THE PROCESSION OF LIFE

THE WORLD NATURAL HISTORY

Editor: Richard Carrington
Associate Editors:
Dr L. Harrison Matthews FRS
Professor J. Z. Young FRS

The Procession of Life

ALFRED S. ROMER

Alexander Agassiz Professor of Zoology, Emeritus,
Museum of Comparative Zoology, Harvard University

THE WORLD PUBLISHING COMPANY

CLEVELAND AND NEW YORK

Published by The World Publishing Company
2231 West 110th Street, Cleveland, Ohio 44102

First World Printing 1968

Contents

List of Illustrations

Acknowledgements

The publishers wish to thank the following for providing photographs for this volume: Paul Popper Agency, plates 2, 18, 26, 35; American Museum of Natural History, plate 3; Karl H. Maslowski, plate 6; New York Zoological Society, plates 17, 27, 29, 37, 39, 40, 41; Zoological Society of London, plates 19, 20, 24, 25, 42, 43; Jane Burton, plate 21; Richard Carrington, plate 22; Photo Researchers, plate 28 (photograph by Joe Van Wormer); Patricia Caulfield, plate 34; J. Allan Cash, plate 38; British Museum, plates 44, 45, 46, 47, 48 (drawings by Maurice Wilson).

The following were used as sources in preparing the figures: Barnes, *Invertebrate Zoology*, figures 2, 6, 7, 15, 16, 17, 19, 22, 29; Buchsbaum, *Animals without Backbones*, figures 5, 6, 8, 10, 12, 13, 28; Parker and Haswell, *Textbook of Zoology*, figures 17, 23, 24, 26, 34, 39; *Scientific American*, figure 1; Fisher and Peterson, *World of Birds*, figure 4; Grove and Newell, *Animal Biology*, figures 7, 9; *Traité de Paléontologie* (ed. Piveteau), figures 19, 50; *Traité de Zoologie* (ed. Grassé), figure 21; Darwin, *Monograph on the Subclass Cirripedia*, figure 20; Nuttall, *Ticks*, figure 23; Imms, *General Textbook of Entomology*, figure 25; Longfield, *Dragonflies of the British Isles*, figure 25; Storer and Usinger, *General Zoology*, figure 29; Alder and Hancock, *British Nudibranchiate Mollusca*, figure 30; Janus, *Molluscs*, figure 30; Schrock and Twenhofel, *Index of Fossils of North America*, figures 32, 33; *British Mesozoic Fossils* (published by the British Museum (Natural History)), figure 33; Hyman, *The Invertebrates*, figures 34, 35, 36; Delage and Hérourard, *Traité de Zoologie Concrète*, figures 34, 38; Colbert, *Evolution of the Vertebrates*, figures 39, 40, 50, 55, 58; Romer, *Vertebrate Body*, figures 37, 38, 40, *Vertebrate Paleontology*, figures 43, 53, 56, 58; *Vertebrate Story*, figures 43, 50; Marshall, *Life of Fishes*, figure 42; Colbert, *Age of Reptiles*, figure 47; Creer, *Discovery*, 1965, figure 48; Stirton, *Time, Life and Man*, figure 56.

The reconstructions used in plates 1, 4, 7, 8, 9, 10, 11, 12, 13, 14, 15, 16, 23, 30, 31, 32, 33, 36, and the figures in the text, were drawn by Design Practitioners, under the supervision of Dr C. B. Cox.

THE PROCESSION OF LIFE

Chapter 1

Evolution

WE see all about us on this earth a great host of living things, plant and animal. There are, it is thought, more than a million different species of animals in existence today; the number of individuals is beyond counting. Hardly a man exists to whom the nature and life of animals is not of some interest, even if that interest is merely that of an angler or sportsman or bird observer. And it is well that we should be interested; for it should not be forgotten that we ourselves are part of this world of animals, and that in studying the nature and lives of other living things we may gain insights into the nature of man.

There are many aspects to the study of the animal world, many questions which come to mind and seek an answer. The structure, the physiology, the habits of animals all present problems of fascinating interest to scientist and layman alike. In this work we will deal with one category of such possible questions – that of animal history. We know well that some animals, some even of rather highly evolved types, have been in existence for some 600 millions of years, and it seems highly probable that animals of lowly sorts, at least, were present vastly farther back in time. Animals have evolved in the past, and, one feels sure, these evolutionary paths are still being followed today, although a fleeting human lifetime is too short a period to give us any perspective on the drama as a whole. How, and in what fashion, has this bewildering array of forms present today come into existence? What are the evolutionary paths which their ancestors followed? And what is our own place in this history of life of which we are a part; who were our forebears? Through what evolutionary channels did our ancestors, over so many hundreds of millions of years, rise from primitive types to our present estate?

In the chapters which follow we will attempt to give the available evidence – all too fragmentary and incomplete in many cases – as to the evolutionary history of the major animal types. But before doing this, we must spend a bit of time on some general topics. What are the

I

mechanisms which underlie the evolutionary story? Upon what types of evidence can we draw to plot out the family tree of animal life?

Evolutionary Theory

The story we have to tell is, thus, one of animal evolution. In his great work, published in 1859, on *The Origin of Species*, Darwin presented such a thoroughly documented case that the *fact* that evolution had occurred was accepted within a very few years by nearly every worker of standing or intelligence in the field of biology. But the *how* and *why* of the evolutionary story were questions to which answers were then far from clear, and it is only in recent years that there has been even an approach to general agreement on this subject. What are the forces underlying this great story of the evolution of life? What are the mechanisms which have operated in causing the marvellous radiation of primitive organisms into the millions of different animals and plant types which exist today?

Non-biologists have from time to time suggested that evolution may have been caused by a deity or some other type of supernatural agency. For example, a dozen years or so ago one Du Noüy published a work entitled *Human Destiny* which gained considerable attention (and sales). In this he proved, to his own satisfaction, that evolution could not be interpreted as being due to natural agencies, and hence there must be some sort of divine direction behind the evolutionary process; following his supposed proof of supernatural intervention in the evolutionary process, he wrote eloquently (and at length) on the attractive vistas open to man's future along the path in which he is being supernaturally directed. The latter part of the book I never read, for the first part was so full of misstatements of fact that I found it difficult to believe in the author's sincerity.

By the nature of the underlying assumptions one cannot, of course, prove or disprove theories of supernatural agencies by scientific research or experiment; but before resorting to such unprovable hypotheses, a scientist should attempt to explain the pertinent phenomena of nature in terms of natural laws. To consider a simpler example of the same sort. If a person were to tell me that my automobile is activated by a small, invisible daemon who resides beneath the hood or bonnet, I could not, from the nature of the case, prove him wrong. But although the internal workings of a modern automobile are so complex that I do not fully understand them, I do have some compre-

2

hension of the nature of an electric spark and the explosiveness of such hydrocarbons as petrol-gasoline. Despite my own ignorance, I am sure that a natural explanation can be found for the way in which an internal combustion engine operates, and the daemon is unnecessary and might well be left out.

In the same category as hypotheses of supernatural intervention are those which suggest the presence of some urge or desire within the animal itself which pushes it forward along an evolutionary path. The French philosopher Bergson believed in the existence of a mysterious, driving force which he termed an 'élan vital'. But this gets us nowhere; he fails to define the nature of this force in understandable physical, chemical, or biological terms. As Sir Julian Huxley has remarked, the naming of an 'élan vital' explains no better the workings of an organism than would the attempt to interpret the operation of a railway engine as due to an 'élan locomotif'.

Let us leave these cloudy regions for the domain of science, and discuss theories to the proof or disproof of which scientific methods may be applied. Of these, the first to be seriously advocated was that of the inheritance of acquired characters, of the influence on heredity of the environment, as set forth more than a century and a half ago by the distinguished French naturalist Lamarck (or, to give him his full, imposing name, Jean Baptiste Pierre Antoine de Monet, Chevalier de Lamarck). Some of the differences between the individuals of a race or species are, of course, due to inheritance of differences present in their parents. Others are obviously differences which have developed during the lifetime of the individual, and can be seen to be clearly related to the circumstances under which he has lived, the vicissitudes he has encountered, his mode of life. The environment certainly influences the characteristic of the individual, and Lamarck made the seemingly reasonable assumption that the characters acquired during the life of the individual could be transmitted to his (or her) offspring; that organs or structures of the body that were vigorously used would tend to be more highly developed in succeeding generations, and those little used would dwindle.

To cite examples used by Lamarck himself. The giraffe, seeking to browse higher and higher on the tree branches in search of the leaves on which it feeds, stretches its neck; and as a result of this habit, continued for generation after generation, the giraffe's neck and front legs have gradually grown longer. Again, the ancestors of the snakes were assumed to be lizard-like animals, living in regions of thick, tall grass

3

where the feet could not comfortably reach the ground. Travelling over such savannas could, however, be accomplished by wriggling motions of the body and tail, without use of the limbs; use of this undulatory motion as a means of progression over the course of time led to decrease in size of the unused legs and their eventual disappearance.

This is an attractive theory and seemingly a very logical one, which one is tempted to accept as a matter of course. Unfortunately, there is not the slightest scientific evidence that acquired characters are ever inherited, although time after time, over the past century, experiments have been made to test the validity of the theory. An early experiment, for example, consisted in cutting off the tails of mice, cutting them off again in the offspring, and so on. If, in theory, disuse of an organ tends to reduce it, its utter absence should have even stronger effects. Not at all. When, after many generations, no knife was applied to the tails, they developed in full and wriggling vigour.

This experiment was objected to, perhaps rightly, as being rather crude in nature. But let us turn to a positive, rather than a negative type of experiment on the subject, and one having to do with mental development. We may fondly hope that if we read learned works and become lovers of art and poetry, our offspring may be born to be, by nature, more intellectual and cultured, and − looking at it from a broader point of view − perhaps the whole human race might gradually rise to higher inborn intellectual levels by constant emphasis on education.

Can we gain evidence that mental acquirements can be inherited? It is, of course, impossible to make properly 'controlled' experiments on man, but that useful laboratory animal, the white rat, is available. A distinguished psychologist made a series of experiments in each of which rats were taught to run a maze (with a food reward if the right turnings were made), their offspring were trained to run the same maze, and so on. The results, when first published, seemed promising and comforting. Generation by generation, it seemed, the rats were becoming brighter and brighter, learning faster and faster.

But when the experiments were closely scrutinized and attempts made to repeat them, fatal flaws appeared. For example, not all of the offspring at every generation were kept and trained, for by twenty or thirty generations the numbers would have been astronomical. Only a few were 'selected' at each generation to go on with; and it is probable that, without intention of fraud, those selected were usually

4

among the brighter members of the litter. Again, in one experiment, the figures showed constant improvement in maze running for nineteen generations. At this point, the man who trained the rats died and, in the next generation the maze-running ability of the rats slumped badly. It rather looks as if, here, it was the trainer who was improving – not the rats.

All in all, few if any scientists today believe in the inheritance of acquired characteristics – much as we might like to.

The first valid attack on the problem was that given by Darwin in his famous work, *The Origin of Species by Means of Natural Selection*. In this, as we have said, he convincingly stated the evidence that evolution had actually occurred, and, in addition, suggested a possible mode of operation in evolutionary advance. This is explicitly stated in the book title – *natural selection*. Darwin did not have all the answers; other fields of science were not then sufficiently advanced to supply them; but although modern beliefs as to how evolution has operated have advanced far beyond that of his day, natural selection is still the basic principle upon which modern evolutionary theory is grounded.

Darwin pointed out that in all animals individual variations constantly occur, apparently more or less at random, and that many of these variations are inherited. Familiar to all is the fact that in animals and plants under domestication, man has been able to select artificially variations which were potentially valuable, or struck his fancy, and by breeding for them for generations he has been able to develop flower types far more brilliant than those seen in nature, to produce vastly more productive strains of corn or to develop breeds of dogs as strikingly different as a borzoi and a pekinese. May there not be similar processes at work, albeit more slowly, in nature? Reflection strongly indicates that something of this sort is constantly happening. It is obvious that only a fraction of all the animals that are born or hatched survive to maturity and reproduce. What fraction? To some degree, survival is a chance affair. But frequently individual differences may make all the difference between life and death; on occasion, a swifter or more alert form, or one better able to obtain a supply of food may succeed in reaching maturity and giving rise to a new generation, while his more sluggish brother may become extinct. Given variation among individuals, those with advantageous variations are the ones most likely to survive. By a process of natural selection, those best fitted triumph, in the long run, in the constant struggle for existence.

5

Each advantageous variation may be small, but over the many millions of years of geologic time, major evolutionary changes can be brought about.

Darwin's exposition of the idea of natural selection laid the groundwork for a reasonable theory of evolutionary mechanisms, but his ideas were open, for decades, to numerous objections. These were due, primarily, to the fact that for his theory it was assumed that variations capable of being inherited came constantly into existence; but we then had no real knowledge as to the mechanisms of inheritance or to the way in which variations originated. Today, the science of genetics has given us a clear understanding of inheritance and considerable knowledge of the origin of variations. But it was not for many decades after Darwin's day that this science developed.

Actually, a basic piece of work was done in Darwin's time by an obscure monk named Gregor Mendel, who bred peas in the quiet gardens of his Moravian monastery and published the results. Mendel's work was neglected, and it was Thomas Hunt Morgan and his colleagues at Columbia University who, at about the period of the First World War, established the basic principles of modern genetics.

Breeding experiments were, of course, the proper basis for a study of heredity, and what was needed was an animal which would breed easily, rapidly, and in great numbers. The little fruit fly, *Drosophila*, proved to be the ideal for such work. Put two fruit flies (properly assorted) into a pint bottle with a bit of banana or other food, and in ten days there are five hundred or so young fruit flies. It was assumed that the basal mechanisms of inheritance, once worked out in such an animal, would be found to be similar to those of other forms, and this has proved to be the case.

The work progressed favourably and rapidly. One thing which soon became apparent was that inheritance is not, as some had thought, a sort of blending process, the offspring splitting the difference, in a general way, between the sum of the characters of the two parents. Inheritance, it was found, is particulate, rather than a general blending. It soon became clear that not only the germ cells – egg and sperm – which produce the new generation, but every cell in the whole body of every individual, contains thousands of discrete hereditary units, to which the name 'genes' was given; even in a little fruit fly there are some thousands of these units. It was at first thought that each gene had a single specific activity, but this is not the case; we find, for example, in a fruit fly, a number of genes which influence eye colour,

6

but some of these are definitely known to have other, non-related effects on other structures or functions of the fly. The work of the Morgan laboratory, further, was able to spot the position of these genes in the organism (figure 1). In every cell there is a nucleus which appears to control the cell's activities; within the nucleus are a number of long, slender structures termed chromosomes, and breeding experiments proved that the genes were arranged in linear fashion along the chromosomes. In recent years, advances in biochemistry have enabled us to determine the basic chemical structure of chromosomes and genes. In each chromosome is a long spiral thread-like molecule of a complex compound, for which the full name is desoxyribose nucleic acid, but for which, fortunately, the abbreviation 'DNA' (a term familiar to every modern student in biology) is available. These DNA molecules are of the essence of life itself; little chemical chains along the length of the DNA spirals are essentially the materials which act as genes. The original interest in the work on genetics and the resulting discovery of genes were due to interest in inheritance. But it is important to note that the genes not only control the development of the young individual, and thus demonstrate its inheritance, but continue to control the activities of the animal throughout its whole life. From the DNA molecules in the chromosomes, chemical 'messengers' are sent out into the rest of the cell and regulate its activity; and the conduct of the organism as a whole is the total result of the gene-directed processes going on, busily and continuously, in every cell of the body. Each time a cell divides, each chromosome is, as if miraculously, able to form an exact duplicate of its whole structure, so that each daughter cell is fully equipped.

But this is, literally, only half the story. Every cell in the body has not merely one full set of chromosomes and their pendant genes, but two full sets. One complete series comes, *via* egg or sperm, from each parent; when sex cells are formed, each contains a single full set so that in the resultant offspring the double set is again present.

If there were no variations in genes, this 'doubling up' of chromosomes and genes would appear to be of little significance. But each gene in the series may vary as to how it acts. There is, for example, a specific gene in the fruit fly which is important for wing development. As usually present, its effect helps produce a fully developed wing. But there crops up, occasionally, a variant of this gene whose effects are to produce a stunted, vestigial wing. It is obvious that if both of the pair of genes in an individual are of the 'normal' type, the fly will

7

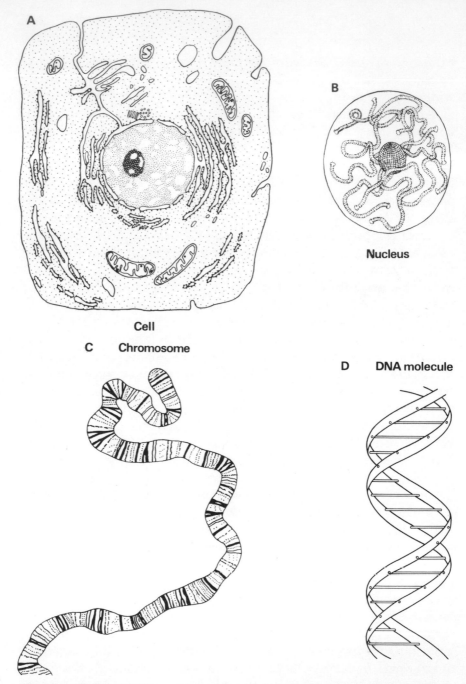

A

B

Nucleus

Cell

C   Chromosome

D   DNA molecule

Figure 1. A. The complete cell contains various specialized structures including the controlling nucleus. B. Within the nucleus are the thread-like chromosomes; there is often also a round nucleolus. C. An enlarged view of part of a chromosome shows dark bands of varying thickness, whose arrangement reflects the linear order of the genes. D. This diagram shows how the DNA molecule is composed of complex spiralling threads.

exhibit to the observer normal wings; if both members of the gene pair are of the 'vestigial' variant, the fly will only develop vestigial wings.

But what if the gene pair includes one of each type? Here there is a conflict of interests. One might imagine there might be a compromise; but this is seldom the case. Usually one of the two variants dominates over the other. Here the gene for full wings is the 'dominant', and the individual shows, to the observer, good wings, even though he is carrying within him a 'recessive' gene which would tend to reduce them.

Here, then, is a mechanism, basically simple in nature, of which early students of heredity and evolution never dreamed, thinking, as was reasonable, that any inheritable factor that an animal possessed would show itself in the structure of the individual. Not so; recessive characters may go for generations without making themselves visible. This explains many things which puzzled former workers on heredity and animal breeding. For example, why is it so difficult to breed unfavourable characters out of a strain? The answer, as is clear from our modern knowledge of genetics, is simple; if the character is a recessive and not too common, it may long persist in a stock without ever coming visibly to the surface.

A species of animal, thus, is not genetically uniform, even though most individuals conform generally to a uniform pattern. The population carries within itself, in a variety of recessive genes, a reservoir of variation. Even without the incoming of any new characters, the potentialities already present in the stock might be sufficient to allow the animal to adjust to new conditions, should they occur, and evolve along lines different from those previously common and fit. As a simple example, let us take the reduced wing variant already described. Under normal conditions this character is disadvantageous, and whenever, by inheritance of this gene from both parents, the fly exhibits itself in short-winged form, natural selection would tend to eliminate it. But suppose that a colony of fruit flies establishes itself on an island with heavy winds, what then? The normal long-winged flies would tend to fly up, get caught in the gales, blown out to sea, and perish; the short-winged type would, on the average, survive more frequently, and there might evolve, in such a situation, a new short-winged species of fruit fly.

We have, thus, a pattern of inheritance under which natural selection can act effectively on characters already present. But how do the

9

variants arise? Here there is less positive information, but the general picture is clear. The genes are, essentially, chemical materials, and a change – technically termed a mutation – is quite surely a chemical change in the pertinent part of the chromosome and its DNA spiral. We know some specific ways in which such changes, resulting in gene mutations, can be caused. Certain chemicals which can penetrate the cells are known to be able to do this. Bombarding animals with X-rays has been definitely proved to cause mutations; cosmic rays constantly reaching us through the atmosphere are probably responsible in great measure for the modest amount of mutation, good or bad (mainly bad) that constantly occurs in the members of any animal species; the greatest menace of possible atomic warfare is not the immediate loss of life, but the probability that the mutation rate would so increase as to endanger the future of all life on earth.

But really, the wonder of the situation is not that mutation does occur. As we have said, the entire complicated chromosomal mechanism must be exactly duplicated at every cell division; an exact mate must be created for every DNA molecule and every one of its side chains, time after time after time. Any slight imperfection in the reduplication process will result in a mutation. It is close to miraculous that 'mistakes' occur so seldom and that stability is so generally maintained.

To sum up: Darwin, in natural selection, supplied a principle which is the underlying base of all modern concepts of evolutionary processes; our knowledge of genetics shows us an interesting and effective mechanism of heredity through which selection can operate. Modern workers on evolutionary problems can, in general, explain their results in terms of known biological facts and principles, and see no reason to call upon supernatural intervention or mysterious forces of nature.

Homology

Let us now turn to a consideration of the types of evidence upon which one can draw in attempting to sort out the evolutionary patterns with which we are to be concerned. In some groups we can rely in part on the evidence of fossil forms to aid us in determining their evolutionary story; in others – particularly soft-bodied types – such evidence is sparse or non-existent, and in attempting to trace their history we have nothing to go on except what can be deduced from the group representatives alive today. A careful study of the anatomy of an adult animal and comparison of its structures with those of possible relatives can be most instructive and valuable. If we compare any structure – say, the limb of a vertebrate – with the same structure in another form, it is reasonable to conclude, barring evidence to the contrary based on other factors, that the closer the resemblance, the closer the probable relationship. This type of study uses the concept of 'homology'; the thesis that specific organs of living members of an animal group have descended, with modification, from basically similar organs present in their remote common ancestor. For many decades following the acceptance of evolution, the tracing of homologies played a major role in zoological and anatomical work. The results were nearly always of importance, often very interesting, and sometimes startling in the conclusions reached. For example, man and other mammals all have three tiny ossicles inside the ear drum which aid in hearing; reptiles have but one; fishes none. What are the equivalents – the homologues – of these tiny bones in lower vertebrates? The answer is one which we would hardly suspect. These ossicles, in higher fishes, were part of the jaw apparatus; in lower fishes and their ancestors, lacking jaws, they were part of the supports for the gills. Structures originally associated with breathing became adapted for eating and finally for hearing; but their homology throughout this series of changes in function is unquestioned. In recent decades this story has been confirmed by increasing knowledge of fossils; but the evidence derivable from living forms alone was sufficient in itself to prove the case.

Evidence from Embryology

In the attempt to trace out the history of homologous organs and the modifications which they have undergone in the course of evolution, much can be told from the structure of the adult. But the study of embryology, of the development of the individual from egg through embryonic stages and, in many animal groups, through a distinct larval stage, can contribute greatly to an interpretation of the evolutionary history. Adult man lacks a tail; but our belief that man has descended from more primitive monkey-like primates possessing this structure is reinforced through the fact that a human embryo does have a tail, later resorbed. Fish breathe by means of a set of gills, formed as pouches on either side of the throat, which gain openings to the exterior. An adult man, of course, has no gills; but in the human embryo such pouches do form, much as in the young fish.

From discoveries of this sort, Haeckel, a German disciple of Darwin, in the last century came to advocate a 'theory of recapitulation'; that in its embryonic development an animal passes successively through the types of structure possessed by its ancestors at successive stages of its evolutionary history. 'Ontogeny recapitulates phylogeny', was the usual brief statement of the recapitulation theory. The history of the individual repeats the evolutionary history of the race; the embryo climbs its own family tree.

An attractive theory, and one that stimulated much work in embryology. But a theory which, as time elapsed, proved to rest in great measure on false premises. After all, would one expect that, over millions of years, embryos would devote their energies to faithfully repeating their phylogenetic histories for the purpose of furnishing information to students of embryology? Hardly. The function of an embryo is the production of an adult; it appears to be frequently the case that the most successful method for attaining this goal is to follow, for some distance at least, the same developmental path which his ancestors followed. A human embryo, at one stage, develops gill pouches in its throat as does a fish. But these do not open to the surface as formed gill slits as in a mature fish; it is not the fish adult which the human embryo resembles, but the fish embryo.

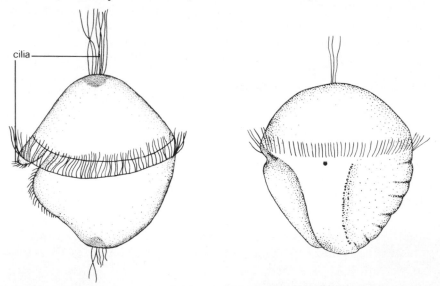

Figure 2. Though these two trochophore larvae look very similar, with cilia in equatorial bands and apical tufts, that on the left will develop into a marine worm and that on the right into a mollusc.

We come, then, to a conclusion less spectacular than that which old Haeckel believed in; but one which is nevertheless very useful in studying animal relationships – similarities in embryonic development in two animals offer strong proofs of relationship.

As we said above, young individuals of various groups often assume forms as larvae which are quite different from those of the adults; the caterpillar larva of a butterfly, the grub of a beetle, the tadpole larva of a frog, are familiar examples. A comparative study of larval forms may furnish strong hints of relationship. For example, marine annelid worms (cousins of the ordinary earthworm) begin life as tiny ciliated larvae of a type termed the trochophore. A mollusc, such as a clam or oyster, is very different from such a worm in adult structure; but molluscs have trochophore larvae very similar to those of annelids (figure 2). This gave grounds for a belief that molluscs were, despite adult differences, derived from such worms or forms related to them; recent discoveries of primitive molluscs of somewhat intermediate adult structure are now adding weight to this hypothesis of relationship based on larval studies.

The Record of the Rocks

For the first part of our story, dealing with small and generally soft-bodied animals, with little or no hard parts, we must, of necessity, rely almost entirely on evidence gained from a study of forms with us to-day. But in many groups there are present shells or skeletons which may be preserved as fossils and tell us much about the former life of the world and the ancestors of the animals we see about us. It is much more satisfactory to find concrete evidence of an actual ancestor than to try to deduce, indirectly, what that ancestor might have been. And so, we will, wherever possible, draw heavily in later chapters on the evidence gained from fossils. In another volume in this series[1] there is discussed the geological history of the earth and the nature of the successive faunas which inhabited it, age after age. Here too we shall treat of the animals of the past, but from a different point of view. We will not be concerned with faunas as units but, rather, with the individual components of these faunas as part of an evolutionary story; what are the relationships of a given form?; what were its ancestors?; to what later creatures, if any, did it give rise? The treatment

[1] *The Earth* by Carl O. Dunbar.

of past life by the historical geologist is, so to speak, a series of horizontal views; ours here is an attempt at a vertical, evolutionary treatment of the units in this series of past landscapes.

To discuss intelligently the fossil record of the evolution of any group, it is necessary to make frequent references to the geological position of the ancient forms concerned; and hence we must briefly outline the nature of the geological timetable.

When mention is made of an extinct animal, the first question invariably put to a paleontologist or geologist is 'How many years ago did it live?' This embarrasses the scientist, for he does not think in terms of years. We are, today, gradually accumulating data which do yield approximate dates in terms of years, or rather millions of years. But even now our figures are none too accurate, and to workers in early days time estimates were almost impossible, although they could be sure that the times were exceedingly long. The best they could do was to give *relative* ages; determine which forms occurred higher or lower in the complex layer cake of the earth's sediments, and hence which was relatively early or relatively late.

The sedimentary rocks which cover most of the surface of the earth were obviously laid down, layer by layer, over aeons of time as successive sheets of sand or mud or lime on river deltas or along shallow

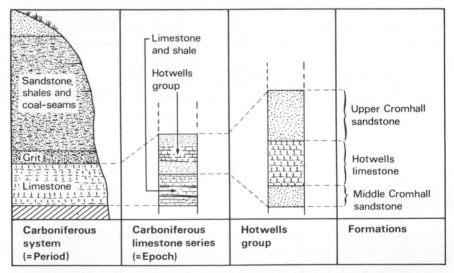

Figure 3. This diagrammatic example shows how the rocks of the Carboniferous system near Bristol are successively subdivided into series, groups and formations. The names of equivalent divisions in time are given in brackets (see also Table 2, p. 17).

14

shore waters. Nearly two centuries ago it was discovered that many of these layers could be traced cross-country for considerable distances, and even where gaps were present, one could often identify the same bed in a different part of the country, or even in another distant area, by the nature of the materials or, better, by the presence of similar fossils contained in it. By this means, over the years, geologists were able to assemble much of the succession of these layers of shales and sandstones and limestones into a complex, many-layered series, not all of them, of course, present and visible in any single region. The individual layers, if of any reasonable thickness, could be called formations; a set of associated formations could be called a group, a set of groups, a series; a number of series, taken together and forming a great thickness of rocks which must have taken a long time to accumulate, is called a system (figure 3).

We can, thus, name the substance of the rock layers. But what could be done to make a time scale? This could not be done in older times on a basis of years or centuries; but terms could be – and were – invented to designate the time period during which the various types of rock units may have been laid down. The time equivalent of a rock series was termed an epoch; that of a system was named a period. And, finally, the whole sequence from the oldest known fossil-bearing rocks on to the latest was divided into three grand units, termed eras. The assembled time structure is outlined in the accompanying table. The three eras are: Palaeozoic, the era of ancient life, when marine invertebrates and, later, lower vertebrates, dominated the scene; Mesozoic, the 'middle ages' of life, essentially the days of the dinosaurs; and Cenozoic, the era of 'modern' life, which witnessed the rise of mammals. Each era is divided into periods, named generally after some region where rocks of the period are well exposed, some tribe inhabiting such a region, or some characteristic of the included rocks. Thus, Cambria is another name for Wales; the Devonian is named from Devonshire, the Permian from the Perm region of Russia, the Jurassic from the Jura Mountains; the Ordovices and Silures were Welsh tribes inhabiting regions where appropriate rock systems are well represented. The Carboniferous contains much of the world's major coal beds; the Triassic is sharply divided into three parts in most European regions; the Cretaceous was a major time of deposition of chalk rocks. The Cenozoic consists of two periods, the Tertiary and Quaternary, the last including modern times. These two terms come from an old-fashioned system of nomenclature, under which the

Palaeozoic Era was called 'primary', the Mesozoic 'secondary', and so on. These first two terms have been abandoned, but 'tertiary' and 'quaternary' are still useful.

Table 1 Geologic Periods
[*Times in millions of years*]

Eras	Periods	Duration	Time since beginning
Cenozoic	Quaternary	1+	1+
	Tertiary	69	70
Mesozoic	Cretaceous	65	135
	Jurassic	45	180
	Triassic	45	225
Palaeozoic	Permian	45	270
	Carboniferous	80	350
	Devonian	50	400
	Silurian	40	440
	Ordovician	60	500
	Cambrian	100	600

Periods can be divided into epochs. In general, we need not consider them for our purposes. But for the evolution of the mammals and man it is useful to relate events to the epochs of the Tertiary and Quaternary, and these epochs are listed in Table 2. Each epoch is given a name ending in '-cene' indicating the relative modernity of the fossils living at the time.

Here, then, we have a table from which we can tell the *relative age* of any given fossil or fossil group. If, for example, we say that dinosaurs became extinct at the end of the Cretaceous, and that the first mammals appeared at the end of the Triassic, reference to the table will show that the mammals lived with (or under!) the dinosaurs for two full geologic periods – obviously a considerable period of time.

Table 2 Cenozoic Subdivisions
[*Times in millions of years*]

Periods	Epochs	Duration	Time since beginning
Quaternary	Recent		
	Pleistocene	1+	1+
Tertiary	Pliocene	10	11
	Miocene	14	25
	Oligocene	15	40
	Eocene	20	60
	Palaeocene	10	70

But how to express such time intervals in an absolute, rather than a relative fashion?

Even in the early days of earth study attempts were made to estimate the length of periods and eras. Darwin, among others, attempted it. One method was to estimate the rate of deposition at the present time of mud flats in deltas and so on, and applying these figures to the sediments of the past, compute the time that must have been necessary to lay down the great thicknesses of rocks that were formed, at one place or another, around the world, during a given period or era. These older computations gave figures on the order of five millions of years for the Cenozoic, fifty millions of years for the whole elapsed time since the beginning of an abundant record of life in the Cambrian.

But such figures were, of course, open to great possibilities of error. Rates of deposition vary greatly today. And most especially, these calculations at best give an estimate of the *minimum* time needed. They give the time required if deposition had been continuous. But it obviously was not. Around the world today there are only a few great river deltas in which there is any great or rapid deposit of muds or sands which are to be the geologic shales and sandstones of the future.

17

In the rest of the world, little rock formation is taking place. The same situation was presumably true in times past. There were obviously long time gaps with no deposition, which are not included in the computations. Quite surely these older time estimates were too short.

Too short they have proved to be – with a vengeance! The actual figures appear to be, on the average, ten times those which were once accepted. The newer data have come from the study of radioactive rocks in recent decades. At various times in the earth's history, there have been laid down rocks which can be placed accurately in the table of geologic periods and which contained radioactive substances at the time of deposition. Such radioactive minerals gradually break down into simpler elements – uranium, for example, forms lead and helium – and the physicists have measured quite accurately the rate of this disintegration. If, then, we analyse with care a sample of rock which contained uranium at deposition, and find out what percentage of this material still remains as uranium and how much has metamorphosed into lead (and helium), we can estimate the age of the rock rather closely. There are, of course, possibilities of error in work of this sort, but methods are constantly being refined, and we are now able to give the ages in years of the periods and eras of our geologic table with a fair degree of accuracy.

The upshot of it is that the older workers underestimated geologic time by a factor of ten or more! The Cenozoic, the age of mammals, was thought to have had a duration of 5 million years or so; the actual figure is on the order of 70 millions. The beginning of the fossil record in the Cambrian was judged to have been about 50 million years ago; radioactive tests show this to have taken place some 600 million years or so ago.

The Pre-Cambrian

Our narration of the evolutionary history of the various animal groups will make necessary numerous references to the table of geologic periods from the Cambrian on, which are tabulated in the chart. This is a considerable period of time – 600 million years of it. But does this period cover the entire history of the earth, or of life on the earth? Far from it. The actual age of our planet is uncertain, but studies of ancient radioactive rocks yield ages for their deposition of as much as 3,000 million years – five times as far back as the beginning of the

18

Cambrian, and current estimates of the earth's age by astronomers and geophysicists run to two or three times this figure. One would, hence, expect our story of the evolution of animal life to extend much farther back than the Cambrian. There is, however, a very puzzling quirk in our story.

In rocks deposited in the lower Cambrian seas we find a flourishing array of marine animals of varied sorts – molluscs, echinoderms, brachiopods, arthropods, for example; except for our own phylum, that of the chordates and vertebrates, almost every known major group of animals is present in the Cambrian. In most of these groups the forms present then were, to be sure, quite primitive by the standards of later periods, but the various phyla were already quite distinct, and the members of the various groups often highly varied. The evolution of life, and even the evolution of complex animal types, had evidently gone on for a long period preceding the Cambrian.

In various parts of the world there are abundant sedimentary rocks older than the Cambrian – hundreds and thousands of feet of such sediments. The earliest stages in the evolution of living things would, we assume, have been concerned with tiny soft-bodied forms unlikely to be found as fossils. But the presence of a variety of well-advanced shelled invertebrates in the Cambrian would lead us to expect that exploration of pre-Cambrian rocks would enable us to trace the history of animal life well before that period, albeit with fewer and fewer fossils as we pass downward towards life's beginning.

But we find nothing of the sort. Plentiful as the older strata are, they are almost destitute of signs of life. In rocks not long (geologically) preceding the Cambrian, there are remains of primitive water plants and there are a few traces of such plants in two localities of considerably greater age. This is not much, and the animal record is even more scant. It is confined to a few remains in deposits not far antedating the Cambrian; most of these are poorly preserved and mostly doubtful in nature. A record of pre-Cambrian animal life, it appears, simply does not exist.

Why this lamentable blank? Various theories have been proposed; none is too satisfactory. It has been suggested, for example, that all the Pre-Cambrian sediments were deposited on continental areas, and the absence of fossils in them is due to the fact that all the older animals were sea-dwellers. But that all these older sediments were continental is a theory which opposes, without proof, everything we know of deposition in later times. Again, it is suggested that the Pre-

19

Cambrian seas were poor in calcium carbonate, necessary for the production of preservable skeletons; but this is not supported by geochemical evidence. Yet again, it is argued that, even though conditions were amenable to the formation of fossilizable skeletal parts, the various phyla only began to use these possibilities at the dawn of the Cambrian. But it is, *a priori*, hard to believe that the varied types present in the early Cambrian would all have, so to speak, decided to put on armour simultaneously. And, once again, it has been argued that the whole evolution of multicellular animals took place with great rapidity in late Pre-Cambrian times, so that a relatively short gap in rock deposition would account for the absence of any record of their rise. Perhaps; but the known evolutionary rate in most groups from the Cambrian on is a relatively leisurely one, and it is hard to convince oneself that a sudden major burst of evolutionary advance would be so promptly followed by a marked 'slowdown'. All in all, there is no satisfactory answer to the Pre-Cambrian riddle. We must accept the presence of this blank in our knowledge and, regretfully, accept the necessity of reconstructing the story of Pre-Cambrian life from the evidence afforded by the Cambrian fossils and from that deduced from study of their modern representatives.

Changing the subject completely – but briefly – I cannot refrain from mentioning, in contrast to Pre-Cambrian gloom and murkiness, an exceptionally bright spot at a somewhat later point in the geological story. I will lament frequently the fact that many animal types are soft-bodied and hence are almost never preserved as fossils. There is a fortunate exception to this nearly universal rule in the mid-Cambrian – close to, although not quite at the beginning of the well-documented record of fossils. A half-century ago there was discovered, near Burgess in British Columbia, a hillside with abundant exposures of a dark-coloured shale of unusually fine texture. In this have been found numerous specimens of soft-bodied Cambrian invertebrate animals. The remains are preserved merely as flattened carbonized films, but in many cases much of the structure can be made out. Some of the remains are those of worms and other groups of which there are little or no fossil remains known at any other time or place. And still others are forms of whose position in animal classification we are entirely ignorant. It is quite certain that there have been in past ages many types of animals now long extinct and of which the fossil record tells us little or nothing. The Burgess shale gives us a tantalizing glimpse into this mysterious ancient world.

The Names of Animals

In later chapters it will be necessary upon occasion to use technical scientific names, rather than 'popular' ones, for the animals being described, and it is well at this point to discuss briefly the nature of *systematics*, a branch of zoology which has to do with establishing uniform names, in Latin form, for animals, and arranging the various sorts of known animals in a system of classification. The use of scientific names is a necessity in many cases, since for most fossils, and even many of the less familiar living animals, there is no general popular name. But even where popular names do exist, it is often unwise to use them, for not only do such names change from language to language, but even vary in usage from one region to another amongst speakers of a common language. For example, the American 'robin' is only distantly related to the English bird to which that name was first applied (figure 4). The European red deer is called an elk in America; the European elk is the American moose. In the little New England town where this is written, there is a $1.00 bounty on 'hedge-hogs'. There is not, of course, a hedgehog within three thousand miles of this town, for they are European animals. The bounty is one on porcupines; but early settlers, encountering a prickly animal unfamiliar to them, transferred the hedgehog name to this inhabitant of their new homes (figure 4).

We do, then, need scientific names, which can be used by people of all countries, for animals, whether familiar or not. The system used was devised by a great Swedish naturalist of the eighteenth century, Linneaus. The basic unit is the species, an interbreeding population of animals of the same kind, which may differ a bit individually, but possess characters in common which set them off from populations of somewhat similar type. For example, despite all the variations bred into them by man, all dogs, as both man and dog recognize, belong to a single species. The wolves form a comparable but distinct species population; so, too, do the jackals of the Old World tropics and the coyote of the American West (plate 1). We recognize the relationship between these species by including them in a unit – the next higher group above the species in the system of classification – the genus. Every animal form is properly known by two names, that of the genus, followed by that of the species. Thus dogs, wolves, jackals and coyotes are all members of the genus *Canis*; the dog species is *Canis familiaris*, the wolf *Canis lupus*, and so on. We can, to discuss matters common to all members of a genus, use a generic term such as *Canis* without

21

specifying any one species; never, however, can we use a specific name alone.

Figure 4. Though not at all closely related to each other, both the red-breasted birds shown here are called 'robins' and both the spiny mammals are called 'hedgehogs'. Those on the left come from Great Britain, those on the right from the USA.

22

Higher categories, however, are needed if we are to include the whole animal kingdom in a single system of classification. Family, order, class, and phvlum, are, in ascending order, the major terms used; we may refine points in the system by adding such prefixes as sub- or super- to these names. For example, the dog-wolf group which forms the genus *Canis* is related to the foxes and a number of related dog-like and fox-like forms; all these together make up the family Canidac. The Canidac, in turn, arc related to other flesh-eating mammals, such as cats and weasels, and all these are bracketed together to form the order Carnivora. The carnivores are, like ourselves, warm-blooded hair- or fur-bearing animals which nurse their young; all the very numerous animals of this sort, from men to cats to bats to rats and what have you, form the class Mammalia. The mammals, as animals with a backbone and so on, are related to birds, reptiles, amphibians and fishes; these comprise the subphylum Vertebrata, the main component of the phylum Chordata.

In early days this type of classification, of bracketing similar forms together into larger and larger assemblages, was thought of as merely a sort of filing system, whereby any animal might be 'pigeon-holed'. But when, a century ago, evolution became generally accepted, zoologists realized to their astonishment and pleasure that a classification of this sort, if founded on basic characters rather than merely superficial resemblances, had real evolutionary meaning in expressing blood relationships of the forms in any given category. The species within each genus have presumably descended from a common ancestor; the gencra within a family owe their similarity to community of descent. All in all, the bracketing together of animals into larger and larger categories may express not merely similarities, but actual relationships; classification prepared zoologists for the study of evolution.

Chapter 2

First Steps

WE need not concern ourselves here with the fascinating problem of the origin of life; of the appearance, perhaps several thousands of millions of years ago in the youth of the world, of organic compounds which eventually gained the power of reproducing their own chemical structure and hence could be claimed to be living matter of a sort; nor of the progress from such a beginning stage to the perfecting of the organization of cells, with a central directing nucleus and its surrounding body of living protoplasm. This story is being told in two other volumes in this series.[1] And, further, since we are here restricting ourselves to the history of animals, it is beyond our province; for the origin of life is the story of the origin of plant life; the development of animals was, in a way of speaking, an afterthought.

Animal *v*. Plant

Plants came into existence before animals; plants could exist today without animals, but animals could not exist without plants. Shortly we shall review the world of primitive one-celled living creatures to sort out which of them can be called animals rather than plants. And in attempting to define and sort out the memberships of the two great groups of living things, the fact soon appears that (humiliating as it may seem to us, as members of the animal kingdom) animals are, in a sense, mere parasites on the plant world.

The presence of carbon compounds, thought to be derived from living organisms, in slates about 2,000 million years old gives us a time at which presumably some primitive type of plant life was already in existence. Almost nothing is known of animal fossils older than about 600 million years ago, but as we have already mentioned, some of the forms found in rocks of that age are quite advanced forms.

[1] *The Origin of Life* by J. D. Bernal, and *The World beneath the Microscope* by J. David Robertson.

Hence, we feel sure that the first living things that could have been definitely animal in nature could have arisen considerably earlier; as a pure guess – nothing more is possible – about a thousand million years may be the total span of animal life to the present.

Quite certainly the first animals were single-celled forms. Many thousands of single-celled organisms are living today. Most of them lack any hard parts capable of preservation, and the same appears to have been true of their ancestors. Hence, in attempting to draw up a picture of the early history of animal life, we have little to go on except such deductions as can be made from a consideration of lower living forms.

Of unicellular organisms, some seem respectably plant-like, are claimed by the botanists, and included by them in the Algae – a term used broadly for almost any lower type of water-dwelling plant. Other unicellular forms are claimed by the zoologists, and are often considered to form a major animal group as the phylum Protozoa. But still others cannot be placed so definitely in either group, and seem to combine both animal and plant characters. In consequence, many biologists would insist that the attempt to sort out these lowly forms accurately into plant and animal categories is a vain one; they would, instead, call them all Protista, and not assign them to either plant or animal kingdom.

Even if we accept this conclusion, we should, for our purposes of attempting to discover the origins of animal life, attempt to sort out possible animal ancestors and relatives among the unicellular creatures – keeping in mind, of course, that even though they may not have evolved far, they cannot be expected to have remained absolutely unchanged for a thousand million years or more. But here we at once encounter a major problem – how does one tell an animal from a plant?

With the higher members of both kingdoms, there is little difficulty. Any fool can tell a dog from a tree. But as we descend the scale in either group, the problem is less simple. What have we to go on? Animals generally move about actively; plants are generally fixed. But, as will be seen, there are various animals – some of them quite highly organized – which are sedentary attached forms (our own ancestors may have been of this nature for much of their evolutionary history), and some one-celled forms which are definitely plant-like are nevertheless mobile.

Basically, the distinction comes down to the matter of food supply.

Every organism, plant or animal, is composed in its living substance of a variety of types of complex chemical compounds – carbohydrates, fats, proteins, nucleic acids – consisting primarily of oxygen, hydrogen and carbon, a certain quantity of nitrogen, and lesser amounts of other elements, notably phosphorus. Both plants and animals can modify such compounds, use them as 'fuel' sources of energy in their life processes, break them down into simpler units, and refashion them into new complexities. But – and here is the sharp distinction – animals, although it is literally vital that they possess such organic chemical materials, cannot make them. Plants can. Using, in the main, solar energy captured through the medium of the chlorophyll that gives most plants their green colouring, the plant manufactures organic compounds from water and air and from minor but important chemical fractions obtained from materials present in soil and water. Animals must obtain their organic materials, directly or indirectly, from plants; they must eat food, and cannot create it. All animals are completely dependent upon the plant world.

Protozoans

With this major clue to identity in mind, let us review briefly the major types of unicellular forms in existence today, try to sort them out into plants (Algae) and animals (Protozoa), and see what clues these living forms can furnish as to the events of a thousand million or so years ago which gave rise to the first simple animals.

Most unicellular forms can be grouped into four major types, of which the seemingly most simple – and perhaps, for our purposes, the most important – is that of the Flagellata. Typical flagellates are, as seen under the microscope, tiny bodies generally slender in shape, with little complexity in internal structure. The one special feature, to which the group name refers, is that at the front end there projects a long whip-like projection, the flagellum; this is the little creature's locomotor organ; it can lash about vigorously and draw the body forward after it.

Some of these flagellates are definitely to be included in the plant kingdom; for example, *Euglena,* a form frequently so abundant in fresh waters that it produces a green scum on the surface of a pond (figure 5). *Green* scum; for within the body of each *Euglena* there are accumulations of chlorophyll. *Euglena* eats no food; it manufactures its essential organic compounds from water, oxygen and other

26

chemical materials from the water surrounding it. It is definitely a plant.

So are many other flagellates. But not all members of the group, by far. Sitting, so to speak, on the fence between animal and plant kingdoms are a number of flagellates which have chlorophyll and the ability to manufacture food, but do not always utilize it. Still other members of the flagellate group have lost the ability to make organic compounds, and live by taking small food particles into the body – an animal mode of life. We cannot, of course, be at all sure, but quite possibly the flagellates represent the basal stock from which there arose, on the one hand, higher plant types, and, on the other, the basic stock destined to give rise to all later animals.

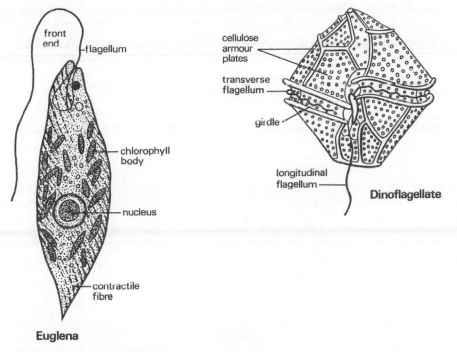

Euglena

Figure 5. Two types of flagellates.

Although some flagellates seem to have persisted to the present day as seemingly simple and primitive forms, we cannot, of course, expect that the group as a whole would have failed, over the course of a thousand million years or so, to have gained evolutionary diversity. Some living flagellates have departed far from the primitive pattern.

27

We may mention, for example, the dinoflagellates, relatively large forms, which have encased themselves in little armour-plates of cellulose (figure 5). They are marine, and sometimes reproduce in enormous numbers, to such an extent that one form, with a pigmented body, may cause a 'red tide' in the ocean in such areas as Florida and Southern California. Again, some flagellates have become true parasites inside the bodies of animals of higher types; most notable of such forms are the trypanosomes which cause the African type of sleeping sickness and are carried from host to host by the tsetse fly.

We may turn now to some groups of unicellular forms that are definitely animal in nature, since they are quite unable to manufacture food and must capture it from other organisms – or their remains. Of the group termed the Sarcodina, a characteristic form is one whose name is almost a household word – *Amoeba* (figure 6). We frequently hear the phrase 'From amoeba to man', with the implication that, just as we consider ourselves the highest of animal forms, the amoeba is to be considered the lowest and most primitive. I am far from certain that either implication is correct; at any rate, the amoeba may not be as primitive as he appears to be.

In the microscope an amoeba appears as a little amorphous lump of clear gelatinous protoplasm, with no obvious structural features except the vitally necessary nucleus and a round blob, a vacuole which can contract and thus pump excess water out of the body. One tends to get, as a first impression, an idea that the amoeba is little more than a bit of primaeval slime, hardly up to the level of life. This is, actually, far from the case. The amoeba is simple looking; but it knows well, so to speak, what it is about, and conducts its little affairs with competence. There is no fixed body shape; its outlines are constantly irregular and constantly changing. This does not indicate indecision on the part of the amoeba. On the contrary. The changes in shape constitute the amoeba's mode of locomotion. A blunt, finger-shaped projection, reasonably termed a pseudopod, an 'imitation foot', may flow out of the amoeba's body mass in the direction it is travelling; this becomes attached to the underlying surface, and the rest of the animal's bulk gradually flows forward to join the original projection. A new process may then form, and the body again flow ahead. An effective method of progression, although a slow one. There is a further reason for the throwing out of pseudopods. The members of this group of organisms are definitely animals, in that they are incapable of food manufacture and must 'eat'. If something edible (often a smaller protozoan or unicellular plant) lies nearby, pseudopods may extend out, surround it, and fold it into the substance of the amoeba's body.

The amoeba then is, even if simply built, an efficient organism. And it is very probable that it is not a truly primitive type; its simplicity may be secondary. In some flagellates it has been found that at times an individual may lose its flagellum, abandon its oval body shape, and, for a time, move about like an amoeba. Very probably the amoebas are descended from forms of this sort which have permanently abandoned the flagellate stage.

Although the amoebas are presumably the most primitive and generalized members of the Sarcodina, this group, like the flagellates, has evolved over the course of the ages into a variety of specialized types. Even some close relatives of the amoeba have evolved simple shells as protective coverings, and there are three distinct groups of amoeboid descendants which have evolved varied shells of complex nature (figure 6). The foraminifers secrete chalky, calcareous shells. In a later chapter we shall describe the way in which the ancient cephalopod molluscs and the living pearly nautilus form complex shells, often of spiral form with numerous chambers. These little protozoans secrete tiny shells of very similar pattern. The marine radiolarians form about their bodies elaborate skeletons of silica, spherical in shape but with varied types of projecting spines and with openings through which pseudopodia may project. Somewhat similar are fresh-water forms, the heliozoans. For soft-bodied protozoans there is, of course, almost no fossil record. But as regards the shelled protozoans, the story is a different one. These little skeletons, tiny but very numerous, are almost indestructible. They abound on modern sea bottoms. A large fraction of the floor of the oceans is covered by a grey mud called the 'Globigerina ooze' because it is largely composed of accumulated shells of a foraminifer of that name; several millions of square miles of the Pacific bottoms are covered by a comparable 'radiolarian ooze'. Many of the marine rocks in the geologic column were formed from similar 'oozes' on the floors of earlier oceans; the white cliffs of Dover and the widespread chalk deposits of Kansas are formed almost entirely of tiny foraminiferan shells. Further, foraminifers are so distinctive in shell patterns and so varied in time of geologic appearance that they are exceedingly useful to the stratigraphic geologist in sorting out the succession of rock formations. Foraminifera are definitely known in every period from the Ordovician onward, and may have been present in the Cambrian; the

29

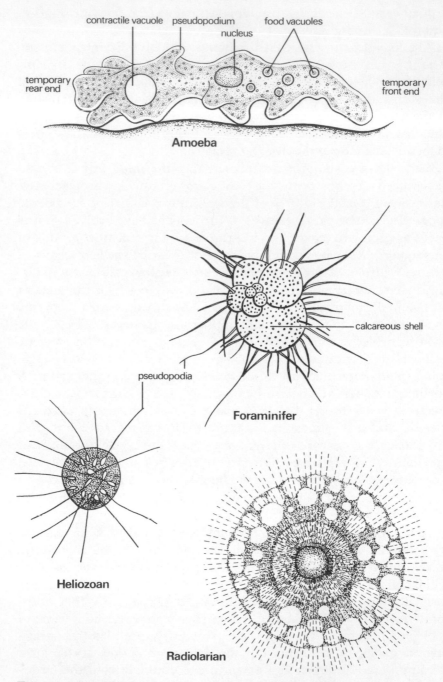

contractile vacuole   pseudopodium   food vacuoles

nucleus

temporary
rear end

temporary
front end

Amoeba

calcareous shell

pseudopodia

Foraminifer

Heliozoan

Radiolarian

Figure 6. *Amoeba* and some of its relatives in the Sarcodina.

radiolarians are definitely known in the Cambrian, and there are doubtful late Pre-Cambrian reports. The early geologic appearance of these forms is not too surprising, since, after all, the first protozoans may have been present at a far earlier time in earth's history, and several hundreds of millions of years would have been available for the evolution of specialized types.

We will mention but briefly a class of protozoans termed the Sporozoa, a varied series of protozoans of which the malarial parasite is the best known member; all are parasites, and under this term are probably included a variety of degenerate side branches of the flagellate and amoeboid stocks. Like most parasites, the various sporozoans are successfully adapted in evolutionary fashion to their degenerate modes of life, but are sterile side branches of the evolving tree of animal life.

As protozoans, the most highly evolved, and in many ways the most interesting forms are those included in the class Ciliata. As the name implies, the distinguishing character of the group is their mode of locomotion, in which not flagella nor pseudopods, but cilia are the effective agents. These tiny hair-like structures are present not only in this group of protozoans but may be found in various regions of the body of many kinds of animals of advanced structural types. Like flagella, cilia are whip-like structures which are locomotor aids; but they are much smaller in size, compared with the animal or cells concerned and, most especially, they are, when present, exceedingly numerous, generally arranged in multiple rows to the number of hundreds or thousands. A single cilium is not too effective; but through little-understood mechanisms they are co-ordinated so that the cilia beat in rhythmical waves in very effective fashion. A typical ciliate, frequently used in laboratory work, is *Paramoecium* (figure 7), a cigar-shaped form which can move through the water, by the beating of its 2,000 or more cilia, at good speed (for a protozoan) in search of food. All ciliates are little predators, even supplied (unlike sarcodines and flagellates) with funnel-shaped gullets in which the prey may be engulfed. Quite in contrast with other groups, the structure of ciliates may be quite complex. For example, various ciliates have developed, by the fusion of sets of cilia, slender structures with somewhat the appearance of spider legs, by means of which they can move about in hopping fashion, and there are even developed strands of tissue which co-ordinate their movement, forming a sort of intracellular nervous system. There are no known connecting links, but

31

one may hazard a guess that the ciliates are greatly modified descendants of more primitive protozoan types, such as the early flagellates. Certainly the more highly evolved ciliates, at any rate, cannot be ancestral to advanced multicellular animals. But they are of interest in showing what a degree of complexity may be attained in the evolution of unicellular animals.

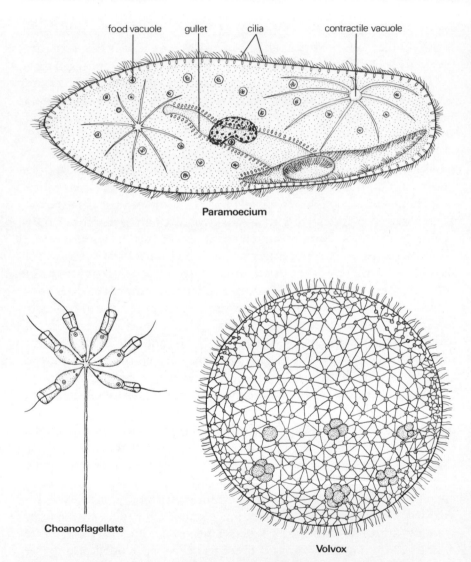

Figure 7. *Paramoecium* is a highly organized ciliated protozoan. The choanoflagellate and *Volvox* show different types of association of cells into colonies.

Sponges

The possibilities of evolutionary advances are limited in unicellular animals, despite the ends achieved by the ciliates. Such forms reproduce, as do most protozoans, by a cleavage of the cell into two daughter types; and this process necessitates a nearly complete destruction of the complex body pattern and a rebuilding of it in each of the two offspring. The activities of a cell are under control of the nucleus; it seems obvious that nuclear control becomes difficult in the case of a single-celled animal of complex structure, and especially so if there were a trend for increasing size.

Looking back at what actually happened, the proper mode for further evolutionary advance seems obvious to us – the development of a multicellular instead of a unicellular body. Subdivision into a series of cellular units would make for more effective nuclear control. And if, in addition, differentiation of cell types could take place, so that different groups of cells, forming tissues, could serve different functions, it would make for still greater efficiency.

This was, of course, the way in which the evolution of higher animal types was achieved. The result was an integrated multicellular organism – a metazoan, as zoologists term all such higher forms, in contrast to a single-celled protozoan. None of the actual animal types which made the transition from protozoans to metazoans has survived; but we can, here and there, pick up clues from existing forms as to the course followed.

It would seem reasonable to believe that the first stage would be a trend toward an aggregation of cells all of similar pattern; in other words the development of a colony of individuals, not yet forming a coherent organism. A tendency toward colony formation is seen in some of the flagellates of animal type, the collar-flagellates (or choano-flagellates), so called because the base of the flagellum is surrounded by a transparent cylindrical collar (figure 7). These flagellates, unlike most members of the group, are sessile, attached to the bottom by a stalk. Usually each collar-flagellate lives by itself in solitary fashion. But at times when the cell divides, the daughter cells remain attached to the same stalk, and a few divisions of this sort may lead to the formation of a small colony, all its members close to one another, but each living its own life.

For a slightly more advanced type of organization, we may turn to another flagellate, *Volvox* by name (although here we are dealing with a non-animal form, since *Volvox* contains food-manufacturing

33

chlorophyll and in consequence is technically to be regarded as a plant flagellate). Here we have a colony which may include some thousands of individual flagellates, embedded over the surface of a spherical ball of a jelly which they have secreted (figure 7). All the cells are exactly alike and, except that there seems to be some co-ordination of the action of the flagella in the swimming about of the sphere, there is no correlation between the activities of the cells. Each cell is an individual; they do not form an integrated organism.

Somewhat higher up the scale we reach, in the sponges, the phylum Porifera, animals consisting of a multiplicity of cells which are not merely a cluster of similar units, but are arranged in a definite pattern

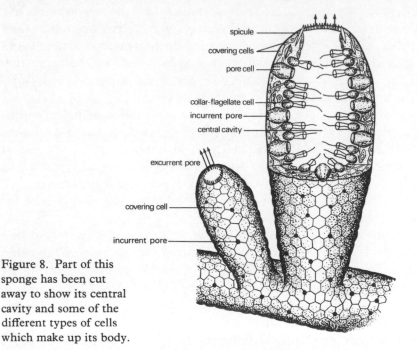

spicule

covering cells

pore cell

collar-flagellate cell

incurrent pore

central cavity

excurrent pore

covering cell

incurrent pore

Figure 8. Part of this sponge has been cut away to show its central cavity and some of the different types of cells which make up its body.

and have differentiated into a number of cell types serving different functions; we are not dealing here with a colony, but with a multi-cellular organism, albeit one of lowly structure. The sponges are a varied group, large and small, simple and complex; those familiar with the group recognize three major subdivisions and a host of distinct families. The basic pattern, however, is the same throughout.

The simplest smaller sponges are vase-shaped, attached at the lower end, with a large central cavity, a large opening at the top, and small pores perforating the side walls (figure 8); the larger ones, of more complicated build, are essentially elaborations of the same pattern, with subdivisions of the cavities and complexities in the passages between them. Water passes into the interior through the pores at the sides and passes out through the large excurrent pore at the top. The current is caused by the beating of flagella of numerous cells which line the entire interior of the sponge. These are collar-flagellates, very similar to the forms of that name which we described among the protozoans, but here they are not individuals, but cells of an organism. Like the protozoan collared forms, they ingest food particles, which come to them in the water current created by the flagella; they are responsible for the nutrition of the organism as a whole.

Were there no other cells in a sponge's body than this inner sheet of collar cells, we might still think of this structure as a colony. But although they are the most numerous, they are not the only kind present; we have in a sponge cell differentiation as well as multiplication. A series of flattened cells covers the outer surface of the sponge; the pores are lined and guarded by other types; still others form hard spicules of skeletal material which stiffen the bodies of many large sponges. These cells are not individuals; they are here parts of an organism, each contributing its share toward the maintenance and well-being of the whole.

As would be expected, the sponges appear to be a very ancient animal group, and since there is a tendency in many types for the formation of a stiffening skeletal structure, a fair number of fossils are known. They were already present in the Lower Cambrian in considerable variety, and hence their origin must have occurred at a considerably earlier time. Although this is disputed, the presence here of the peculiar type of cells known elsewhere in the collared flagellates strongly suggests that they took origin from that flagellate group of protozoans.

But interesting as are the sponges in furnishing an example of a primitive stage in the evolution of a multicellular type of organism, it is universally agreed that they do not form part of the main evolutionary line leading from protozoans to higher animal types. They are a sterile side-branch of the family tree.

Primitive Metazoans – the Coelenterates

If the sponges are not actual transitional forms between unicellular animals and higher forms, where are we, then, to look for evidence as

35

to the route that was followed upward? It is too much to hope that actual intermediate types would have survived unchanged over the many hundreds of millions of years since this major advance took place. However, by taking a broad view of the nature and structure of the advanced animals of today, and tracing downward from more complex types to simpler ones, we can gain some general idea of the nature of the first well-organized multicellular animals, the primitive metazoans, from which all later groups were to be evolved.

When we examine any one of the advanced sorts of metazoans – whether lobster, insect, fish or man, for example – we find them to be highly complex in structure, with a variety of body tissues and numerous organs of complicated build. But among marine animals, such as the various types of worm-like forms, we find simpler structures, fewer and simpler organs. In such creatures, most of the cells of the body tend to be arranged in three layers – an outer sheet of cells, essentially a surface skin layer, technically termed the ectoderm; a middle body layer, the mesoderm; and an inner layer, the endoderm, lining the digestive cavity. Further, in some of these lowly types we find that the digestive tract, which in all higher types is a tube, with mouth at one end and anus at the other, has but a single opening. Still lower down the line of living things we reach forms in which the middle body layer is absent (or practically absent), and there is little to the creature but an outer sheet of skin cells, the ectoderm, and a layer of digestive cells, the endoderm, lining a pouch-like gut cavity. Simple little animals of this sort are found today amongst the coelenterates, which we will discuss presently; it would appear that here we are very close to the ancestral metazoan pattern.

Evidence supporting such a conclusion can be gained by a study of the development of the individual among the higher animal groups; there are many variations, but in a majority of cases a general pattern emerges. As we have said, old Haeckel's ideas of recapitulation, that 'ontogeny repeats phylogeny', are not to be taken too seriously; but animals tend to be conservative in their modes of embryological development, and it is suggestive that many higher types show in early embryonic life a series of developmental stages which parallel closely the series of stages which we believe may have happened in the evolutionary progress from protozoan to metazoan (figure 9). The individual starts life as a fertilized egg cell, corresponding, in phylogeny, to the protozoan. Repeated divisions of the egg cell result in the formation of a spherical structure, comparable to a phylogenetic colonial stage, such as seen in *Volvox*. Then there occurs, in many cases, a phenomenon technically called gastrulation, whereby the sphere becomes a two-layered structure, by the pushing of the sheet of cells of one half of the sphere into the interior of the other hemisphere, somewhat as one may, with one's thumb, push one side of a soft rubber ball into the other half. The result of this process gives us an embryo with two sheets of cells; an outer layer on the surface, corresponding to the 'skin' layer, the epidermis, of the adult, and an inner layer surrounding the future gut cavity, forming the endoderm. In all advanced animal groups, embryonic history, of course, proceeds much farther; but at this stage we have a miniature replica of the body structure which we believe to have been present in the first metazoan animals of a long-past era.

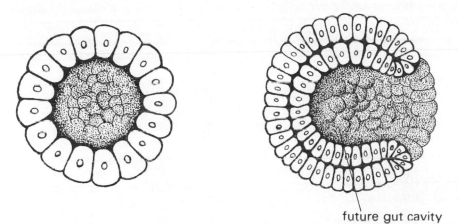

future gut cavity

Blastula　　　　　　　　　　　**Gastrula**

Figure 9. The blastula and gastrula are early stages in the development of many higher animals.

So far we have been talking in vague terms of a hypothetical ancestral type. Let us now see how closely we can approach this ideal in terms of actual present-day animals. The forms which best fill the bill are members of the phylum Coelenterata. As we shall see, there are certain specializations which debar typical coelenterates from a directly ancestral position, but a majority of workers agree that some of them are close to the ancestral type.

The better-known coelenterates are such forms as the corals, sea-anemones and jelly-fishes; for general descriptive purposes, however, let us deal with a tiny animal named *Hydra,* abundant, but seldom

37

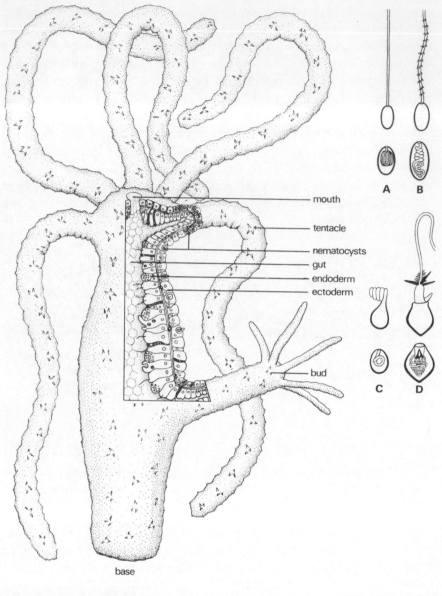

mouth
tentacle
nematocysts
gut
endoderm
ectoderm

bud

base

Hydra

Figure 10. Part of the body of this *Hydra* has been cut away to show the different cells of which it is composed; it is also in the process of growing a new individual, or 'bud'. Enlarged views of different types of nematocyst before and after discharge are shown at right: A and B are adhesive types, nematocyst type C winds around its prey and type D injects poison into the prey.

observed, in fresh-water ponds (figure 10). *Hydra*, when fully extended, is but half an inch or so in length. There is a slender, vase-shaped body, with a stalk below, by which it is usually attached. At the upper end is an opening surrounded by a series of slender arms or tentacles. The animal's cells are nearly all arranged in two simple layers, corresponding to the ectoderm and endoderm of our hypothetical ancestor. Most of the cells of the outer layer form a protective skin; most of those within have digestion of food as their sole function. They surround a cavity which is that of the gut – a simple sac, with the upper opening of the sac acting both as a mouth for food reception and as a point for discharge of digestive wastes. The only major structural departure from our concept of a simple ancestral metazoan that *Hydra* exhibits is the development of a circle of tentacular arms, which aid in obtaining food, around and above the mouth. All the features mentioned may have arisen through a series of stages of cell multiplication and differentiations parallel to those which produced the sponges, but here formed a body equally simple in nature but of a rather different type.

There is, however, one specialization found not only in *Hydra* but in every member of this phylum which shows that coelenterates *as we see them today* are not the direct ancestors of other metazoan groups. This is their possession of specialized stinging cells. We shall later mention a number of other sessile types which have much the appearance of a *Hydra* (although with more highly developed internal structures). Sessile forms of this type are mostly filter-feeders, who depend for a living on straining small food particles out of the waters surrounding them. Modern coelenterates, however, are more ambitious in their feeding habits and can kill and capture larger prey by means of their stinging cells. Scattered over the surface of the body – and particularly abundant on the tentacles – are the so-called thread cells – nematocysts (figure 10, A–D). These contain a cavity, open to the exterior, in which there is a coiled-up thread of protoplasm. When these cells are stimulated, the threads can be shot out rapidly and penetrate the body of a nearby animal, whether enemy or potential food supply. Most prominent of several thread-cell types are those which have barbs, making them tiny harpoons; these can sting and inject a poisonous substance with the ability to paralyse or kill a small animal. By means of these weapons, offensive as well as defensive, a seemingly innocent-looking little coelenterate is able to become, even if sessile, a carnivore, eating prey of relatively large size.

39

Certainly such specialized structures were not present in the ancestral metazoans; they are universal in modern coelenterates, but are known in no other group. The ancestral metazoans may well have been animals much like a *Hydra*, but without these stinging cells. For the most part, the descendants of these ancestral forms progressed to become originators of more advanced lines: but as a result of the evolution of these stinging cells, one set of descendants were able to achieve, as coelenterates, a moderate degree of success while still remaining on a lowly level of organization.

For the modern coelenterates are a varied and successful group. *Hydra*, which we have described, is a dweller in fresh water, but most coelenterates (as probably was the ancestral metazoan) are sea-dwellers. Many of the marine forms are similar in structure to *Hydra*, but generally are found in colonies, much of the increase in numbers of individuals coming about by budding off of new individuals from old, rather than by normal reproductive processes. A second group of coelenterates – purely marine – produces individuals which can be

Figure 11. This piece of coral shows several living polyps. Below them are the limestone columns which they have secreted.

40

termed polyps, which are in general rather larger and more stoutly and complexly built than the tiny and delicate members of the *Hydra*-like group; the sea-anemone and, especially, the numerous varieties of corals, are representative. Notable, of course, in the corals is the fact that each polyp secretes about itself a protective cup of limestone (figure 11). The limestone reefs off tropical islands are formed by the accumulation of the skeletons of generations of dead coral polyps, whose living descendants populate the reef surface; and many limestone formations in the geologic column are composed of fossil coral cups.

But when we have described the various types of polyps found among the coelenterates, we have, literally, covered only half of the story of this phylum. For there exists within the phylum a second and very different type of body plan – the medusa (students of coelenterates seem to like fabulous monsters!) of which the jelly-fishes are typical. A medusa is, in strong contrast to a polyp, free-floating and unattached, and can even, by contraction and expansion of its 'bell', do some swimming under its own power. Its general appearance is quite different from that of a *Hydra* or other polyp, but the basic structure is the same. A jelly-fish is essentially a polyp turned upside down. The original lower surface, forming a stalk in a *Hydra*, is spread out above to form the umbrella-shaped 'bell'; the mouth, originally opening upward, opens downward; the fringing tentacles, too, are directed downward rather than up.

What is the relationship between polyp and medusa? One group of coelenterates, that of the corals and sea-anemones, includes only polyps in its membership. A second includes jelly-fishes, often colonial in structure and including a considerable number of budded-off individuals in a single floating assemblage; some of these, such as the Portuguese man-of-war, may be of great size and dangerous to meet. Most show no evidence of a polyp structure at any stage. But another situation is met with in a third, and probably more primitive, group, to which *Hydra* belongs. Here we encounter the curious fact that some of these animals lead a double, Jekyll-and-Hyde existence, with an alternation in successive generations between life as a polyp and life as a small jelly-fish (figure 12). Some forms closely related to *Hydra*, such as *Obelia*, may live for some time as a polyp, but then bud off a small free-swimming medusa. This, if fortunate, mates, and an embryo is formed which develops into a polyp and thus begins a second cycle in this curious phenomenon of alternation of generations.

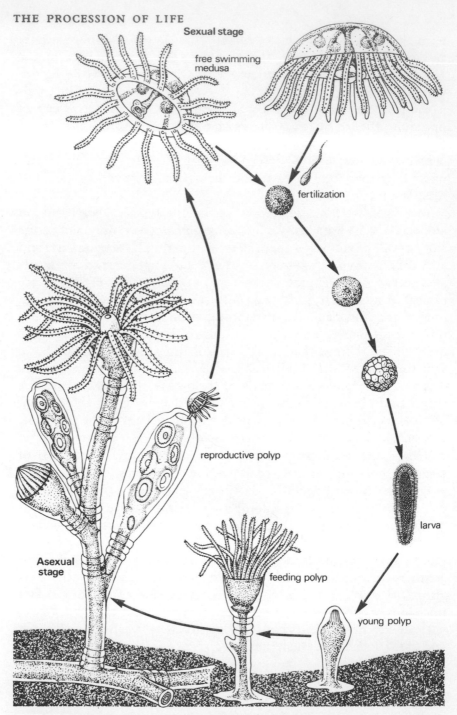

Figure 12. The life-cycle of *Obelia*, a colonial coelenterate.

We cannot be sure which of the two body types – polyp or medusa – is the primary one, but it is reasonable to conclude that the polyp, more simply built, is the ancestral form. A polyp is normally attached, but not tightly attached; and if, by the budding process so common in coelenterates, a polyp were produced that could free itself from the parent and float a bit, even if only for a short distance, this could well be advantageous in permitting the populating of new areas of the sea bottom. The medusa as we see it today may have evolved by gradual improvements of floating and swimming adaptations from an ancestral free-floating polyp. And the complex types of oceanic jelly-fishes probably represent forms whose ancestors alternated generations, but which appear to have become so completely adapted to the medusa type of life that interpolation of a polyp phase was without survival value and was reduced or eliminated.

Symbiosis is a term describing the condition under which we sometimes find two animals or plants living together in mutually profitable combination. Among plants, for example, a lichen is not a simple organism, but a combination of a green alga and a fungus, each of which supplies features useful for the success of the whole. Among animals, the sessile coelenterates show examples of this condition. For example, a hermit crab living in a snail shell and a sea-anemone attached to the shell may be mutually beneficial. The stinging cells of the anemone protect the crab from attack; on the other hand, the anemone may be nourished by scraps from the prey which the crab has killed and partially devoured. Many polyps, such as little *Hydra*, normally include in their tissues single-celled green algae; the algal cell utilizes the waste carbon dioxide given off by the *Hydra* cells, and in return gives off, as a result of its metabolic processes, oxygen useful to the animal.

Because of the soft-bodied nature of a jelly-fish or a hydroid-like polyp, our geologic history of coelenterates is a fragmentary one. As regards the corals, we have, as we would expect, abundant records of their shells of varied types as far back as the Ordovician. And even in the Pre-Cambrian there are impressions of forms of medusa-like structure. The coelenterates are a very ancient, as well as a very primitive group of metazoans. And it is not impossible that some of the older types included in the phylum by the palaeontologists lacked the specialized stinging cells, and hence may have been close to the truly ancestral metazoan types.

A clue is afforded by the Ctenophora, sometimes included among

43

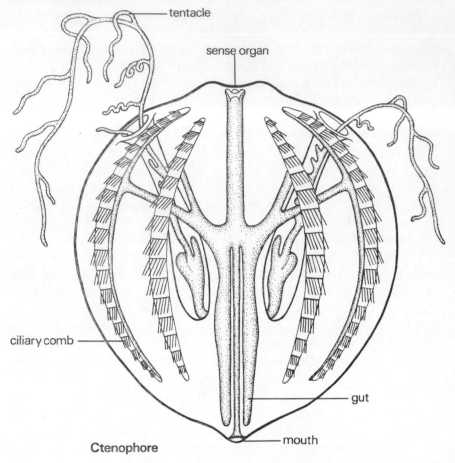

Ctenophore

Figure 13. *Pleurobrachia*, a little ctenophoran about an inch across.

the coelenterates but currently generally regarded as a separate, if minor, phylum. The ctenophores, or comb-jellies, are small, soft-bodied, translucent, free-floating ocean forms which are usually globular in shape (figure 13). Like the coelenterates, they are simply built, with little structure except an outer 'skin' layer and a stomach lining. They lack the diagnostic stinging cells of the coelenterates; but, on the other hand, they are characterized by the presence of a radially-arranged series of comb-like structures to which they owe their name. Each 'comb' consists of a row of cilia, the beating of which affords the animal a mild means of movement. The comb-jellies are

44

unknown as fossils. But it is possible to imagine that there existed in the pre-Palaeozoic seas small metazoans which had not developed either the specialized stinging cells of the coelenterates or the equally specialized ctenophore comb-rows. The ancestral metazoans may well have been forms of this sort.

Chapter 3

Worms

IN the last chapter we traced out, as best we could from such clues as are available, the probable course of early evolution of animals from single-celled forms to simple multicellular forms – simple metazoans with differentiation of functions between cell types, but with, in general, few complications in structure and with differentiation in function mainly confined to the establishment of an outer layer – the ectoderm – and a gut lining – the endoderm – within. Once such primitive metazoans became established, there began a major radiation into the vast range of higher animal forms seen in the fossil record and present with us today. The almost countless types of metazoans known to students of zoology are grouped by them, on the grounds of similarity and probable relationships, into major groups termed phyla (making use of an old Greek word meaning 'tribes'). The chapters which follow make an attempt to trace out the evolutionary story of such major groups. I shall consider the nature of the membership of each group, attempt to follow the evolutionary development within the phylum, and consider the probable position of each group on the evolutionary 'family tree'.

But in doing this, I shall not attempt to be encyclopaedic (nor more than necessarily boring). Most zoologists recognize more than a score of phyla. A good part of them are major groups, worthy of our attention. But a few 'lesser breeds', little groups of little animals not very important in themselves or in their evolutionary significance, I will frankly neglect. In this category, for example, are the chaetognaths, or arrow worms; the tiny water bears, or Tardigrada; the pentastomids, odd little parasites that nestle in the breathing apparatus of snakes and crocodiles; and so on. Let us confine ourselves to the larger and, I hope, more interesting groups.

What types of evidence are available in attempting to work out the evolutionary patterns among the higher animals? In the early stages of the evolution of animal life we were forced to rely on the study of modern survivors in obtaining clues to events which had occurred in the far past youth of the earth. In studying the metazoan phyla we frequently have available material of actual ancestral types, for members of many phyla have shells or other hard skeletal parts which can be preserved in fossil form. But even here we are restricted in various ways. As was mentioned previously, many of the major groups of higher animals were already fully differentiated when fossils first became abundant in the early Cambrian. Hence, in the case of phyla which do have skeletons, the fossil evidence, while giving us valuable information about evolutionary progress and differentiation *within* the group, tells us nothing as to its ultimate origin. And, further, even among the metazoans, many groups remained soft-bodied and hence are seldom represented in the record of the rocks.

But in more advanced metazoans the living animals, due to the complexity of their structures, can give us more to go on than was the case with simpler forms. As we shall see later in this chapter, body layers may become more complex in nature and arrangement; body cavities of one type or another may appear; varied complex organs evolve in this group and that; there are varied patterns of symmetry. All these structures of the adult living representatives of the different phyla yield clues of value. Further, the mode of embryonic development of complex adult structures is seen to vary in significant fashion from group to group. Still again, many of the types to be considered are water-dwellers among which the young are for a period tiny free-floating ciliated larvae; larval types have varied patterns and may furnish clues to relationships which would hardly be suspected from inspection of adult animals alone.

Some of the features of adult and embryonic patterns of significance will be mentioned later in this chapter. But there are, besides matters of structure, complex weaving patterns of behaviour associated with food-getting which can be followed throughout the successive phyla we shall study. Most of the structural adaptations we shall describe are devised to facilitate the obtaining of a livelihood. Although there are all sorts of variations, there are two basic ways of making a living: the animal can sit and wait for food to come to it, or it can actively seek it; it can be, to put it simply and crudely, a 'sitter' or a 'go-getter' (figure 14).

Very likely, sitting motionless and waiting receptively for the arrival of food materials in the water currents flowing past was a very primitive mode of metazoan existence. The coelenterates, as we have

47

seen, are animals more or less of this sort, but they were able to be somewhat predacious in nature through their possession of stinging cells; in a later chapter we shall describe other sessile forms of a simpler nature as regards their mode of living, existing as filter-feeders on food particles brought to them by passing waters. Animals of this sort generally lack the bilateral symmetry, with right and left sides, characteristic of more active animals. Essentially, they only know top and bottom; the lower end attached to the sea bottom, either directly or

Figure 14. The passive and active methods of obtaining food.

by a stalk, the upper end opening, so to speak, to the world. The animal is arrayed around a vertical axis; it makes little difference as to where, around the circuit of the body, any structures are placed. A form of this sort tends to acquire more or less of a radial type of symmetry.

Fundamentally different in pattern is a typical food-seeker. Movement – primarily in the search for food – is the keynote. A lengthwise horizontal build is the best type of body plan, with front and back ends, top and bottom sides, and bilateral symmetry, one side of the usually slender body being a mirror image of the other; an arrow-like shape is the ideal. This type of structure is attained, for example, by various types of worms, utilized with major success by the great group of arthropods, such as crustaceans and insects, and also attained, tardily but successfully, by our own group, that of the backboned animals.

The contrast between these two major types is, I am afraid, an

48

oversimplified one as presented above. The story is not a simple and straightforward one of clear separation of active and passive groups early in history and a wholehearted adherence to the life pattern first adopted. Far from it. As we shall see, various descendants of once active animals have slumped to sloth or, more shocking still, have become parasitic in habits; and on the other hand, the story of our group, that of the vertebrates, shows that activity and aggressive success may follow a beginning in sedentary simplicity.

Let us begin our survey of the higher metazoans with an account of the various types of worms, which well illustrate the arrow-shaped type of body characteristic of animals which lead, or are at any rate capable of leading, an active life. Once all forms in this general category were lumped as a 'phylum Vermes'. But serious study soon showed that a great amount of difference existed between the various types of worms, and, in fact, it is now realized that there are some four separate phyla of worms of various degrees of complexity of organization, to say nothing of half a dozen minor groups which are worms of a sort, but so aberrant that they are likewise accorded phylum rank.

Logically, of course, our account should begin with the simplest-built and most primitive of worms and work upward. But it perhaps makes the story simpler to understand if we reverse things, begin with a description of the most advanced worm types, get an idea of how far in evolution a worm can go as a worm, and then attempt to trace the story backward and downward to simpler beginnings.

Annelids

Without question the most highly organized worms are forms belonging to the phylum Annelida. The common earthworms belong to this phylum. But the earthworms form a side branch, and probably a rather degenerate side branch, of the annelids. It is in the oceans that we find the more highly organized and typical members of the phylum.

Such a typical member is the worm named *Nereis*, a marine form about a foot in length, common on seashores nearly the world over (figure 15). *Nereis* may swim about freely by graceful undulations of the body, aided by two long rows of little paddle-like appendages. More frequently, however, it is to be found, at rest but alert for prey, beneath a rock or partially hidden in a burrow.

I will devote a considerable amount of time to a description of the

49

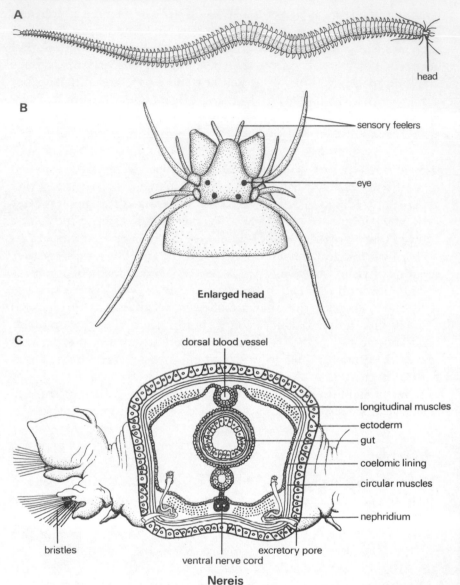

Nereis

Figure 15. A. Complete ragworm, *Nereis*, seen from above while swimming; the undulation of the body and its division into a series of segments, each with a pair of small paddle-like appendages, can be seen. B. View of its head region from above, showing the eyes and sensory feelers. C. Section through the body of *Nereis*, showing the coelomic cavity which surrounds the gut and main blood vessels, and the little excretory nephridia. On the left can be seen one of the paddle-like appendages.

50

anatomy of *Nereis*, not because I am particularly fond of worms (I am not) but because this annelid, as a worm of advanced type, exhibits many of the structural features to be found in advanced metazoans of any sort; once we have an idea of *Nereis*' anatomy, we can note the structural features of other groups in much briefer fashion.

The long slender *Nereis* body is, of course, bilaterally symmetrical in plan. Most active animals tend to develop sense organs, which enable them to swim effectively and to locate enemies and – most essential – their prospective prey. The natural place for the location of such organs is, of course, the front end – technically the anterior end – of the body, and in active forms this tends to result in the formation of a head region (figure 15 B). Formation of a head is not far advanced in *Nereis*, but we do find here, close to the tip of the animal's body, a series of little 'feelers', tentacles which appear to be useful not merely as tactile organs, but also as the seat of a primitive sense of smell. Further, *Nereis* has eyes – two pairs of them, small but apparently fairly effective organs of vision. Light perception is, of course, a means by which an animal can obtain information of the utmost value about his surroundings, and we find that light-perceiving organs have evolved, apparently in independent fashion, in a great variety of animals, some on a much lower level of organization than *Nereis*.

A most obvious feature of the *Nereis* body is that it is divided lengthwise into a series of rings, or segments (a feature to which the name annelid refers). Segmentation is a basic feature of the annelid body plan and is, we shall see, developed with variations in a great variety of animal types. Except for the head region, almost every segment of the worm's body appears externally almost like every other, and this same segmental repetition is found in great measure in its internal structures as well.

Internally *Nereis* is a much more complexly built organism than such a simple metazoan as a coelenterate. As in those more lowly animals, there is, of course, a gut for food reception and digestion. But whereas in coelenterates there is but a single opening, annelids (and most other forms of any degree of complexity) have notably improved the gut's efficiency by the development of separate mouth and anus, setting up one-way traffic in the digestive tube. The worm's mouth, with small but efficient jaws, is situated on the under side of the head; the second opening, the anus, is at the far end of the body.

In a coelenterate almost the whole of the animal's simple structure consists merely of an outer layer, the ectoderm, and the inner gut

51

lining, the endoderm; the annelid worm is far superior in internal construction, for there is here formed – as in all other metazoans of any degree of advancement – a middle body layer, a mesoderm, in addition to the ectoderm and endoderm of simpler metazoans. Much of this mesoderm is arranged in sheets which form the lining of a liquid-filled body cavity, technically the coelom, a further important structure in advanced animal types, which occupies much of the space between the skin externally and the gut within (figure 15 C). The presence of a well-defined cavity of this sort is very advantageous, for it allows freer play for the animal's musculature and for movements and readjustments of the gut tube and other internal organs. Small and simple animals can 'breathe' – that is, obtain the oxygen needed for their metabolic processes – by absorbing it over the general surface of the body, and can also get rid of liquid body wastes by passing them outward into the water through the general area of the skin. *Nereis* is rather big for this, and its skin in general too stout, and there have developed special organs to serve these functions. The paired rows of paddle-like structures have a delicate surface structure and serve as gills for obtaining oxygen; to get rid of nitrogenous wastes, a pair of tubules is present in each segment, which serve as a battery of little kidney-like structures, termed nephridia.

But we have still not exhausted the citing of advanced structures developed by *Nereis*. In a coelenterate there is a bit of nerve tissue, but it is poorly organized – merely a diffuse net of fibres and cells. For the movements of an active animal such as this marine worm, nervous system control and co-ordination are needed – and provided. There runs the length of the body, beneath the gut, a stout cord of nerve fibres; the cell bodies to which the fibres pertain are, in successive segments, clustered into swellings on the cord termed ganglia. Since the animal's activities are influenced in major fashion by the sense organs of the head, it is reasonable to expect, and find, that the head contains a particularly large ganglion – rather, a pair of connected ganglia – which is a brain of a primitive sort.

And, finally, there is a well-developed circulatory system. In a small and primitive form materials such as food from the intestine and oxygen taken in from the air can reach all the individual cells of the animal by diffusion through the liquids of the body. *Nereis* is too big and too complex in structure for this to be effective. Instead, there is an efficient system of blood vessels, with the blood completely walled off from the general body fluids. Blood flows forward through a dorsal vessel above the gut, backward through a ventral vessel below it. The two are connected by smaller tubes, the capillaries; numerous little vessels of this sort pass through the side 'paddles', where oxygen is picked up, or traverse the gut walls, collecting digested food materials.

At first thought one would have tended to be contemptuous of such an animal as *Nereis* and dismiss him as a 'mere worm'. Worm he is, but an exceedingly well-organized little animal at that. This annelid has already developed, or at least begun to develop, almost every type of organ present in advanced forms of any sort. Some of the groups described in later chapters have inherited their structural patterns, and in some cases the mode of development, from forms of the general *Nereis* type. Other advanced forms have attained structural complexity, we believe, quite independently of annelid worms (vertebrates, for one). But even so, a comparable organization has developed.

Nereis is one example of a great variety of marine annelid worms found in the seas today. Also members of this phylum, as we have mentioned, are the earthworms, which possess most of the basic structural features of their marine cousins, but are presumably a degenerate annelid branch. Still another side-branch, highly specialized for blood-sucking, are the leeches. Since annelids are soft-bodied, their fossil history is poorly known. However, we are fortunate in knowing a few specimens of earthworms as far back as the Ordovician; and as regards the marine annelids, the mid-Cambrian Burgess shales reveal the presence of about a dozen genera at that early date. The annelids are an ancient group, despite their highly developed body organization.

Lower Worm Groups

If, now, we attempt to explore the pedigree of the annelids and try to discern the path along which worm evolution passed on the way upward from simple ancestral metazoans, we meet with only indifferent success. There are living today several phyla of worms more simply organized than the annelids; but most are obviously specialized, and many are parasites which are quite surely degenerate and far off the main evolutionary track. Further, none of these groups is known in fossil form.

Our best view of a worm type which, although quite surely not a

53

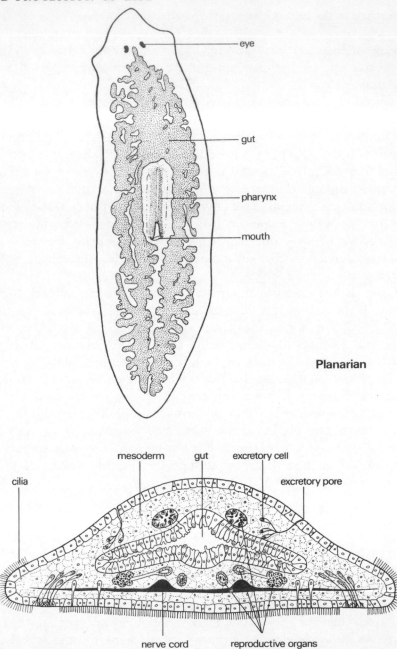

Planarian

Figure 16. Above, a complete planarian, which is about a quarter of an inch long in life. Below, a section through its body, showing the organs lying in the loosely-built mesoderm.

54

direct ancestor to the annelids, shows many of the features to be expected in such an ancestor, is to be found in the phylum Platyhelminthes, the flatworms, and especially a group of small free-living flatworms abundant in fresh waters, termed planarians (figure 16). As we shall see, these small creatures are far below the annelids in their structure, but, on the other hand, they are far above the coelenterates. Planarians are definitely capable of active, directed movement, and are very definitely bilaterally symmetrical in build; the flat body is more or less elongate, and in some the head, at the 'leading' end, is a broad triangle, giving the animal the shape of an arrow. In some regards, the planarians show a development of organ systems which does not compare too unfavourably with the annelid condition. There is a developed nervous system, which here consists of a pair of lengthwise cords, and a pair of swellings for a brain of sorts in the head. There is a pair of eyes atop the head, although these are inferior in structure to those of typical marine annelids. A good series of excretory tubules is present as in annelids to perform kidney-like functions, and reproductive organs are well developed. And there is a mesoderm.

So far, so good. But in many basic features the flatworm level is far below that of the annelids. To begin with, although a third body layer is present as mesoderm, there are not the well-formed body cavities constructed by the mesoderm of an annelid; instead, the mesoderm is merely a loosely built web of tissue forming a sort of stuffing for the body between skin and gut. Again, there is no circulatory system. Still again – and still more important – is the fact that there is no segmentation; the body is, as in ancestral metazoans, a single unit structure (and one, in fact, so loosely organized that a fair fraction of it can regenerate a whole new animal). And, finally, the digestive tract is still on the coelenterate level. There is a mouth opening midway of the underside, within which branches of the gut tube ramify into all parts of the body. But there is no anal opening; waste must return whence it entered.

The planarians exhibit, despite some specializations of their own, the type of structure to be expected in a simple metazoan which had begun to follow the active type of bilateral organization leading, with greater success, to the annelids. But none of the numerous other worm types are of much aid in rounding out the evolutionary picture of progress, for most appear to have, so to speak, evolved sideways instead of forward (figure 17). For example, the roundworms of the

55

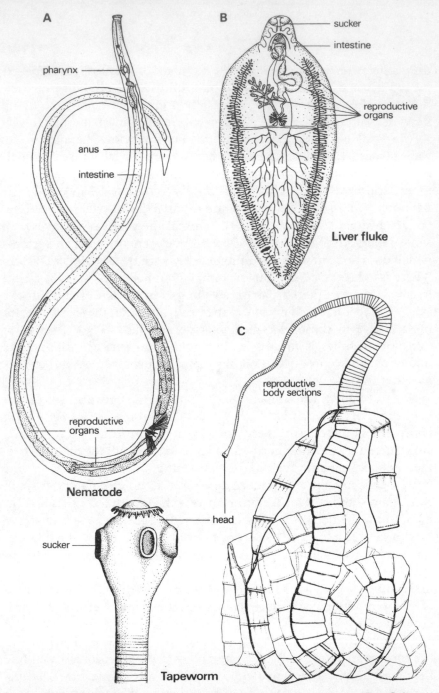

Figure 17. Some types of parasitic worms. A, *Ascaris*, a roundworm. B, a fluke showing the sucker with which it grasps the host's tissues. C, a tapeworm; the head (of which an enlarged view is also shown) is embedded in the host's tissues and constantly buds off reproductive body-sections which grow in size.

phylum Nematoda include numerous tiny forms which are more advanced than the planarians in the fact that there is a developed anus, but are much more lowly than the planarians in nearly every other regard. The great majority of lower worm types, however, have become parasites, frequently with a high degree of specialization combined with structural degeneration. Among the roundworms, some are free dwelling, and present in the soil in fabulously large numbers; but many are parasites, and the group includes not only the ordinary roundworms which may be mildly annoying visitors to the intestines of man and other mammals, but more serious parasites, such as the hookworm, once very common in the southern United States, the trichina, and the filaria, which may cause a human limb to grow to elephant-like proportions by blocking lymph vessels. Among the flatworms, relatives of the harmless planarians are the flukes, which have developed suckers for clinging to a host. Some are relatively harmless external parasites, but others are invaders, including the dangerous liver fluke. Still another flatworm group is that of the tapeworms, remarkably degenerate in that they have completely lost the digestive tract, relying for sustenance on absorption of the intestinal juices of their hosts.

Chapter 4

Arthropods

IN this chapter we will describe the evolution of the phylum Arthropoda, and at some length. For this phylum includes a vast array of animals, from the crabs and lobsters and their crustacean relatives in the sea, through the scorpions and spiders and the centipedes and millipedes, to the myriad insect hosts.

Arthropod Structure

The name arthropod means 'jointed feet'; but this is a modest way to put it. It is not only the feet which are jointed; it is the whole animal. Perhaps the simplest way to give a broad picture of the nature of an arthropod is to imagine a progressive annelid which has developed a pair of legs on all, or nearly all, the segments of his body, and has then encased himself, trunk, legs and all, in armour – armour with well-developed articulations between the body segments and good joints between the successive segments, often numerous, of each leg.

It is not too difficult to describe the structure of a typical arthropod; but it is difficult to see just what it is that has made the arthropods so successful. To begin with, arthropods are generally active seekers after food and hence, as would be expected, have the bilateral body build of a 'go-getter'. Apart from the armour and the legs, the arthropod body is basically that of one of the better annelid worms – with improvements. As in an annelid, the whole body is a segmented one (in the embryo, at least) with such structures as the digestive tract and the nerve cord (on the under side, as in annelids) traversing every segment, from stem to stern, and with many structures repeated in one segment after another. But there is more of a trend for consolidation and concentration than in any annelid. We have seen that in that worm group there is some concentration of nervous and sensory structures at the front end of the animal. This is emphatically the case in arthropods. In all members of the group the first six segments are,

58

even early in the embryo, fused together and set off as a well-defined head. But many arthropods go further in differentiating body parts. Primitive arthropods appear to have had a long series of body segments. Behind such head as he has, an annelid pays little attention to which segment is which. But many arthropods, as if in search of efficiency, have tended to reduce the number of segments and to concentrate most of their body organs in a relatively few expanded segments behind the head region (figure 18). This region, the thorax, may be more or less consolidated with the head (as is obvious in the dinner-table lobster) or set off distinctly, as in insects. The word 'thorax' is,

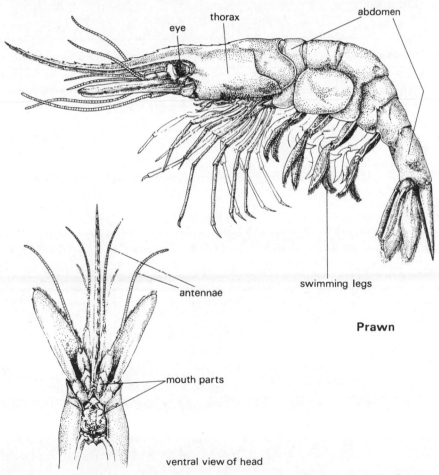

eye
thorax
abdomen
antennae
swimming legs

Prawn

mouth parts

ventral view of head

Figure 18. The muscular abdomen of the prawn is quite distinct from the thorax, in which lie most of the body organs. The head bears sensory antennae and eyes, and the more anterior limbs are modified into specialized mouth parts.

59

of course, borrowed from human anatomy, where it refers to the chest. But a human chest contains only heart and lungs; the arthropod thorax, when well developed, may contain many important parts of the digestive tract, liver, and reproductive glands. Behind the thorax is the abdomen, mainly muscular, and hence not too comparable to the abdomen of a vertebrate such as ourselves. We tend to think of this series of segments in a lobster as the tail; but it is not really comparable to the tail of a fish or a monkey, for the animal's intestine and reproductive tubes traverse every segment to the end – or nearly the end, at any rate.

Armour apart, typical arthropods show a whole series of features in which they are advanced and specialized over their annelid ancestors. We have noted that typically six anterior segments are efficiently fused to form the arthropod head. Here there is a strong tendency to accumulate a considerable mass of ganglionic nerve tissue to form a brain of sorts, capable of working the jaw parts and of receiving sensory impressions and passing pertinent instructions along the nerve cord to the appropriate muscles of the body and appendages. Sensory structures are usually well developed in these active animals. The most anterior pair of appendages are generally transformed into sensitive feeling organs, the antennae (figure 18). Many a lowly invertebrate may develop eyes of a simple sort. These may persist in arthropods, but most arthropods have unique structures in a pair of compound eyes. Such an eye, often of large size compared to the bulk of the animal, consists of hundreds or even thousands of units, arranged something like the cells in a honeycomb, to form a bulging hemisphere. Each 'cell' is a simple structure, which only sees a tiny portion of the available view; but the sum total of the whole mosaic, received by the arthropod brain, gives him very good vision indeed; vision surpassed, it is probable, only by the eyes of some vertebrates. Some, but not all, arthropods have structures comparable in a way to our ears, which give a sense of balance or hearing or both, and in addition there may be sensory bristles back on the body or limbs. An efficient blood circulation is necessary; this is attained in arthropods not by complexity, but by simplification as compared with the worm ancestor. A heart is present dorsally as a pulsating tube; from it arteries lead to various parts of the body. But the system is not a closed one; there are no capillaries, and the blood, after bathing the various organs, oozes back to the heart through a series of large blood cavities. Small animals with a soft body surface can readily breathe through the skin;

a chitin-covered arthropod cannot. Instead, water-dwelling arthropods develop gills beneath the thorax or abdomen – thin-walled plates or filaments, extending from the body wall or connected with the limbs, through which oxygen and carbon dioxide can easily pass.

The armour in which the whole arthropod is encased differs basically from that which is found among our own relatives, the vertebrates. In a turtle or an armadillo, for example, the bony surface armour is produced by living cells lying well within the skin, and even the horny scales of a lizard are made of modified cells of the lizard skin. In contrast, the arthropod armour is secreted at the skin surface and laid down completely external to the live parts of the animal. Usually there is first formed a thin waxy insulating layer; beneath this, however, the main bulk of the outer skeleton is made of chitin, a horny material similar to our fingernails. It is tough, but generally flexible; however, especially in many crustaceans, it is stiffened by having mineral salts laid down in its substance, so that it becomes, for its thickness, as unyielding as bone.

This arthropod outer skeleton forms a highly useful set of structures. As a major feature, of course, it holds the whole body tidily in shape; even in the original water home of the arthropods, a soft bulgy body would be hard to manipulate, particularly for an animal of any size. If the entire body were encased in a single solid structure, there would be a great loss of manœuvrability; but since the armour is basically built in segmental pieces, flexibility is retained. To be sure, as we have said, there is always some consolidation at the front end of the body, to form a head and often a thorax; but the back part of the body is usually persistently segmented, with movable joints between successive segments which allow good up-and-down movement (although not much from side to side).

The development of limb armour is highly advantageous. For swimming in the waters which were the ancestral home of the arthropods, a segmental series of stiffened 'oars' do a much better job than a set of softer structures. Many water-dwelling arthropods are essentially bottom-dwellers, and even in the water a leg stiffened by a chitin skeleton is more efficient for walking than a soft appendage. When arthropods attained the land, they could, with these firm structures, walk about erect, clear of the ground, instead of belly-crawling, as a worm or slug must do.

But limbs can be used for other purposes than locomotion, and are so used by arthropods. We have already mentioned that one pair of 'limbs' in the head region has been transformed into antennae. Again, how to eat? A small marine animal may take in tiny food particles by the beating of cilia and the setting up of water currents which reach the mouth. But if an ambitious arthropod of any size attempts to feed on larger objects, how is it to gather this food and get it into the mouth?

Our own group, the vertebrates, solved this problem by taking some of the skeletal bars already present between the gills (and thus accessory to breathing purposes) and modifying them into biting jaws. Ancestral arthropods had no such structures available. But plenty of legs were at hand. An anterior pair of appendages is some-times enlarged as grasping claws for seizing prey. Others may shorten, cluster about the mouth, and aid in treating the food and stuffing it into the mouth, to begin its satisfying course through the digestive tract.

Protection is, of course, a major advantage of an external skeleton. Our own internal skeleton is a very efficient structure for support and locomotion, but leaves us defenceless from attack; if a vertebrate is to be protected, it must add a second, external skeleton, with an in-efficient increase in ponderousness. The arthropod obtains support and protection combined.

When we speak of protection, we tend to think, of course, of protec-tion from predators. But the arthropod armour is also a protection against vicissitudes of other sorts, both physical and chemical. Any highly organized animal contains body fluids in its tissues which must remain stable in amount and chemical composition if it is to sur-vive and function properly. The armour is highly useful as an insulat-ing device in such regards. In the water, an animal with a soft and permeable skin is liable, because of osmotic passage of water, to be-come too salty internally in the sea, too dilute in fresh waters; in the case of land forms, there is danger of water loss, dehydration and death. From such dangers the almost impenetrable armour of the arthropod is an efficient protection.

Essentially, it appears, armour makes the arthropod. Once this major 'invention' had been attained, other improvements, in sensory structures, nervous system, and other features, could profitably fol-low. But there is one major disadvantage. How can an arthropod grow? It emerges from the egg as a tiny animal far smaller than the adult which, with good fortune, it is destined to become. But it is presently encased in chitinous armour. This may give and bulge a bit in flexible fashion, but it cannot stretch or expand. What to do? The only solution is that found in every arthropod – moult. Time after time, in almost every arthropod's individual development, the armour splits and is cast off; the soft body which lay within expands, and presently secretes and is encased within a new set of armour. Once the new shell is formed, all is well for the time being. But in the interval, the little animal is soft, helpless and unprotected. The necessity of repeated moulting is a problem which has been met with and solved, with greater or less success, by all arthropods, from crustaceans to insects. But it remains as a perpetual threat to arthropod existence and progress.

One further disadvantage in the arthropod structural pattern is that it results in limitations in volume. In the sea a lobster or crab may attain a very respectable size. But on land, a grasshopper, dung-beetle, centipede or scorpion represents about the maximum of arthropod bulk. The functional reasons for the failure of land arthropods to attain greater stature are varied. One, however, has to do with the inability of the arthropod limb to support and move a bulky body when away from the buoyant aid of the water. Chitin, even when reinforced by the laying down of mineral salts, is far inferior to the bone of our own legs in supporting weight; furthermore, the fact that in arthropods all the muscles and tendons of the leg must be contained within the restraining limits of the leg armour places them at a considerable mechanical disadvantage. The arthropods flourish all too well without being able to grow to great size. And for this we should be profoundly thankful. Only in nightmares need we dread giant crabs as large as horses trundling about with claws extended for human prey, or wasps as big as ostriches, with stings which could pierce us through like swords.

Peripatus

It is universally accepted that it was from marine annelid worms, which they basically resemble in structural pattern, that the arthropods sprang. But, since we find full-fledged arthropods already on the scene at the beginning of the fossil record in the early Cambrian, the evolution of the group must have begun well back in Pre-Cambrian times. It is thus improbable that we will ever find, as fossils, the actual forms which made the transition. But a curious type of small and obscure animal found here and there in moist areas of tropical lands appears to be a little-modified descendant of a half-way stage in this development.

63

This is *Peripatus* (figure 19), to give him his scientific name (the animal is too little known to have gained a popular title). If in the rain forests of Panama (for example) one were to poke over masses of damp leaves one might come upon such a creature. Superficially it would

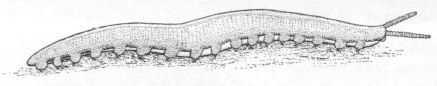

Peripatus

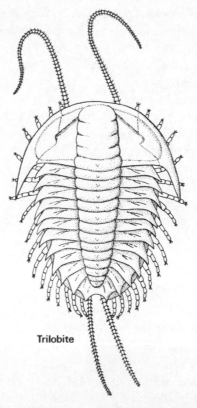

Trilobite

Figure 19. Two clues to arthropod history. Unlike *Peripatus*, the trilobite has chitinous armour, so that the limbs are jointed, but there is still little development of specialized feeding mouth parts.

64

look much like a caterpillar, two or three inches long, with a velvety skin, tiny eyes, a pair of long antennae, and numerous stubby legs, each one ending in a claw. Internally the little creature shows an interesting combination of primitive annelid, advanced arthropod, and specialized structures. Notable arthropod features are found in the circulatory system and, most especially, in the head region. Although the typical arthropod type of head is here not fully developed, three segments are, at any rate, definitely fused to form a head, with the beginnings of the arthropod brain, and with a pair of legs already transformed into jaws. On the other hand, *Peripatus* is far from being a full-fledged arthropod; the legs, for example, are not jointed and, notably, there is here no development of the hard chitinous skeleton which is the outstanding arthropod patent. So marked is the animal's half-way structural position that it is generally accorded a unique position of its own as the sole member of a separate phylum Onychophora.

The modern *Peripatus* is not, of course, in itself the ancestor of the arthropods. For one thing, the actual form transitional from worm to arthropod must have lived well over 500 million years ago, and it would be too much to expect that it would have remained unchanged for all this stretch of time. Further, *Peripatus* of today is a land animal (albeit restricted to moist places). The true ancestor was surely a water-dweller, and *Peripatus* has made its way ashore independently of the parallel shift made by many of its arthropod nephews. For unarmoured animals of this sort, the fossil record is sure to be a scanty one. A fortunate find is one from the Cambrian deposit in British Columbia, mentioned before, where remains of soft-bodied animals have been preserved. Here is found *Aysheaia*, a little animal very similar in all ways to *Peripatus* – caterpillar-like body, long antennae, stumpy legs and all – but a sea-dweller, and hence much closer to the true ancestral type. Still farther back, one of the few animal fossils found in Pre-Cambrian rocks is a fragmentary specimen which appears to be of much the same type, tending further to testify to the antiquity of the primitive onychophoran group.

Trilobites

The ancestral arthropods were surely sea-dwellers. The crustaceans are the prominent, and almost the sole marine arthropods in the seas today; hence one would expect the crustaceans to figure prominently in the early geologic history of arthropods. Not so. The Crustacea amounted to very little until relatively late in geologic history. When the curtain rolls up on the scene of marine life in the Lower Cambrian, an arthropod group already plays a prominent role. But that group is not the Crustacea, but one long since extinct – the trilobites, present in great numbers and variety (figure 19). In size, trilobites ranged from half an inch or so to two and a half feet in length. The body was broad and flattened; there was a proper arthropod fusion of half a dozen anterior segments to form a head, covered by a single, broad shield; behind this, however, there was no trend for formation of a thorax; every segment was movably jointed to its neighbours, except that a variable number at the back may have fused to form a terminal blunt 'tail' structure. The body was very flexible, so that the whole animal could – and the fossil remains indicate that it very often did – roll into a hedgehog-like ball for protection. Each segment was divided by longitudinal furrows into three lobes (whence the trilobite name). The central portion carried the essential organs of the animal; the two side wings appear to have been mainly a protective shield for the appendages which lay beneath. The head was large and typically broader than the rest of the body, with a backwardly projecting 'horn' at each margin. Mouth, jaws, and antennae were tucked away beneath the head shield; above, the central portion of the shield may show cross-furrows indicating some of the points of fusion of the segments making up the head, and at the sides a pair of well-developed compound eyes.

Trilobites are common fossils in rocks of the earlier Palaeozoic periods. Actually, however, most of our finds are not those of the animal itself, but of armour discarded in moulting; this contains some mineral stiffening of calcium and hence tends readily to be preserved. But even when the animal itself is preserved, it is often partly disarticulated and has lost its appendages. These, fortunately, have been found in rare cases, and the complex anatomy of the trilobites' under surface restored. Except for the antennae, all the limbs were built on a common plan. Each leg was split into two branches; the upper branch ended in a thin frilled sheet of material and acted both as a gill and as a swimming organ; the lower, with half a dozen or so jointed segments, was for walking purposes (figure 22 A). Very primitive for an arthropod was the fact that, apart from the feelers, the appendages of the head region were essentially similar to those farther back, and were little modified for feeding purposes. The trilobites were quite surely not active swimmers, but bottom-dwellers in the main, crawling about over the mud flats, or burrowing into them, in search of food. Because of the lack of grasping claws or good biting mouth parts, the food supply must have consisted of animals of small size and, not improbably, disintegrating carrion. But whatever its nature, the food supply was obviously a satisfactory one, for it carried the trilobites through a long career of about 300 million years. They began to decline in abundance, however, after the Ordovician, and were rare in the Carboniferous; the last stragglers are found in the Permian. New forms of life were by then taking over the place they had long occupied in the life of the ocean floors.

The trilobites are the best known of early arthropods. But in themselves they are obviously not ancestral to the other arthropods, despite such primitive features as their lack of specialized feeding legs. The very broad body with lateral lobes is surely a specialization, even if an early and, for the time, successful one. We would expect the true ancestral arthropod to have a more slender body, like *Peripatus*, but with proper legs and proper chitin armour; a form which would have had somewhat the appearance of a modern centipede, but would have been aquatic rather than terrestrial. Such forms are, in fact, reported in Palaeozoic rocks, from the Cambrian to the Carboniferous, but they are rare, and none has survived to the present to give us a glimpse of a truly primitive living arthropod.

Crustaceans

From such ancestral types there sprang early not only the trilobites but the crustaceans as well. Members of this group are present in the Cambrian, but they did not attain prominence until a much later time. Our mental picture of crustaceans is mainly derived from the lobsters and crabs of the dinner table. These are quite advanced forms, as well as being among the largest members of the class Crustacea, but nevertheless show the diagnostic features of the group. A conspicuous advance over the trilobites seen here is that there are now limbs modified into effective mouth parts, making the larger crustaceans very efficient predators. Crustaceans are unique among arthropods in the possession of two pairs of antennae. There may be a variable number of specialized walking legs, but there always persists more or less of a series of primitive two-branched appendages like those of trilobites, used as gills as well as for swimming. And especially characteristic is the general make-up of the body. There is always

67

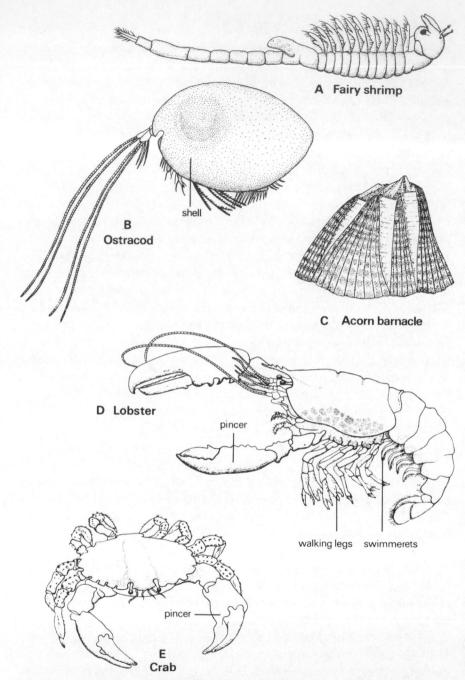

A Fairy shrimp

shell

B
Ostracod

C Acorn barnacle

D Lobster

pincer

walking legs swimmers

pincer

E
Crab

Figure 20. Some types of crustaceans. Fairy shrimps swim upside down; nearly all the appendages are alike. Both the active ostracods and the sedentary acorn barnacles somewhat resemble molluscs. The lobster has developed strong thoracic walking legs and abdominal swimmers, while the less active crab has reduced the strong swimming abdominal region.

68

a series of flexible abdominal segments, with a terminal 'tailpiece' technically termed the telson. But the whole front part of the body, head plus much of the trunk, is fused in the adult crustacean into a single unit; chitin forms a solid carapace over the top and sides of the whole structure, and extends down at the sides as a partial protection to the gills and limb bases beneath it.

There are various methods of classifying the numerous varieties of living and fossil crustaceans. There are perhaps some eight or so sub-classes, some of minor nature; we shall note only a few of the major groups. Most primitive are the members of the Branchiopoda, such as the fairy shrimps and water fleas, all of very small size and today living mainly in fresh-water ponds. Among the primitive features of the group is the fact that nearly all the pairs of appendages form a uniform series of little swimming organs; to each is attached a small gill plate, thus the name 'gill-feet'. Even more primitive in some regards are small burrowing crustaceans recently discovered in Long Island Sound. Here even the more posterior mouth parts have not yet differentiated from the row of more posterior appendages. Nothing is known of the ancestors of these newly-found forms. But the branchiopods, which are nearly as primitive, have a pedigree stretching back to the Cambrian dawn of fossil history; the more generalized members of the subclass are, one may believe, not too far removed from the ancestry of the crustaceans as a whole.

The presence of a carapace is in itself a protection for a small animal, and amongst the crustaceans the very small members of the subclass Ostracoda, persistently present in the fossil record from Cambrian to modern times, make the most of it. The carapace is stiffened by calcite and, further, expanded to form a tiny two-valved shell, superficially like that of a tiny clam, which can cover the whole animal (figure 20 B). The ostracods are not of great evolutionary interest; they are, however, useful to the stratigrapher as guide fossils. Their little shells preserve well, and differ from formation to formation; finding such shells in cuttings from oil wells, for example, will give good clues as to what formation the drill is penetrating.

Still another subclass of crustaceans, the Cirripedia, is that of the barnacles, which form the sole exception to the rule that arthropods are active food-seekers (figure 20 C). They have shifted to a sessile life and, like forms which we shall meet with in later chapters, wait for food to come to them. The larval barnacle, fresh from the egg, is a tiny free-swimming little fellow, very similar to the larvae of other

69

crustaceans. Soon, however, the larva settles down, attaching to a rock, head on and upside down. In addition to the normal carapace, the barnacle develops about its body hard and sharp-edged calcified plates (annoying to the bather on rocky shores). In the middle of the plates is an opening through which the animal can extend its feathery appendages, which sweep through the water like a casting net to entrap food particles and tiny animals.

We may scorn the barnacles as degenerate forms; but the barnacles do very well in their modest way. And some of their relatives, having, so to speak, discovered the advantages of sloth, successfully degenerated still further to become parasitic. An example familiar to zoologists is *Sacculina*, which begins life as a typical crustacean larva, but then attaches to the underside of the abdomen of a crab, loses every proper crustacean feature and makes its living by sending off root-like feeding processes into the substance of its unfortunate host. As might be expected from their specialized nature, the barnacles appear to have evolved at a relatively late date. There are reports of fossils which might pertain to this order from the Palaeozoic, but there are no positive proofs of their presence until Jurassic times.

Quite the opposite is the story of the members of the subclass Malacostraca, which includes the crustaceans more familiar to us, as well as a large fraction of the total crustacean population. These, the proper progressive members of the class, first appeared in the Ordovician, but only gradually came to play an important part in ocean life. The lobster is one of the larger members of the group, but is a typical and rather generalized form (figure 20 D). Here the abdomen may carry relatively primitive two-bladed 'swimmerets', but farther forward, in the thorax region beneath the carapace, there develop stout walking legs, and in some malacostracans (but far from all) an anterior pair of legs may develop as a stout pair of pincers. Prominent among the larger members of the Malacostraca are the numerous and highly varied crabs (figure 20 E), which have abandoned swimming almost entirely, shortened the abdomen and tucked what remains of it away ventrally beneath the chest.

Merostomes

The crustaceans, then, have evolved into the most successful of marine arthropods. But discussion of trilobites and crustaceans does not exhaust the list of ancient and primitive aquatic arthropods. Not too important in themselves, but important from an evolutionary point of view, are two ancient aquatic types which are related to the spiders, scorpions and their kin. These are the Xiphosura, such as the horseshoe crabs, and the eurypterids, now entirely extinct, but prominent in Middle Palaeozoic fresh waters. The two types have sometimes been brigaded with the arachnids, but they are quite distinct from the scorpions and spiders in many structural features and differ in their persistently primitive aquatic mode of life as well; hence the modern tendency is to consider them as members of a distinct class Merostoma, related and ancestral to the arachnids, but distinct from them.

The two classes have a number of common distinctive features. One such is important but negative. Almost all other arthropods have well-developed antennae, and the crustaceans even sport two pairs of them; the merostomes and their arachnid descendants lack these useful sensory structures. A second, and this time a positive character, also has to do with appendages. Few other arthropods have grasping claws, and when they do occur, as in crabs and lobsters, they are developed on one of the thoracic limb pairs, well behind the mouth. All members of the two present orders have pincers, termed chelicerae, sometimes small, sometimes powerful (as in scorpions and some eurypterids) and in contrast to crustacean claws, they are formed from the farthest forward pair of appendages, in front of the mouth. A further common feature of merostomes and arachnids has to do with arrangement of body parts. The trilobites had a specialized head, but left the rest of the body in a primitive segmented condition; the crustaceans, in strong contrast, have fused head and much of the body into a single compounded unit, leaving the remaining part, the abdomen, as little more than an appendage. Merostomes and arachnids have, so to speak, compromised between the two extremes. There is a well-fused anterior part of the body, which includes not only the head proper, but a thorax region, bearing walking legs; but there remains a considerable length of trunk behind this 'head' region, which contains a large part of the internal organs of the body. Primitively this remained segmented; but in all advanced members of both classes these segments may fuse to form an abdominal structure which, in contrast to the crustacean abdomen, is not a swimming apparatus, but is an important part of the body proper. A further distinction between these two classes and those considered before lies in the fact that normal appendages, including the walking legs, are found only in the 'head' region; in contrast with supposedly primitive conditions, more posterior ones are present only in much modified form, mainly as gills or lung-like structures.

Oldest and most persistent of the two merostome types is that of the Xiphosura, of which *Limulus*, the modern horseshoe 'crab', is the only survivor (figure 21). *Limulus* is found today only along the Atlantic coast of North America and the Pacific coast of Asia; in these regions this lone modern representative of an ancient group is locally abundant along the shores as a seemingly substantial if staid and sluggish citizen of the aquatic community.

The horseshoe 'crab' is not, of course, at all closely related to true crabs; it owes its name to the contours of the head carapace – a broad, arched shield, comparable to a horseshoe in outline, but differing from that formerly common item in that it has considerable length fore and aft, giving protection to a large fraction of the body; limbs, mouth parts and mouth are, as in trilobites, completely hidden by the shield, which shows little above but a pair of good compound eyes (there are also two pairs of tiny simple eyes which only close observation will disclose). Behind the major shield *Limulus* shows one major difference from presumably primitive conditions in that all the abdominal segments are fused into a compact shielded structure, showing from above no evidence of its compound nature except for a series of small spines along each margin. The body terminates in a long stout tail spike. Grasp *Limulus* by the tail and turn him over, and you can study his more revealing ventral surface at leisure (the animal can right itself only by vigorous acrobatics, including use of his tail spike). Anteriorly, beneath the head shield, is a diagnostic pair of small chelicerae in advance of the mouth, and, farther back on either side, five stout legs. Beneath the abdomen are five pairs of broad plates, folded back over one another. These are the animal's breathing apparatus, termed book gills (figure 22 B). The outer surface of each 'book' is smooth; the inner surface, however, has numerous delicate leaf-like folds, on the surface of which the oxygen-carbon dioxide exchange takes place.

Limulus is a persistently conservative, far right-wing member of the arthropod stock, little changed in any major aspect from some of the most primitive arthropod types. The genus itself was established in Jurassic times well over a hundred million years ago, and later members of the clan have, so to speak, found no reason to change their structural pattern; what was good enough for grandfather is good

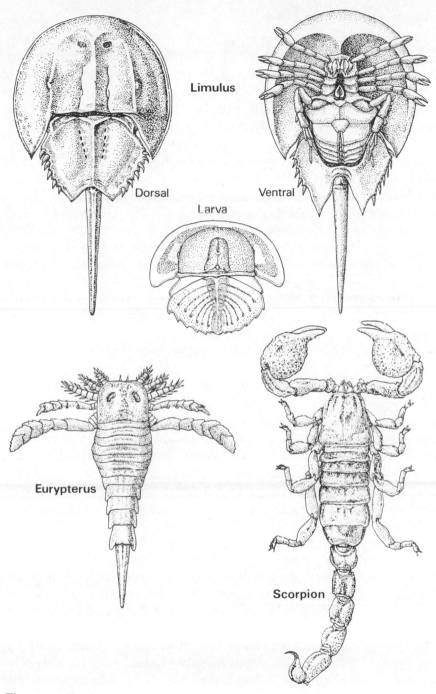

Limulus

Dorsal

Ventral

Larva

Eurypterus

Scorpion

Figure 21. The larva of *Limulus* is very similar to the extinct trilobites (see figure 19). Like the extinct eurypterids and the living scorpions, *Limulus* has pincers but no antennae.

73

enough today. And *Limulus* is, again, not so far removed from still more ancient members of this general stock which trace back to the most ancient of arthropod times in the Cambrian, when there were present such relatives as *Aglaspis*. Here the distinctive horseshoe-shaped head is already well formed, but the abdominal segments are still quite distinct, and instead of little spikes on either side, there are broad flaps, giving the animal somewhat the appearance of one of its trilobite cousins (even today the larva of the horseshoe crab is a bit trilobite-like in appearance, figure 21). Thus *Limulus*, in later times, did bow to progress, to a degree, in tidying up its abdomen by fusion of segments. But no further nonsense!

The second group of ancient arachnid relatives is that of the Palaeozoic eurypterids, sometimes termed 'sea scorpions'. The name is 50 per cent a misnomer. Some of the eurypterids did resemble true scorpions. But although the eurypterids were water-dwellers, breathing by book gills like their *Limulus* relatives, they were not characteristically marine forms. Presumably the remote ancestors of the group were, like all the earliest types of life, inhabitants of the sea; but most eurypterids appear to have inhabited fresh waters (as did, as well, a number of Palaeozoic horseshoe crabs).

Although there was variation within the group, typical eurypterids had somewhat the appearance of more slenderly-built relatives of the most ancient horseshoe crabs (figure 21). The head was relatively narrow; behind it, the dozen or so segments of the abdomen (never fused) tapered backward and sometimes, as in *Limulus*, terminated in a tail spike. The nipping chelicerae varied greatly in development. In some they were reduced to tiny structures (parts of the walking legs aided in feeding); in others they developed into large grasping claws, comparable to those of a lobster or crab (but not homologous to them, of course, for crustacean claws are modified walking legs).

As in horseshoe crabs, the locomotor appendages are confined to the segments of the 'head'. But whereas in *Limulus* the legs are concealed beneath the broad head shield, in these narrow-headed forms they are found in the fossils projecting out into the open on either side, and are sometimes very prominently developed. There are always five pairs of legs, as in cousin *Limulus*. The first four are normal walking legs; the fifth pair, however, are usually expanded at the ends into paddles. Eurypterids, it would seem, mainly trundled themselves along the bottom muds of ancient ponds and streams, but could help themselves along by a bit of semi-swimming.

74

Eurypterids were conspicuous among ancient invertebrates for their relatively large size. On the average, the eurypterids ran to a foot or so in length – very respectable proportions indeed. Some specimens, however, measure six or seven feet in length, and others, less complete, have been estimated to have reached nine feet. These were giants for those days.

And now let us mention, for the first (but not last!) time our own early ancestors, the oldest vertebrates, generally termed ostracoderms. These were little fishes of primitive structure, generally measuring but a few inches in length. They were common in the Silurian and to some degree in the Devonian; most inhabited the same fresh waters in which the eurypterids flourished. Lacking jaws, the ostracoderms appear to have been inoffensive mud-grubbers and bottom-dwelling filter-feeders. Invariably we find that they were covered with a stout armour – a bony armour, in contrast with the chitin-covering of the eurypterids. The water sediments of the Silurian generally contain little trace of any animals other than eurypterids and ostracoderms. And in attempting to figure out the ecology of life in these waters, two questions arise. The eurypterids were large and obviously highly predacious forms; what did they live on? Second, why were the ostracoderms armoured?

Now that we have asked the proper questions, the answers (really one answer) are obvious. Our little ancestors were the eurypterids' food supply; the ostracoderm's armour was a defence against this predation. It is possible that there were in these streams soft-bodied invertebrates not preserved as fossils, which may have formed part of the eurypterids' fodder, but it is reasonable to believe that the little ostracoderms may have been the major prey of these relatively giant arthropods.

The late history of the two groups – eurypterids and ostracoderms – fits in well with this interpretation. The ostracoderms appeared in the Ordovician period, and flourished in the Silurian and early Devonian. In this last period, however, there developed numerous fishes of more advanced type, which were better and faster swimmers, grew generally to larger size, and possessed jaws, giving them not only better defensive ability, but also the potentiality of becoming predators themselves. Parallel to this story, the eurypterids appeared in the Ordovician and flourished greatly in the Silurian and early Devonian. Beyond this point, however, the eurypterids declined sharply in numbers. A few persisted into the Carboniferous; a last lone survivor is

75

reported in the Permian. The story seems clear. As the ostracoderms declined and vanished, to give way to more progressive vertebrate types, the food supply of the eurypterids dwindled and vanished; and the eurypterids themselves followed suit. The vertebrates eventually triumphed; but at the beginning it was they who were the under-dogs.

Arachnids

So far the story of the arachnids and their relatives has been that of water-dwellers. Today, however, only the horseshoe crab remains as a lone survivor of this older phase of arachnid history. We shall now follow the arachnids ashore and witness the progress of the first of two major invasions of the land by the arthropods.

Oldest of known terrestrial arthropods are the scorpions, which appeared in the Silurian (figure 21). This was at a time when the early radiation of aquatic arthropods was still in progress; when the crustaceans had not yet come to amount to much, and when the ancient trilobites, eurypterids and horseshoe crab relatives were still flourishing greatly. A second great land invasion – that of the insects – was yet to come; the scorpions were the first, archaic, members of the invading arthropods.

The eurypterids, as we noted, have often been considered as aquatic scorpion-like types. In part the comparison is a superficial one; for example, the large claws found on many eurypterid forms are chelicerae, whereas the scorpion's chelicerae are, although efficient, of modest size, and the great scorpion claws, projecting forward to grasp the prey are, like those of crustaceans, modified walking legs. Further, while *Limulus* has good compound eyes of orthodox arthropod type, scorpions and other terrestrial arachnids have only 'simple' eyes, although these are often quite efficient. In most regards, however, scorpions and eurypterids are built on the same basic pattern. There is the same 'head' structure, with the appendages concentrated beneath it. But since the first pair of appendages behind the mouth, which in eurypterids were walking legs, have been transformed into powerful pincers, the scorpion (and other land arachnids as well) have but four pairs of normal limbs for locomotion. There is, as tends to happen in all progressive arthropods, some specialization of the more posterior segments. Most of the body organs are concentrated in the first half-dozen units of the abdomen, which are relatively broad. The segments beyond are a slender 'tail', containing little except the end part of the gut tube. And let us not forget that at the tip is the scorpion's defensive

76

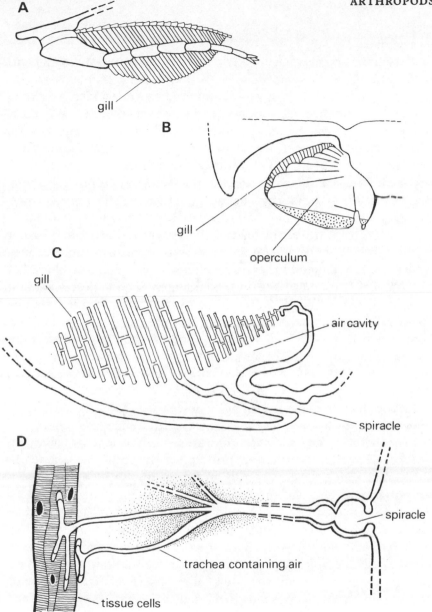

Figure 22. The gill of the trilobite (A) and the book-gill of *Limulus* (B) are adapted to obtaining oxygen from the water. This type of gill has been modified into a book-lung in spiders (C) so that it can obtain oxygen from air without becoming desiccated. This problem has been solved differently in the tracheole system of insects (D) by taking the air, through a closable spiracle, directly to the cells of the tissues.

77

weapon – a short but sharp spike which can inject a painful poison into its enemy.

The change from water to land existence confronts an animal with many functional problems. For an arthropod the problems are less difficult of solution than those encountered by one lacking his chitinous armour. The armour supports and holds together the body effectively in air as in water, and – provided the animal does not grow to too great a size – the jointed legs which enabled the aquatic ancestor to walk along the sea or pond bottoms will serve him well in walking on dry land. The armour, too, insulates the would-be terrestrial arthropod from some of the physical dangers of life in the air – notably desiccation. There remains, however, the problem of breathing; of obtaining oxygen from the air instead of the water, and returning carbon dioxide to it. For the arachnids, an easy solution was found. As we have seen, *Limulus* and his extinct aquatic arachnid cousins breathed by means of book gills beneath the abdomen. The delicate tissues of these gills will still function to obtain oxygen from the air, provided they can be kept moist. In the evolution of the scorpions this has been accomplished; the book gills have, it appears, simply withdrawn into the substance of the front abdominal segments, where they can be kept moist, and connect with the exterior only by narrow openings. The 'book gills' have become 'book lungs' (figure 22).

Although the scorpions cannot be descended from any of the well-known and typical eurypterids, because of differences in such features as the nature of claws and eyes, they are certainly closely related, and are merely a slightly different product of the same basic arachnid stock from which the eurypterids and their limuloid cousins arose in Cambrian and Ordovician days. It is not certain that in the oldest Silurian scorpions the transformation of gills into book lungs had yet taken place; in later periods, however, this change had definitely occurred, and the scorpions flourished modestly as terrestrial forms in the late Palaeozoic. Beyond that time, however, they tended to decline (perhaps because of the rise of their insect relatives) and today play but an inconspicuous part in animal economy.

But well before the close of the Palaeozoic there arose from scorpion-like forms other arachnids which are of greater importance today. These include the spiders and, as well, such forms as the mites, ticks, and harvest-men or (in American usage) daddy-longlegs (figure 23).

Including several extinct groups, as many as a dozen or so orders of

78

Figure 23. The main types of arachnids.

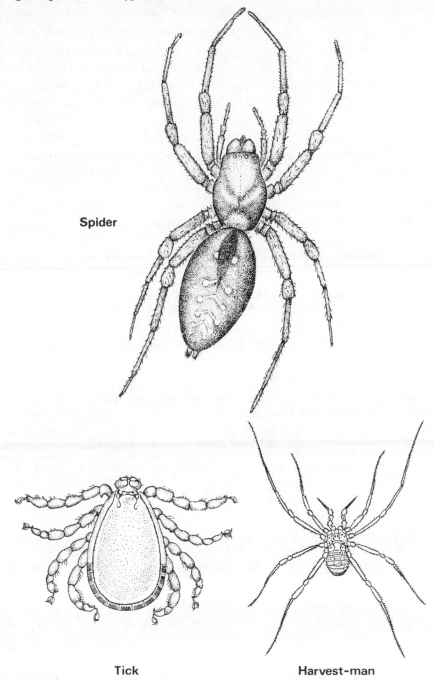

Spider

Tick

Harvest-man

terrestrial arachnids are generally distinguished. We cannot, however, give any connected account of their evolution – this for very practical reasons. Nearly all these forms tend to be of small size and with relatively thin 'armour', so that under the best of conditions their preservation as identifiable fossils would not be too common. Their terrestrial nature is a further handicap. We have seen that occasionally a water-deposited shale or lime may be fine grained enough to preserve small and delicate animals as fossils. But for a tiny and fragile land-dweller, the chances of preservation are poor indeed.

A few points can, however, be determined. A fortunate case of preservation has afforded definite knowledge of a Devonian mite. Several other types, including harvestmen, are represented in the coal shales of the Carboniferous, and there is no doubt that by that time the radiation of arachnids was well under way. Unfortunately our knowledge of the ancient history of the most important group, the true spiders, is very poor. There are doubtful reports of spiders from the Devonian, Carboniferous and Permian, but while one may be quite sure that spiders had evolved before the end of the Palaeozoic, we have no certain evidence of them before the Tertiary.

The evolved arachnid orders share certain basic characters of the class with the scorpions, such as the development of the 'head', the absence of compound eyes, and the presence of four pairs of walking legs (in contrast with the three of insects). There are, however, notable differences. In most, the abdomen is consolidated; the number of segments is decreased, and those remaining are fused, as in *Limulus*, into a broad compact structure which (in spiders but not in ticks and mites) is connected with the head only by a narrow 'waist'. The tail sting of scorpions is absent (some spiders develop poison glands in the head). The fate of the first pair of walking legs differs from that seen in the scorpions. In that group, as we have seen, they were transformed into large claws. In other forms they serve a different but very useful function. As we have seen, the arachnids differ from other crustaceans in lacking true antennae. In most arachnid orders, functionally comparable 'feelers' are gained by transforming the first pair of legs into slender tactile organs.

Myriapods

In following the arachnids to land, we have wandered off the main line of arthropod evolution. The arachnids are, after all, a relatively non-progressive group of arthropods in such features as their failure to develop antennae, flaunted not only by trilobites and crustaceans but by the land forms now to be reviewed, and in the absence in land arachnids of the effective compound eyes found in most other arthropods. Let us now turn to a second invasion of the land by arthropods – one which culminated in the rise and triumph of the insects, but had its forerunners in the centipedes and millipedes.

These are often considered as constituting a single group, appropriately named the Myriapoda; there are, however, two distinct major groups, the centipedes or Chilopoda, which do have numerous appendages, but generally less than a hundred, and the millipedes or Diplopoda, in which legs are still more numerous although not approaching the thousand that the popular name implies. The high count of millipede legs is due to the fact that – unique in arthropods – each segment of the body possesses two pairs of legs. The millipedes are obviously a side branch of the family tree, and we will hence confine discussion to the centipedes.

These little creatures show an interesting combination of primitive and advanced characters. There is a compact little head, with a good pair of antennae and well-formed mouth parts; all features which tie in with the trilobites and crustaceans on the one hand, and the insects on the other, and contrast with the arachnids where true antennae were never present and jaw structures little developed. A somewhat puzzling feature is the absence of compound eyes. These are present both in their aquatic relatives and in the insects; possibly their absence in myriapods is a degenerate feature, as in land arachnids, and the myriapod ancestors may have had them.

Behind the head, the myriapod body is as primitive as in any known arthropod, recent or fossil. Even among the trilobites there was some specialization of body segments and their appendages. In myriapods there is almost none. Except for a pair of poison claws on the first pair of legs, every one of the numerous segments behind the head is exactly the same as every other, and every segment bears a proper pair of walking legs. The body lacks the lateral expansions of the armour seen in trilobites and to a lesser extent in other aquatic arthropods. In most regards a centipede has the appearance one would expect of a truly archaic ancestral arthropod, of a sort expected in the Cambrian or even earlier.

With one notable exception, however. We are dealing with forms already adapted for life on land.

81

As we said earlier in connection with the arachnids, arthropod adaptation for terrestrial life is not too difficult a matter in most regards; the chitin armour suffices in many ways for support and protection, and the arthropod limb for locomotion. But breathing is a major problem. The scorpions were fortunate in that their aquatic ancestors had developed book gills which could be transformed without too much difficulty into protected book lungs. But in the trilobite-crustacean groups, to which the myriapod ancestors were related, the gill system was merely a series of small feathery structures attached to a series of legs, not too well protected or protectable for use on dry land.

Something new was needed, and something new was found – a system of breathing air by means of tracheae – structures found not only in myriapods, but in insects as well (and, in fact, paralleled to some degree among the spiders). In most animals (barring small and simple skin-breathers) the oxygen received in special gill or lung structures, is transported by way of the bloodstream to the cells in various parts of the body; these in turn give carbon dioxide to the bloodstream to return to the gill or lung. Not so here. A completely different and unique system of supply is present. There is no gill or lung. There is no dependence on the blood vessels for gas transport (possibly because the circulation in myriapods and insects is not efficient enough for rapid oxygen transport through the body). Instead, a series of pores are present on the sides of the trunk, from which a series of branching tubules – the tracheae – ramify out into all parts of the body and allow air to come in direct contact with nearly all the body cells. Each cell breathes for itself. (Incidentally, this is a curiously individualistic feature to be present in the body of such a highly organized animal as a typical insect.)

As with terrestrial arachnids, the fossil record of the myriapods is a sparse one. The oldest known forms are Devonian in age. We have no sure clues as to their earlier history. Although related to crustaceans and trilobites, they are not directly descended from either, but stem, surely, from some more obscure stock present in the early Palaeozoic radiation of primitive trilobite relatives. And, in turn, as we shall see, the typical myriapods are not directly ancestral to the insects, although surely closely related.

Insects

Greatest of all arthropod groups, and in many ways greatest of all animal groups, is the class Insecta. In numbers of living species, the insects far outnumber all the rest of the animal kingdom put together. Well up toward a million forms have been described, and because of the staggering numbers surely present, but incompletely studied, in the tropics, the total of species living today is probably on the order of twice that figure. As to numbers of individuals, it is difficult to estimate this in comparison with protozoan populations or those of tiny earth-dwelling roundworms, but a reasonable guess is that at any given moment there may be as many insects alive as a million million million, giving a figure which is (for me, at any rate) incomprehensibly vast.

The insects are, thus, an immeasurably successful group of animals. But although one can cite various efficient features in insect structure and function, it is difficult here, as for arthropods generally, to put one's finger on any one feature responsible for their great success. Another volume in the present series[1] is devoted to a comprehensive account of the insects; we shall here merely note briefly some of their most obvious characters, and plot out what is known of their evolutionary history.

The insects are, of course, good arthropods, and exhibit the basic pattern of the group. They are proper segmental forms which, as in every typical arthropod, have welded six segments into a head region, where are concentrated sense organs, brain, and mouth. There are, as in most arthropods, good antennae, and, in addition to simple eyes, there are highly developed compound eyes, such as are present in marine arthropods (but not in land arachnids nor myriapods). Present, too, beneath the head are several pairs of appendages which act as feeding aids in most cases.

We have seen that in various arthropod groups there has been a trend in more advanced forms for specialization of body regions. There is in insects a precise and uniform pattern in this regard. The three segments following the head are invariably fused into a compact thorax. Here are found the three pairs of walking legs which are characteristic of every adult insect. And, above the thorax, are mounted the wings, present in all but a relatively few primitive or degenerate insect forms. Behind the thorax is the abdomen. Here segmentation – and usually flexibility – is maintained. But insects exhibit efficiency in not wasting developmental energy in growing a long series of relatively useless 'tail' segments. Never, in the adult, are there more than eleven trunk segments, and often the number is

[1] *The Life of Insects* by V. B. Wigglesworth.

83

further reduced. There is no waste space. The thorax, except for containing a storage segment of the gut, is mainly devoted to muscles and locomotion; the abdomen to digestion and reproductive organs.

For most insects, of course, the wings, typically two pairs above the thorax, are structures of outstanding and unique importance. Among vertebrates the wings, when present, are modifications of normal locomotor appendages. Not so in insects; these are new, extra developments, which are quite independent of the legs lying below them on the under side of the thorax. Their substance is a thin layer of chitin; reinforcing it is a network of thicker bars, somewhat confusingly termed 'veins' (which have, of course, nothing to do with circulatory vessels). Within the thorax are powerful muscles, often of exceedingly high competence, which operate the wings. Some of the larger or more primitive insects are only capable of a dozen or two wing-beats per second; but a bee or house-fly has muscles capable of giving a beat of 200 or so per second, and one small fly is reported to be able to vibrate its wings at the rate of more than 1,000 beats in this short period of time.

As in all arthropod groups, the problem of growth to adult size of armour-clad young presents a serious problem. In aquatic arthropods some of the difficulty is avoided by the hatching out of small larvae which lead a life rather different from that of the adult, and, further, the sea offers some opportunities for the hiding of a small, naked animal which has shed its armour for a time, and is helpless and defenceless. On land, the world is harsher – and dryer. The insects have solved the problems of growth and larval development, but have solved them, as we shall note, in a variety of ways.

There are but a dozen or so orders of insects with the members of which the average non-specialist is ordinarily familiar. The entomologist, however, would distinguish twice that number and rather more, and there are, in addition, a dozen or so orders of primitive insects now entirely extinct. We will not (heaven forbid!) go into details concerning all these groups, but certainly the insects are so large and so important a series of animals that in all conscience we must go bravely forward and attempt to present the outlines of the broad picture of insect evolution, as far as the fossil evidence (plus the evidence deduced from the structure and development of living forms) will allow.

As was discussed in the case of the arachnids, the fossil history, for forms as small and fragile as most insects, is, as one might expect, a bit spotty. There are, however, some helpful circumstances. Many of the older insects were of relatively large size and firm build and, through good fortune, many remains have been recovered from coal shales and other shale deposits of the Carboniferous and Permian. For most of the Mesozoic the record is none too good. But for the Cretaceous and Tertiary, much valuable data has been gleaned from amber deposits. Pines and various other trees put forth a resin which soon hardens and may be preserved in 'fossil' form (a widespread trade in fossil Baltic amber was developed even in prehistoric times). When first exuded, the resin is soft and sticky, and an insect alighting upon it may, despite its struggles, be completely embedded in it – and thus preserved for posterity. Thousands of excellent specimens have been recovered from Canadian and Baltic amber deposits, and give us excellent knowledge of a wide range of Cretaceous and early Tertiary insect types. Again, recent discoveries in Kenya and Mexico have been deposits of Tertiary insects preserved, in some almost miraculous fashion, in the round. We do not know the whole of insect evolution; but we do have parts of many chapters of the story.

Wings are, of course, the major glory of the class Insecta. But not all insects have wings. Some of the forms which lack them appear to be degenerate; but others appear to be truly primitive wingless types. The insects of this sort (figure 24) include, as well as some more obscure forms, the bristletails (order Thysanura) and springtails (Collembola). All are of small size, and most tend to inhabit moist places in the soil or under leaves or rotting wood where danger of desiccation is reduced. The only generally familiar member of these groups is the bristletail known as the silverfish (notorious as a lover of books, although starch in the binding, not literary content, is the silverfish's pabulum). The springtails are tiny folk, never more than a small fraction of an inch in length, which are immensely abundant in meadow soils, but almost never observed except by the specialist seeking them. They owe their name to the presence of a forked tail rod folded under the abdomen; this can be suddenly extended and catapult the springtail forward like a miniature flea. The presence of this specialized structure indicates that the springtails are well off the main line of insect evolution. The bristletails, however, are much more generalized in structure. In the absence of wings, some entomologists of a snobbish turn of mind would say that *ipso facto* they should be excluded from the Insecta and relegated to a position of sub insects. But the thysanurans, wings excepted, show all the basic

85

characters for admission to the insect class, and they appear to be exceedingly close to the ancestry of the entire group. Their fossil history is poorly known, and the oldest thysanuran is a Triassic one. But the Devonian of Scotland shows fragmentary remains of a form which appears to be a springtail, and hence it is reasonably certain that the

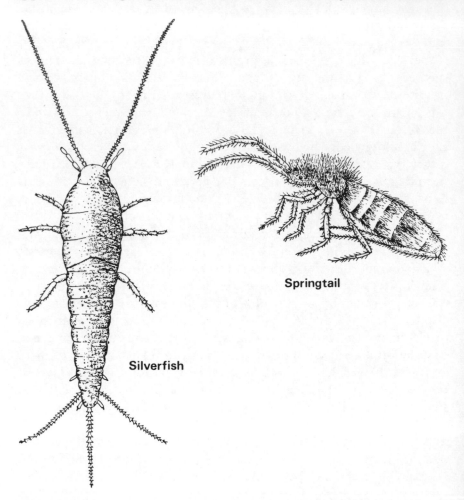

Springtail

Silverfish

Figure 24. Two types of primitive, wingless insects (much enlarged).

more primitive Thysanura must be still older – early Devonian, if not still earlier.

Whence did the thysanurans – and the insects in general – arise? There are various features which negate any close relationship to crustaceans, trilobites, or arachnids. In many regards the centipedes would appear to be primitive and generalized arthropod types from which an insect might have been derived by body shortening, limb reduction and formation of a compact thorax. But there are certain myriapod features, such as the poison glands on the front legs, which throw typical centipedes out of a direct ancestral position. There is, however, an odd group of myriapods, the so-called 'garden centipedes' (Symphyla) which lack some of the myriapod specializations and seem close to what we would expect of an insect ancestor at the myriapod level of evolution. They are, unfortunately, unknown in fossil form.

Above the wingless silverfish level, we arrive at the proper insect stage, with wing development. But concerning the origin of wings, we are very much in the dark. In the case of many important animal structures, we can trace their origin back to elements already present in the body of ancestral types, and very often see how a gradual modification toward the structural type may have occurred. Not so with wings. There is nothing in the pattern of any other arthropod with which they can be compared, or from which they might have developed. The two pairs of wings present in most insects are developed on the middle and back elements of the three segments comprising the thorax. In some primitive insects there are small lobes of chitinous membrane in line with them on the front thoracic segment. It has been suggested that the evolutionary development of wings occurred as outgrowths of such lobes. But as far as we know, these lobes do not seem to serve any specific useful purpose and currently, at any rate, it is difficult to imagine what useful function an expanded lobe of this sort could have served before it came to be large enough to serve as a gliding plane, at least, even if not a true wing. We do not know any transitional stages between no-wings and fully developed wings. In the latter part of the Carboniferous, the Coal Measures, there are plentiful remains of half a dozen different orders of winged insects, and hence we are quite sure that the evolution of wings took place by early Carboniferous times at the latest, and not improbably before the close of the Devonian. But currently we do not have the slightest trace of any winged form of pre-Coal Measures date.

If we attempt to trace out the evolutionary history of the numerous orders of winged insects, we can rather reasonably sort them out into four major series of primitive to advanced forms on the basis of wing structure plus the nature of their life histories. On every count the

87

most primitive orders of living winged insects are those termed the Odonata and Ephemerida, of which the dragonflies and mayflies are representative. Proper members of these two orders are known as far back as the Permian, and the commonest of Carboniferous insects are members of related groups. The dragonflies (figure 25 A) are highly predacious forms which, despite their primitive nature, remain common today. They are among the largest of insect types, one existing form having a wing-span of seven-and-a-half inches, while specimens of a related Carboniferous species measure a full two feet from wing-tip to wing-tip. The wings of both dragonflies and mayflies are very primitive in that they are capable only of an up-and-down beat, and cannot be turned back over the abdomen when at rest. A second feature of both these orders is that the eggs are laid in the water, and the young develop as aquatic larvae, only taking to the air after a marked metamorphosis. The mayflies gain their name of ephemerids from their curious life history. The larvae live and grow in the water for periods up to as much as three years. Then comes a final moulting and metamorphosis, the emergence of the winged adult. This adult's only functions are to mate promptly and die promptly; often the life-span in the air is but a day or so. Very probably the presence of an aquatic larva here is a truly primitive feature; the winged adult is a 'land' form, but the larva still leads the type of existence characteristic of the insects' ancient water-dwelling ancestors.

Somewhat more advanced, but still primitive in many ways, is an assemblage of insect orders of considerable antiquity. Most prominent and familiar members are the cockroaches and mantids, which comprise the order Dictyoptera, and the grasshoppers and their kin, the Orthoptera. Representatives of these two orders were already present in the oldest known faunas of winged insects, in the Coal Measures, and there are in these same beds further forms which may be ancestral to orders of the group which appear only later. Such types include the stoneflies, the termites or 'white ants', the earwigs, and the stick insects. In this whole series of orders the wings have attained greater power of movement, for here (and in later types to be considered) they can be turned backward over the abdomen when the animal is at rest. Within the group, however, the main attention has been paid to the hinder pair of wings; these are often beautiful lacy structures which, when at rest, can be folded fan-fashion; the front pair of wings are in many cases little more than leathery covers shielding the back pair in the resting pose. In these orders the young grow

88

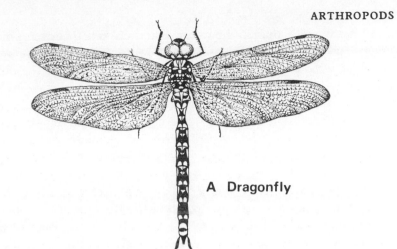

A Dragonfly

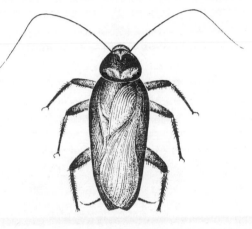

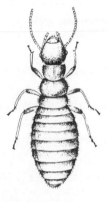

B Cockroach   C Termite

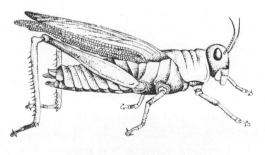

D Grasshopper

Figure 25. A few of the more primitive winged insects.

up on land, rather than in the water. But there is little development of special larval types; the fresh-hatched young (except for the absence of wings, which appear later) is usually a tiny replica of the parents. With growth, there is a series of moults during which, stage by stage, there is a gradual attainment of adult size and structure. As the names we have cited of members of this assemblage immediately suggest, the component types lead a varied series of existences. Everyone is familiar, of course, with the grasshoppers (figure 25 D), which can fly but are mainly leaping types, and many of us are (unfortunately) familiar with the roaches (figure 25 B) which prefer scuttling about to flying. Flying is, again, the exception rather than the rule in the life of the termites (figure 25 C), which have evolved a complex social life paralleling that of the true ants. In contrast to other orders of this group, the 'white ants' are not known in fossil form earlier than the Tertiary, and may represent a late development from cockroach-like ancestors.

A third assemblage of insects is a relatively small – and unattractive – one, including thrips, lice of various sorts, and the varied 'bugs' which form the order Hemiptera. As in the last group of orders, flying tends to be of little importance; many bugs fly only for mating purposes, and other bugs, and the lice as well, have secondarily abandoned flight altogether. As in the roach-grasshopper assemblage, there is generally no marked development of special larval forms; the young bug or louse emerges from the egg as essentially a miniature model of his repulsive parents.

The major order here is that of the bugs, the Hemiptera. There are more than 50,000 known species of bugs, which vary widely in size, appearance, and habits, but agree in one major structural feature – the mouth parts are modified to form a tube by which fluids are sucked from the plants or animals on which they feed. A majority are plant-feeders, some notorious pests; among them we may cite as examples the leaf-hoppers, the plant lice or aphids (figure 26) and the curiously degenerate scale insects. Others have developed a taste for animal blood. Fortunately a majority prey on other insects. The various kinds of water bugs are for the most part predators of this sort, although the larger ones may attack a minnow or tadpole. A very few essay attacks on mammals and birds. Darwin, in *The Voyage of the Beagle,* cites a night in western Argentina when he was practically eaten alive by the venchuca, a large, inch-long black bug of this sort (and a disease carrier, to boot). Others of us are familiar with a smaller relative, the

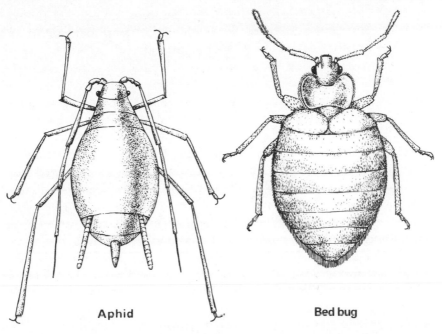

Aphid   Bed bug

Figure 26. Hemiptera or 'bugs', which feed by sucking fluids either, like the aphid (left) from plants, or from animals – as does the blood-sucking bed-bug (right).

'domestic' bed bug (figure 26), sometimes more politely termed the 'crimson rambler'. While we may deplore the frequently unfortunate effects of the indiscriminate employment of insecticides, we can be thankful that their use in a more restricted fashion has greatly improved one's chances of undisturbed rest in hostelries of lower levels of cleanliness. As would be expected from their specialized nature, members of this group of orders are relatively late in appearance. Bugs and some of the less important types are found in late Permian deposits; lice are unknown as fossils. The sucking lice are presumably a late off-shoot from hemipterans of similar habits. All are parasites on mammals. A separate group is that of the tiny biting lice which infest birds. The lice are of considerable interest to the student of evolutionary history, not so much on their own account, as with regard to the evolution of their hosts. In the case of both mammal and bird lice, each louse species is tied strictly to a given host, and generally related lice are associated with animals which are suspected on other grounds of being related to one another. For example, man and chimpanzee are infested (pardon, *may* be infested) by two related species of the same louse genus. This tends to confirm our belief that

91

man and chimpanzee are relatives; the common ancestor of the two louse species presumably made his home amidst the hair of the common ancestor of these two higher primates.

A final major group of insect orders includes all the remaining familiar insects, ranging from butterflies to flies, to fleas, to ants and bees and wasps, to beetles; a vast assemblage, and an exceedingly varied one. But all these familiar types have two things in common – first, all the more familiar orders (as might be expected of 'advanced' forms) appear relatively late in geologic history – none before the Triassic, and some much later; and, secondly, all have changed from direct development to a type of life history with a specialized larval stage of one sort or another. There is here no series of moults with a gradual step-by-step attainment of adult size and structure. Instead, the individual leads, in succession, two very different lives (figure 27). From the egg develops a larva, as grub or caterpillar, which is widely different from the adult in structure and habits. This feeds and grows and then encases itself as a motionless pupa. In this stage the entire anatomy of the creature is radically refashioned into that of the adult which finally bursts out of its pupal prison.

Although major orders included in this advanced assemblage are late in time of geologic appearance, exception must be made in the case of some minor orders included in this assemblage although not listed above. These are the Neuroptera, such as the alder flies (figure 28) and lacewings, Trichoptera or caddis flies, and the Mecoptera, or scorpion flies. All three groups have adults with long delicate lacy wings of relatively primitive appearance; all three are present in the Permian. These lacy-winged types appear to occupy an evolutionary position intermediate between truly primitive insects and the major advanced groups. Their relatively advanced nature is shown, however, by the fact that all of them have developed distinct larval types.

From such forms as those listed just above have probably developed all the major advanced orders. Indeed, it appears to be commonly agreed that at least three varied advanced groups are rather definitely descendants of these groups; these are the Lepidoptera, Diptera, and Siphonaptera.

The Lepidoptera, the butterflies and moths, with both pairs of wings expanded, covered with tiny scales and often attractively patterned, are the latest of any major group of insects in putting in their appearance; none are known before the beginning of the Tertiary, at which time the flowering plants first began to flourish. Indeed, the

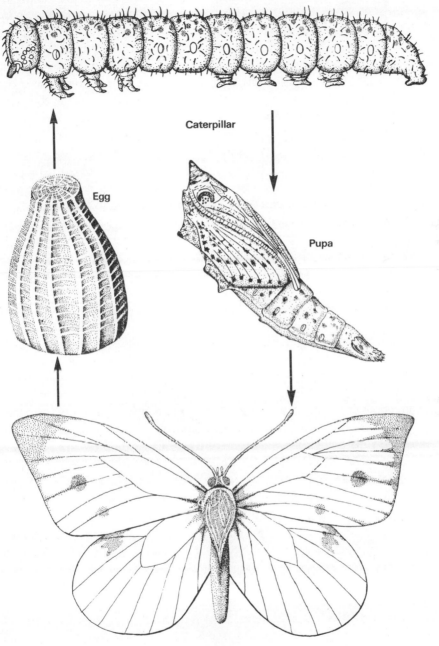

Caterpillar

Egg

Pupa

Adult

Figure 27. The life history of a butterfly.

evolution of the butterflies and the evolution of flower-bearing plants are intimately connected, for the adult butterflies feed on flowers and, on the other hand, flowering plants depend in great measure on butterflies (as well as on flies and bees) for fertilization, by pollen transport from flower to flower. Quite different, however, from the mode of life of the adult is that of larval butterflies. Here there has been developed the caterpillar type, with its numerous podgy legs reminiscent of a myriapod or *Peripatus*. The caterpillar, instead of leading the gay and harmless life of the adult after pupation, typically feeds voraciously and destructively on plant leaves or stems or roots. Most adult lepidopterans have modified the mouth parts into a proboscis for the delicate sucking of nectar (figure 28); some primitive moths, however, still retain biting jaws and are little more advanced in structure than the caddis flies, which are close to the ancestry of the Lepidoptera.

A second major order which, like the butterflies, is relatively late in appearance, and like them is rather surely derived from the lacy-winged orders, is that of the Diptera – the flies and their relatives, such as the mosquitoes. Early members of the group are present in the Jurassic, but their great expansion (like that of the flowering plants and their butterfly cousins) appears to have taken place in the Tertiary. The evolution of the Diptera went in a direction quite different from that of the Lepidoptera. Instead of the four fluttering wings of the butterflies, the flies have, with exemplary if unpleasant efficiency, reduced their flying equipment to two plain but stout wings capable of very rapid motion. Much like the Lepidoptera, most dipterans have adopted liquid sucking as a mode of life; but while most are harmless forms, a number of types, such as mosquitoes and horse-flies, have, regrettably, taken up blood-sucking. Here, as in the case of the Lepidoptera, there are larvae quite unlike the adult. These are seldom as highly specialized as the lepidopteran caterpillar. There is considerable variation, but most dipteran larvae are maggots of simple structure which feed and grow on decaying animal or plant material. Very probably Tertiary derivatives of the blood-sucking flies are the fleas (figure 28), the Siphonaptera, which have entirely lost their wings and acquired a hopping gait; their relationship to the Diptera is strongly indicated by the resemblances between the two groups in their life histories.

Two further major orders remain whose ancestry and relationships are less clear, although they are certainly members of this general

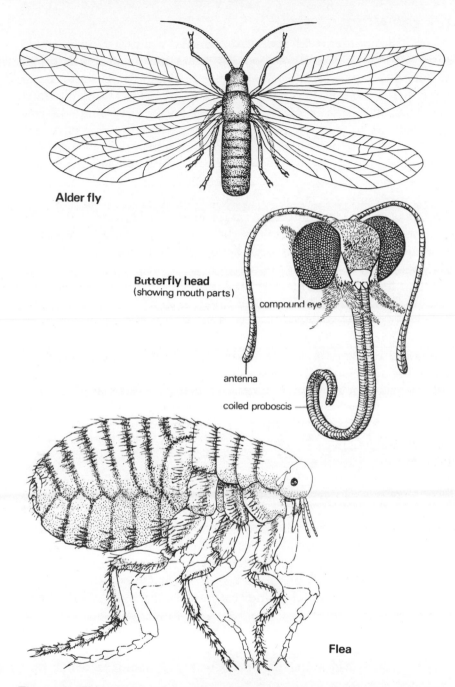

Alder fly

Butterfly head
(showing mouth parts)

compound eye

antenna

coiled proboscis

Flea

Figure 28. The alder-fly (above) has very large, transparent wings. The butterfly head (middle) shows the long, coiled proboscis, which is used for sucking nectar. The blood-sucking flea (below) is a wingless relative of the flies.

assemblage of orders with specialized larval types – the Hymenoptera and Coleoptera. The Hymenoptera are modestly ancient, for an advanced group, since they can be traced back to the Triassic. Relatively primitive members of the order include sawflies, ichneumon flies, and gall wasps; an advanced group of fairly closely related forms includes the true wasps, ants, and bees. This is a highly evolved order; highly evolved as individual organisms and in many instances highly evolved socially, quite in contrast with the individualistic dipterans. The Hymenoptera have gained very efficient flight, as have the Diptera, but in a different fashion. The flies simplified the wing apparatus for efficiency by reducing to a single pair; the Hymenoptera have achieved the same end by retaining both pairs, but hooking the two of each side together so that they act as a single unit. Most of the Hymenoptera, in contrast to their dipteran cousins, show solicitude for their helpless grub-like larvae. A majority of bees and wasps are solitary forms, but many wasps of this sort supply the young with a killed insect upon which they may feed and grow, and solitary bees furnish the larvae with pollen and honey. And beyond this, many wasps and bees and all ants have developed a marvellously complex social organization, with variably specialized individual functions. All labour for the survival of the group – but most especially labour in the care of the young.

And, finally, the beetles, the order Coleoptera, the most abundant of all insects. There are more than 300,000 described species of beetles, and probably as many again awaiting discovery. Fossil beetles are known as far back as the Permian, but the beetle characteristics were already well developed at that time, and we cannot tie them in closely with any other insect order. It is difficult to see just what has made these ungainly trundling creatures so unsurpassedly successful. They are solitary and unsociable, without the slightest trace of the social organization of the Hymenoptera or termites. Unlike the Hymenoptera or the Diptera, they are not good fliers; in fact many have lost the power of flight, and the front wings have been modified to become merely hard sheaths covering the hinder pair over the back. Nor are they solicitous for their young; the eggs once laid, the hatched offspring must shift for themselves, many living as grubs among plant roots, others as caterpillar-like forms with powerful jaws which feed on leaves or prey on other insects.

Perhaps the outstanding feature of the beetles is a negative one – their relative invulnerability to attack. Of all insects, they have the thickest and hardest covering of chitin found in any group. Even the back and wing region, usually an especially weak point in insect defence, is well cased in armour by the heavy pair of plates into which the front wings have been transformed. Few predators prey upon the beetles, few parasites can penetrate their defences. And so, while the positive accomplishments of the beetle are not in any way spectacular, he can trudge toward his modest goals unmolested.

With a mention of this most abundant of orders of the most successful class of this outstandingly successful animal phylum, we conclude our account of the Arthropoda. As vertebrates ourselves, we tend to consider our own group as the pinnacle of the animal world. But had a beetle the sagacity to consider the matter and the voice to express his thoughts on the subject, he would be able to present a strong argument that it is the arthropods which deserve first place. True, an individual arthropod is generally no match for an individual vertebrate, and man, with modern mechanisms and modern scientific knowledge, can often effect mass destruction of insects. But, by and large, man is able to make little impression on the arthropod hordes. Arthropods play a prominent role in the life of the seas; on land and in the air they are omnipresent in overwhelming variety and numbers. And it sometimes seems as if we vertebrates were living on sufferance in an arthropod world.

Chapter 5

Molluscs

IN the arthropods we witnessed the evolution of a group of animals which, starting from a base among the annelid worms, retained and improved upon the organizational pattern present in that group. The efficient segmentation of the annelids provided a structural pattern from which could develop, and did develop, a successful series of highly mobile and progressive bilaterally symmetrical and segmented forms. The history of the molluscs, which include such familiar forms as the snails, clams and squids, is a story of a very different sort. Molluscs, too, are of annelid derivation, one definite piece of evidence being that most have a ciliated larva, a trochophore, which is identical with that of the annelids. But did the molluscs evolve onward from the level of organization seen in annelids? Not at all. They changed; but went, so to speak, sideways rather than forward and, to tell the truth, it is hard to say in what direction they went. Better 'directions' than 'direction'; for the build and mode of life of the molluscs differ so much from one group to another that no general description is possible.

One clear point, however, emerges. The molluscs early in their history developed a mantle, a broad covering over the top and sides of the body; over the surface of this mantle there was secreted a hard shell of limy material (calcium carbonate, that is) under which the body of the animal huddled for protection. Once they had gained this defence against the outside world, the molluscs went their own ways of evolutionary change with complete disregard for the potentialities afforded by the structure of their annelid ancestors. Annelids have a good bilateral symmetry and sharp segmentation; molluscs have for the most part abandoned segmentation and even abandon orthodox symmetry in many cases. Annelids are capable of good locomotion; molluscs in general show little interest in travelling and most are either sedentary or are restricted to a slow crawl by means of a slimy 'foot'. Even the basic character of the possession of a shell is one which is flouted by some molluscs. The shell varies greatly in pattern from one group to another; it may be highly developed, as a single or paired structure, or, on the other hand, it may be reduced to a vestige or lost entirely. Looking at the molluscs as a whole, one fails to find any clear pattern in the story. But despite this, the molluscs have muddled through with reasonable success, and throughout most of the known history of life have formed a respectable part in the faunas of the seas.

Primitive Molluscs

In the case of arthropods it was possible to preface an account of their evolution by a description of the build of a typical, generalized member of the group. As implied by what was said above, this is impossible in the case of molluscs. There are, it is true, a few basic features in their structural pattern which can be traced from one group to another, but there is very little in the anatomy of a clam, for example, that is readily comparable with anything in the body structure of a snail or octopus. The best we can do is to describe as primitive a type of mollusc as can be readily found, and proceed from there.

Unless we were to descend to deep ocean depths, our best examples of relatively primitive types are presented by the chitons (figure 29), little molluscs which are not uncommon on or beneath rocks in the tideway. As seen from above, the animal has an oval shape; it is protected by a hard convex shell, formed of eight plates in a fore-and-aft row, plus a multitude of protective spinelets around the margins. It seems clear that the chitons have, unlike some other molluscs, preserved their ancestors' bilateral symmetry. The oval shape, plus the arrangement of the plates, leads us to conclude (correctly) that we have front and hind ends at the two extremes of the oval. The series of plates make us expect, at first sight, that we have segmentation present. This, however, is not the case; nothing else in the animal's anatomy shows the slightest trace of the presumed segmentation of its ancestors, and the subdivisions of the shield are merely a secondary adaptation for defence, enabling the little chiton, if in danger, to roll up into a ball.

Turning the animal over, we can confirm our ideas of a simple front-to-back bilateral arrangement, for a close look will discover a mouth opening beneath one end of the oval, an anus at the other. Around the margins there may be seen a row of little comb-shaped structures which are the chiton's gill apparatus.

99

Most of the under surface, however, is occupied by a broad flat mass of tissue of rubbery texture which completely conceals the main body of the animal. This ventral structure is, next to the shield, the most distinctive patented device in mollusc organization, and is present, although variously modified, in every member of the phylum. For want of a better term, it is called the 'foot'; functionally, it is more than this, for it constitutes the entire locomotor apparatus of most molluscs. Typical molluscs have no legs to walk upon, no rows of paddle-like structures to help them to swim about; only this curious ventral organ. It is highly muscular, broad and flat in build, but capable of giving a chiton movement – of a sort. Rippling motions of the foot can gradually slide the animal over the rocks in search of the algae on which it feeds. Further, the foot margins can, by adhering tightly to the substrate, form a sort of suction cup which can anchor the little creature firmly in place.

Above the foot, the main bulk of the animal's body is humped up beneath the arched shell. Its structure is simple but effective. There is, we have pointed out, a mouth opening at the front end of the shield, but very little, here, in the way of a formed head or sensory structures. The animal feeds on water plants. Unlike the arthropods, a mollusc is unable to aid itself in feeding by the use of legs modified into jaws. However, the chiton (and other molluscs as well) has gained useful substitutes by the development in the mouth cavity of rows of little tooth-like structures termed radulae. Within the hump are simply built organs for digestion, excretion and reproduction. But in no case is there any trace of the segmental pattern of organs so characteristic of annelids.

Chiton, then, is a relatively simple and primitive mollusc. One can readily deduce from its structure how it has evolved from its worm ancestor, by shortening and flattening the body, covering itself with a hard shell and improvising the curious flattened foot on its under surface as a mode of locomotion. But in the complete loss of any trace of segmentation, the living *Chiton* has departed very far from the ancestral annelid body pattern.

But still more primitive molluscs are known both in the fossil record and, as we now know, in the depths of the modern seas. *Chiton* is a member of one of the five generally recognized classes of molluscs, one termed the Amphineura. Forms very much like the living *Chiton* were already present in Ordovician times; the specialization of a row of armour plates developed, thus, at an early stage. But in addition, there have long been known from the older Palaeozoic rocks a number of forms represented by small oval or roundish shells somewhat comparable to those of a chiton, but not broken into segments, and with a trend toward development of a conical peak at the shell centre over the body hump. Where they fitted into the classification of molluscs was a puzzle. We knew nothing, of course, of the body of the animal apart from the shell. In some of these forms, however – notably the little Silurian *Pilina* – the under surface of the shell shows a short series of scars along either margin. While we could not, of course, be entirely sure about this, it seemed likely that these scars were the points of attachment of a row of muscles, and this in turn suggested that *Pilina* was more primitive than any mollusc living today in having retained traces of primitive segmentation in its musculature, at any rate.

Belief as to the primitive nature of these little ancient molluscs was abundantly confirmed by the discovery by a Danish oceanographic vessel a few years ago of specimens of a modern descendant of *Pilina*, living in deep oceanic waters off the west coast of South America; American exploration has resulted in further finds of this small mollusc, appropriately named *Neopilina*. Not too long ago considerable attention was paid by the public at large as well as by scientists to the discovery, off the African coast, of a fish, *Latimeria*, belonging to a group thought to be long extinct. Little *Neopilina* has aroused little public interest; but scientifically it is far more important than *Latimeria*. The latter merely adds to our knowledge of one sub group of fishes; *Neopilina* sheds much light on the origin of a whole animal phylum.

In the case of the Palaeozoic fossil *Pilina* we had nothing to go on but the few clues afforded by the shell. In *Neopilina* we have the entire body of the animal; and this has been dissected and studied with eager care (figure 29). As the fossil led us to believe, the muscles are laid down in a series, with five successive segments clearly marked out. But it is not only the muscles which are segmented. The comb-like gills likewise are formed in five pairs; the kidney structures, usually consolidated in molluscs, open by five pairs of ducts; the blood vessels, too, show a five-part segmental arrangement. This little form and its Palaeozoic forebears are molluscs; but molluscs of a very primitive nature indeed, their demonstration of retained segmentation partially bridging the worm-mollusc gap.

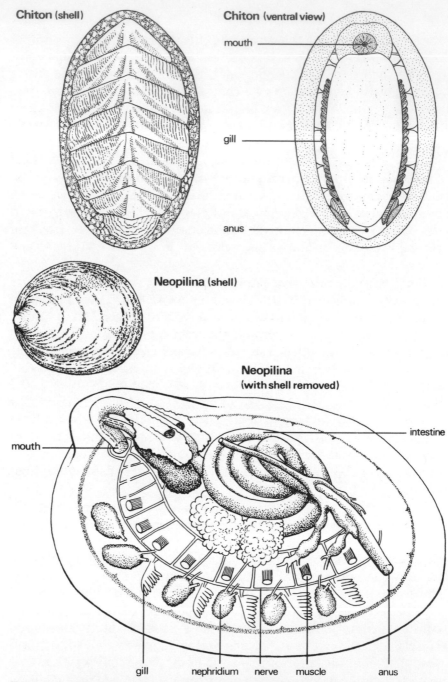

Figure 29. Primitive molluscs – the common shore *Chiton*, and the deep-water *Neopilina*. The diagrammatic drawing of the anatomy of *Neopilina* shows how it has retained traces of segmentation in its gills, nephridia and muscles.

Gastropods

Of the very divergent branches into which more specialized molluscs evolved, the closest in many ways to the primitive forms is the class Gastropoda, including the snails, limpets, whelks and similar types. The components of a snail's body include the same essential features present in a *Chiton* or a *Neopilina*; but the arrangement is a different one. As in these simpler molluscs, the under side of the animal consists of a large muscular 'foot', by means of which the snail can glide, in slow and slimy fashion, over the substrate beneath it. In contrast with more primitive forms, however, there is much more of a development of a head region in a snail; there are sense organs in the form of two pairs of projecting tentacles, one pair apparently the seat of a sense of smell, the second bearing little eyes. Presumably the presence of these sensory structures is related to the fact that – slow as their movements seem to us – the snails are much more active animals than the amphineurans. Whether a developed head was present in the ancestors of the molluscs and its absence in a chiton is due to degeneration, or whether it is a new structure, evolved in the course of snail evolution, is a question for which there is no sure answer.

As in ancestral molluscs, the snail is protected above by a hard limy shell, basically cone-shaped. There are, however, notable differences from primitive forms in the shape and disposition of the shell. In a *Chiton* or a *Neopilina* the mantle and shell cover the entire animal at all times. In a snail, a dorsal 'hump' of tissue remains permanently within the shell, but while going about its perambulations most of the snail's body lies outside it, making for greater ease of locomotion. The cone-shaped shell is, however, sufficiently capacious that when danger threatens the entire body can be drawn back into it, leaving nothing exposed but part of the sole of the 'foot', plugging the opening.

All well and good. But there was a practical problem which demanded solution. If the cone were developed as a simple straight cornucopia-like structure above the animal's back, it would make the snail top-heavy, and the maintenance of balance difficult; further, it would keep the animal from entering (as is often its wont) crevices lacking in height.

In snail evolution the problem has been effectively solved in a unique fashion – by coiling of the shell. As the little snail grows, the shell cone becomes a spiral – and, further, a spiral which is not (as will be seen in cephalopods) a coiling in a single plane, but involves strong growth about a horizontal axis as well as an upward growth. A trend in this direction was apparently a very old one in molluscs, for even some of the oldest of Palaeozoic shells show a slight twist. The end result is the development of a very neat coiled shell structure, snugly placed over the snail's back.

As a result of this, the snail has departed even farther than has a chiton from the primitive pre-mollusc pattern of body organization. Most molluscs have abandoned segmentation; the gastropods have in great measure abandoned bilateral symmetry as well. The asymmetry of the shell demands comparable modification of the snail within it. There is a marked tendency for the reduction of organs of one side of the body, with a resultant strongly asymmetrical build.

Modern gastropods are highly numerous as inhabitants of the seas. A considerable number have accustomed themselves to life in fresh water, and a few, such as the common garden snails, have ventured out onto land. Most have a typical shell; but others, having once evolved it, have reversed the process, reduced it or abandoned it entirely (figure 30). The garden slug is a terrestrial form of this sort. More prominent as shell-less forms are the appropriately named nudibranchs or 'sea-slugs', which are active swimmers in marine waters; the loss of the shell has relieved them of a considerable burden of weight, and swimming has been accomplished by the spreading out of the foot into wing-like expansions.

The gastropods appear, like many other invertebrate groups, in the Lower Cambrian. The earliest types, however, show little coiling, and, with no evidence except what may be gained from the shell, it is difficult to distinguish the earliest members of the group from the primitive molluscs of the *Pilina* type, from which they undoubtedly sprang. Somewhat more advanced forms, of which the modern limpets are the most direct descendants, appear toward the end of the Cambrian; in many of these the shell was (and is) primitive in shape, with little coiling. By the Ordovician, gastropod evolution was in full swing, and fossil snails are common in marine rocks of all later periods. The invasion of fresh waters and the land was a relatively late event. Most snails with pond and terrestrial modes of life are termed pulmonates, because of the fact that they breathe by means of lung-like sacs rather than the comb gills of ordinary molluscs. The earliest records of pulmonates come from the coal swamps of the Carboniferous, but the group became a flourishing one only toward the end of the Cretaceous.

104

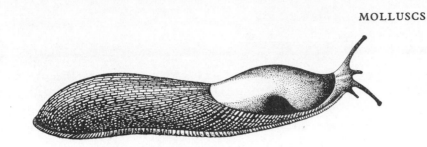

Slug

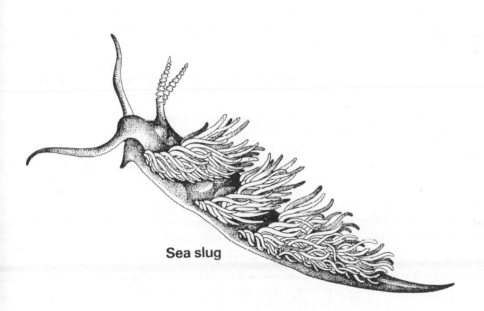

Sea slug

Figure 30. Gastropods which have reduced the shell. There is a small internal shell in slugs, but the sea-slugs have lost it completely.

We shall here mention only briefly a group of marine molluscs, termed the Scaphopoda, or 'tooth shells'. These are mud burrowers, with long slender conical shells, shaped somewhat like a small elephant's tusk, which are slightly curved but never coiled, and open at the narrow upper tip as well as below. There are few living scaphopods and few fossils known, and the group has in general failed to excite the interest of either malacologists (as students of molluscs are called) or of palaeontologists. Let us pass on.

105

Pelecypoda

Next to the gastropods, these forms, the 'hatchet-footed' molluscs, are the most abundant and widespread members of the phylum; clams, oysters, scallops and mussels are familiar and representative. Most show a remarkable uniformity in structure – a structure differing widely from that seen in the gastropods. Very different, too, is their mode of life. The gastropods are, in a mild way, active animals, gliding about in search of food; typical pelecypods are not technically sessile, for they may burrow their way about through mud or sand; but, with very few exceptions, they are a sedentary folk, who do not search for food, but wait for food to come to them.

A clam or mussel well illustrates the general anatomy of a pelecypod. There is a good shell; but it here consists of two parts, hinged above, and so extensive that it can be completely closed below the animal's foot when the clam wishes to become incommunicado, or opened to a moderate degree when the clam is in a more expansive mood. The 'hatchet foot' of the clam is a stout structure which can be extended out from the shell and, like a live and wriggling ploughshare, burrow a path for the clam through the mud (figure 31). Within the shell and the mantle which secretes it lies the soft body of the clam, surrounded by a considerable water-filled cavity – the mantle cavity. Its mode of life parallels that of many of the series of animals discussed in the next chapter, for it is a filter-feeder, existing on small food particles contained in the sea water. Simple in many structural features, it has excellent adaptations for obtaining a supply of water from which its food may be strained. Folds of the mantle form a pair of conjoined tubes – siphons – which can be extruded like the snorkel of a submarine from the mantle and serve to carry, by ciliary action, a current of water in through one tube and out again through the other. The filtering devices are the gills, which fulfil a double function. In other molluscs they are relatively simple and small comb-like structures. In a pelecypod the single pair of gills, one on either side of the body, are much enlarged and complex in nature. The water brought in by the incurrent siphon is strained through the spaces between the bars of the gill comb; the food particles retained are transferred to the mouth and thence to the digestive tract to satisfy the clam's nutritional needs. Robbed of its food materials, the water now passes out again into the sea through the excurrent siphon.

A simple life, but a satisfying one. Presumably the specialized structures which are characteristic of the pelecypods arose during the

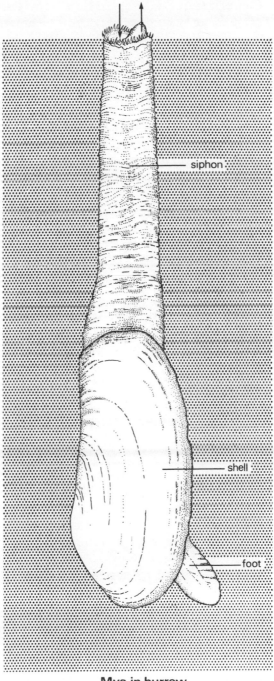

siphon

shell

foot

Figure 31. A burrowing pelecypod, *Mya*, showing the long siphons extending up to the surface, which bear the openings through which water is taken in and later expelled after filtering. The burrowing 'foot' projects below the shell.

Mya in burrow

Cambrian, but it is only in the Ordovician that we can be sure of the presence of true members of this group of molluscs, and many types did not appear until the Silurian or even later periods.

Cephalopods

A final group of molluscs is one which had a most unusual and most spectacular evolutionary history, the Cephalopoda – a name implying, as we shall see, that the head and foot of the animal have gone into profitable partnership. Today the cephalopods are few in number of types, including but a small series of squids and octopuses and the pearly nautilus. But through the ages cephalopods have played a very conspicuous role in marine life. They evolved and ramified in bewildering abundance and variety over a long series of geological periods, and hence afford interesting studies for the scientist interested in evolutionary processes. Further, their shells exhibit such distinctive patterns that the cephalopods have been of the highest value to the stratigrapher in world-wide correlations of strata and the establishment of sequences in the geological time scale.

It is fortunate that there has survived to the present day an archaic remnant of a very ancient cephalopod type – the genus *Nautilus*, of the seas of the East Indies, where it lives, generally, at a considerable depth, swimming near the bottom or crawling over the rocks in search of food. Most of its volume consists of a tightly coiled shell, which in an adult may include half a dozen or so complete cylindrical whorls of increasing size as we progress outward from the centre (figure 32). At the end of the final, outermost whorl is a circular opening, from which, when the animal is active, protrudes a head, with a large pair of eyes, and numerous tentacles; when wishing privacy, these structures can be withdrawn into the shell, and the opening closed.

At first glance one would tend to think that we have here merely a variation on the structure of the gastropods, with their coiled shells. This is not at all the case, however; the structure of the cephalopod body is a very different one, and even the shell, except that it is coiled, has no similarity to that of the snails and their relatives. The snail shell is spirally twisted; the nautilus shell is complexly rolled, but rolled in a single vertical plane, without loss of symmetry. Further, the snail, when withdrawn, occupies the entire length of its shell coil; the nautilus, in strong contrast, lives only in the outermost part of this structure. The remainder of the nautilus shell consists of a long series of empty gas-filled chambers, separated from one another (and from the animal itself at the tip) by solid cross-partitions – septa – and connected with the living animal only by a thin strand of tissue which passes back through the centre of each compartment. This shell

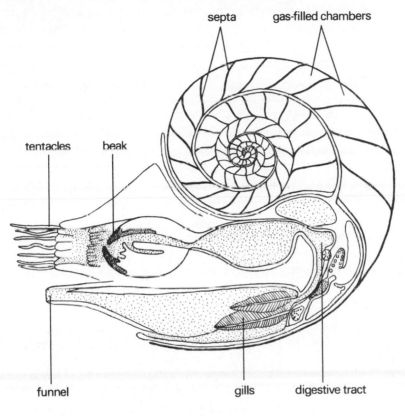

Nautilus

Figure 32. Section through a nautilus to show how the animal lives in the last chamber of the shell.

structure is functionally a very practical arrangement. A heavy shell, while useful as a protective structure, weights the animal down, and is an impediment to free navigation. But the happy device of filling the shell chambers with gas reduces the specific gravity of the nautilus to a point little above that of the water in which he swims. He is protected by the shell, but not hampered by excessive weight. He can eat his cake and have it too.

This chambered type of shell is gradually built during the growth of the animal. The baby nautilus secretes, much like a small gastropod, a tiny conical shell. As the youngster begins to grow, the shell grows with it, expanding a bit in diameter, and begins its spiral curve. But instead of continuing to occupy the old shell tip, the young nautilus abandons it, moves out into the new and wider shell segment, pumps out the water and replaces it with gas, and seals itself off from the tip by a solid cross-partition. Further shell growth occurs; again the growing animal moves out; another septum forms behind it. And so on to maturity.

The nautilus body, too, is constructed in a fashion very different from that of a gastropod. Both cephalopod and gastropod tend to be active food-seeking forms, and, like the gastropod, the nautilus develops a head region which, with large, if simply constructed, eyes peers forward out of the shell opening. Further, there develop from the head a series of slender tentacles which are of major service in obtaining food. Still further, in contrast to the relatively simple nervous system of most molluscs, the cephalopods have a concentration of nerve cells in the head to form a well-developed brain, useful in the co-ordination necessary in seeking prey, and have, as an additional aid in predatory habits, a sharp biting beak at the entrance to the digestive tract.

An effective swimming device is present in all cephalopods – a mechanism for jet propulsion. Below the head and tentacles, the fleshy substance of the foot forms a funnel, with an internal opening to the water-filled mantle cavity and a narrow tip opening to the surface, the whole like a rubber syringe. When desirous of speedy travel, the apparatus can be contracted by muscular action, and a powerful stream of water can be squirted out, giving the animal a propulsive push through the water comparable to that produced in the air by the engines of a jet-powered plane. In normal position, the syringe points forward. Its tip is flexible, and can be turned down and back, so that the animal can be sent forward. But of course the jet is more effective if sent straight out and forward, and hence when rushed, the nautilus shoots itself backward at top speed.

Fortunately for students of cephalopod history, the nautilus appears to be very much of a 'living fossil', a little-changed survivor of a very early stage in the evolution of the group. It is accepted that all of the many hundreds of known fossil cephalopods can be ranged in three subclasses which follow one another in times of appearance and of abundance – Nautiloidea, Ammonoidea, and Dibranchiata. As would be expected of forms with so evolved and complex a structure as the cephalopods, even nautiloids are not known with any certainty amongst the molluscs of the early Cambrian. A few primitive forms are present, however, in late Cambrian days, and in the following Ordovician period the nautiloids evolved in explosive fashion; some specialists recognize up to ten different orders of nautiloids as being present in this early geological period. In late Palaeozoic times nautiloids were still plentiful, but were reduced in variety. In the Mesozoic they dwindled rapidly, their place in the life of the ocean being taken over by their ammonoid descendants. Beyond the Jurassic none was left except forms closely related to the modern nautilus, and from middle Tertiary times onward, *Nautilus* itself is the sole survivor of this once great host.

The fossil nautiloids are, of course, known only from their shells. But these shells are so varied in nature, and the history of the forms which bore them so complex, that even the cephalopod specialists have never entirely succeeded in untangling the evolutionary lines and relationships within the group. Some nautiloids have straight, uncoiled shells, looking like long cornucopias; others have loosely coiled or partially coiled shells; in still others the coil is tight and complex. One would *a priori* expect that the first forms would have had straight shells and that coiling would have come later. Very probably some of the straight shells found in the Palaeozoic are primitive in this regard; but there is evidence that in some cases the descendants of a nautiloid which had wound himself into a good spiral changed their minds, so to speak, reversed the direction of their evolution, and uncoiled again.

Succeeding the nautiloids came the Ammonoidea. The name comes from the Egyptian god Ammon; shells of this group, common in Egyptian limestones, may fancifully be considered as being the horns – in some sense – of that deity. The ammonoids, unfortunately, are entirely extinct, so that we know nothing of the animal which inhabited the abundantly known fossil shells of this group. Not improbably they would have been in the flesh fairly similar to the nautiloids and, in fact, their shells are, on the whole, fairly similar to those of their nautiloid ancestors. The two groups, however, can be readily distinguished on the basis of details of shell structure. In nautiloids the partitions between successive segments of the shell are simple in construction, and generally show on the surface as a series of simple circular markings along the length of the shell. In ammonoids, in contrast, the surface markings show a complex wrinkling pattern, the internal septa tend likewise to become complex in build, and, in addition, the shell surface may acquire a varied ornamental sculpturing (figure 33). The first ammonoids appear in the Ordovician as a modest side-branch off the nautiloid stock. In the late Palaeozoic the group began to acquire prominence, and in the Mesozoic era they are the dominant cephalopods, flourishing in immense numbers and variety and pushing their nautiloid kin to the wall. They continued in abundance until the end of the Cretaceous; then, in a fashion parallel to that of the dinosaurs, they vanished completely from the oceans in a geologically short period of time, leaving us with almost no clues as to why great success was followed so rapidly by complete failure – and extinction.

The third and final group of cephalopods is that which alone (except for *Nautilus*) survived the Cretaceous. This is the sub-class Dibranchiata, including the cuttlefish, squids and octopuses (figure 33). The name means little; it simply refers to the fact that these forms have but two gills, whereas the living nautilus has four, and presumably the ancient shelled cephalopods had the same. Molluscs in general surprise one by the peculiar turns taken in the evolution of the group. And no turn in mollusc history is more astonishing than the sharp reversal in evolutionary trend exhibited by these 'modern' cephalopods. It almost seems as if the older cephalopods gloried in their great and complex shells, which they proudly carried about for hundreds of millions of years. The modern cephalopods, one might believe, are ashamed of shells; in these forms they are hidden and reduced, and play no part in the animal's life.

Commonest of modern forms are the squids. These are mostly small creatures, although a giant deep-sea squid reaches a length of fifty feet (including the arms). The body is cigar-shaped, tapering at one end. The contours are such that one can imagine the ancestor to have inhabited a simple conical shell. This was presumably the case; but in the modern squid the shell, although it begins to develop in the young, never amounts to much, and in the adult is only a feather-shaped horny plate, buried deep within the animal's leathery covering. Projecting from the broad end of the cigar are the head and 'foot'. In part the structures we see are comparable to those of the more primitive *Nautilus*. There is a good siphon, and the squid is capable of rapid locomotion – especially in backing away from trouble.

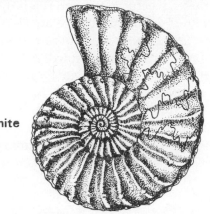

Ammonite

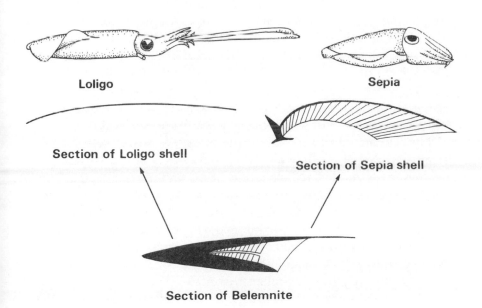

Loligo

Sepia

Section of Loligo shell

Section of Sepia shell

Section of Belemnite

Figure 33. Some of the sutures between successive chambers can be seen on the surface of the ammonite shell. Though the shell is internal and straight in the dibranchiate cephalopods, vestiges of the old system of a sequence of chambers separated by partitions can be seen in sections of the shell of the ancestral dibranchiate *Belemnites* and of the modern squid, *Sepia*, though not in that of the cuttlefish, *Loligo*.

113

9

Eyes and tentacles are present in *Nautilus* and likewise in the squid; but in the build of these structures the two types differ greatly.

The nautiloid eye is of good size, but relatively simple construction. There is no lens; and the sensory structure of the retina, lying in a pocket with a small opening to the surface, is bathed in sea water. Vision in a nautilus is surely imperfect. Quite otherwise is the build of the squid (or octopus) eye. There is a well-formed lens which can focus the image accurately on the retina, accessory focusing devices, and even an iris. Vision is probably as acute in a squid as in a vertebrate, and the build of the eye is closely comparable in the two cases. We have here an excellent example of parallelism in evolution. The molluscs and the vertebrates are not related, except in the most remote degree, and quite surely the common ancestor was a simple eyeless form. Both types have, over the course of the eras, evolved almost identical structures; but have evolved them independently in parallel fashion.

Modified, too, are the tentacles. In *Nautilus* they are numerous, but simple and non-adhesive in build. In 'modern' cephalopods they are fewer in number (ten in a squid, eight in an octopus, as his name indicates) but more evolved in build. The slender tapering tentacles of the nautilus are of some use in bringing food to the mouth; in the squid the arms, two of which are notably long, are supplied with rows of effective sucking disks. The squid can aggressively seize its prey and bring it to the mouth, which has a powerful horny beak.

The dibranchiates were, as one might expect, a relatively late group to appear. Small shells which may have been borne by squid-like animals are found in late Palaeozoic strata, and remains of true squids and the related cuttlefish are known from the Jurassic. Most specialized of living cephalopods are the octopuses, first found in the late Cretaceous. These have abandoned the elongate squid shape to become rather formless globular large-eyed masses of tissue without even vestiges of a shell, and with but eight arms – all of which, however, are highly effective prehensile organs.

One gets the impression (perhaps ill founded) that hosts of Palaeozoic and Mesozoic cephalopods, floating about with their buoyant shells, were essentially a peaceful folk, feeding only on smaller types of food materials and not, in general, molesting their more prominent contemporaries. In the 'modern' cephalopods we see an attempt to change the whole pattern of existence by becoming aggressive predators. To some degree they have succeeded in the attempt. But

despite the acquirements of such adaptations as the prehensile tentacles and the jet propulsion system, their basic structural pattern is
not one well adapted to the role they have attempted to play. Their
success has been little better than that of Mussolini in his efforts to
transform the peace-loving Italian populace into a horde of blood-
seeking aggressors.

In the evolution of many animal groups there appears to be some
sort of general trend in the direction of their evolution, often leading
people of a philosophical turn of mind, as we have seen, to suggest a
'purpose' behind the evolutionary story, due to some supernatural
directive or to some internal urge. This is certainly not the case with
the molluscs – as was pointed out at the beginning of this chapter, and
as has been obvious from a recital of the history of the various components of the phylum. The molluscs have followed not one path, but
many, and even shown sharp reversals of trends once begun. Their
course has been somewhat comparable to that of the messenger of
legend, who mounted his horse and dashed off in all directions.

Chapter 6

Filter-Feeders

IN the last several chapters we have described a series of invertebrates – worms, arthropods, molluscs – which are for the most part active animals, basically bilaterally symmetrical, often segmented, and generally aggressive in the search for food. To be sure, some of them have departed from this pattern, to seek food but seek it as parasites, as in the case of many worms, or to degenerate into a sessile mode of life, as the pelecypods and barnacles have done. But in all these cases the ancestral background is one of active food-seeking.

In the present chapter we turn to consider the evolution of a series of forms in whose pedigree, as far as we can tell, no such activity was ever present; a series of forms which, from the beginning of their metazoan history, may have been sessile food-gatherers. Attached, as adults, upright on the sea bottom, they stand with outstretched ciliated arms gathering food particles for provender. These are all filter-feeders, in a broad sense of that term. Most prominent of such forms are the little bryozoans, or moss animalcules; the brachiopods, or lamp shells; and (as regards their more primitive members) the echinoderms, the crinoids or sea-lilies and their cousins.

The three groups just named are the principal ones with sedentary filter-feeding habits. But all are specialized in one direction or another, with varied adaptations and structures diagnostic of each group. Quite possibly they are related to one another, but this is doubtful or capable of little proof. They may, however, represent three surviving end-types of a broad radiation of sessile filter-feeders of early days in metazoan history, which may have originally included other types now extinct and of which (since they were presumably soft bodied, for the most part) we have little or no fossil record.

Phoronids

There are, however, a few odds and ends of seeming survivors of this radiation in addition to the three major types presently to be

116

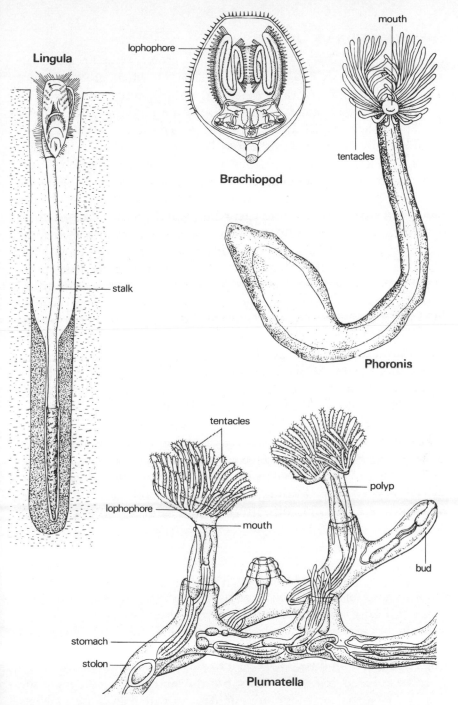

Lingula

lophophore

Brachiopod

mouth

tentacles

stalk

Phoronis

tentacles

polyp

lophophore

mouth

bud

stomach

stolon

Plumatella

Figure 34. Three different types of filter-feeders. *Lingula* is a brachiopod which has a long flexible stalk anchoring it into the mud. The internal view of a brachiopod (above, middle) shows its horseshoe-shaped lophophore, which can also be seen in *Phoronis*. Part of a colony of the bryozoan *Plumatella* is also shown.

discussed. One is that of the Phoronidea, a group of rare little animals which includes only a dozen or so species, but which are so distinct from any other invertebrates that they are generally considered, despite their insignificance, to form a separate phylum of the animal kingdom. They dwell, buried in mud or sand flats, in tubes which they secrete about themselves; tube and body are slender, but elongate, and may reach a number of inches in length. The body may be withdrawn into the tube, but generally the upper end is a bit emergent for food-seeking. Nearly completely surrounding the upper end of the body, and rising above it into the water, is a horseshoe-shaped sheet of tissue, considerably folded, termed a lophophore (we shall meet similar structures in later groups). From this extend numerous little tentacles, so called (figure 34). But unlike the tentacles of a coelenterate or a cephalopod, these are not grasping organs; instead they are ciliated, and the beats of the cilia of the tentacle rows carry down to the mouth food particles gathered from the passing water currents. The animal has a simple body structure; as must needs be for an animal of any degree of organization living in a tube closed below, mouth and anus are both present on the upper surface, within the fold of the lophophore, the digestive tract being in consequence U-shaped; there are nervous, circulatory, reproductive and excretory organs of a simple sort.

Phoronids are not surely known as fossils, although some fossil tube structures in Palaeozoic rocks have been interpreted as possibly made by such forms. They do, however, represent a very primitive stage in the evolution of filter-feeding food-gatherers, and may well be close to the ancestry of some or all of the remaining forms mentioned in this chapter.

Bryozoans

On the shores of the oceans, streams, and ponds, are frequently present a variety of small and primitive plants, broadly termed algae. But appearances are sometimes deceptive. Some of the small clusters of plant-like things which one may find on a rock or wharf or piling, often branched and with little flower-like tips to the branches, prove, when closely examined, to be not plants, but tiny animals – members of the phylum Bryozoa, or moss animalcules, so called because of their appearance. (Polyzoa is an alternative term.) There is considerable variation amongst bryozoans, but a common type is that shown by

Plumatella, a fresh-water member of the group (figure 34). This is a colonial form, as are nearly all bryozoans, the individuals, which look rather like the polyps of a hydrozoan coelenterate at first glance, lying at the tips of a branching connecting stem, or stolon. The colony is begun by normal reproductive processes, but increases and ramifies by budding. In the production of a new bud, there is formed a stout body wall enclosing the base and sides of the body and, within it, the soft body of the 'polyp'. The body of the individual within the case is basically rather similar to that of the phoronids already described: the digestive tract is U-shaped, with both mouth and anus opening on the upper surface, and there is a horseshoe-shaped lophophore, bearing a long series of ciliated food-gathering tentacles. It is obvious that we are dealing with an animal which has the same basic build as the phoronids. But in the course of a long evolutionary history the bryozoans have accumulated various specializations. The taking up of a colonial life is one item, but they have other and curious features. For example, a 'polyp' may degenerate, its cells cluster into a brown mass of tissue which may be carried out, and a new 'polyp' forms within the old body sheath. Again, just as is true of the polyps of colonial hydroids, we find a variety of types of individuals among the budding 'polyps' of a bryozoan colony. As a most curious type may be mentioned the sort of individual termed an 'avicularium', which may bud on a short stalk off the side of a normal 'polyp' in some bryozoans. As the name suggests, a little animalcule of this sort looks like a tiny bird's head with a sharp beak and a movable jaw. If some roving little animal comes in contact with it, the jaws snap, and the intruder is caught in a tiny vice.

We have described *Plumatella* as a rather generalized bryozoan. Most forms have a fairly comparable structure. But there is an important point to be noted. In this little animal and a majority of bryozoans, the anus lies outside the sweep of the lophophore, and these forms are hence called, reasonably, the Ectoprocta (*proctos* being the Greek word for anus). In a number of forms, however, termed the Endoprocta, both mouth and anus are within the circle formed by the lophophore. This point in itself might not be of great importance, but there are other features in which 'ects' and 'ends' differ. The latter group is much simpler in nature, and, amongst other items, lacks proper coelomic spaces. It is, therefore, argued that the two groups are quite distinct and related only distantly, if at all. However, the matter is none too clear. Possibly the endoprocts are a simpler ancestral group; on the other hand, they may be a degenerate side-branch of the major ectoproct division of the bryozoans.

We cannot settle this point; but on another front we do have data. For the bryozoans (the ectoprocts, at least) have an extensive fossil history. The soft material of the 'polyp' is never preserved; but the stalks of the colony and the cases enclosing the individuals often contain considerable calcareous material which may be preserved. A wide range of fossil materials of diverse types of bryozoan colonies is known from the later Cambrian onward. Obviously many of the specializations of the phylum had already been established early in the Palaeozoic, and hence the time of occurrence of the most primitive of lophophore filter-feeders, from which the bryozoans and other forms of this ilk arose, must have been back somewhere in the Pre-Cambrian.

Brachiopods

The lamp shells, or brachiopods, are an insignificant group of sessile marine organisms today; the world over, there are about a hundred or so species, belonging to a small number of genera. But in early geologic times, particularly in the Palaeozoic, the situation was very different. Brachiopods were then exceedingly abundant and exceedingly varied and prominent members of the ocean fauna. Known Palaeozoic families are reckoned by the scores, genera by the hundreds, species by the thousands, and brachiopods are the main interest of a considerable fraction of workers in invertebrate palaeontology.

The main characteristics of the group are readily defined. They are, like the phoronids and bryozoans, lophophore-bearing filter-feeders, different from the phoronids in being supported by a distinct stalk and from the bryozoans in being solitary rather than colonial forms. They further differ from both of these groups in having the individual – lophophore and all – enclosed within a two-valved shell.

A well-known modern member of the group is *Lingula* (figure 34), found here and there in mudflats in all parts of the world. All brachiopods are sessile forms, living on muddy or sandy bottoms; some are deep-sea types, but most today – and probably in the past – prefer shallow waters. The animal is supported by a flexible stalk, which attaches to a rock beneath or is anchored firmly in the mud. At the top a pair of shells enclose the animal. In *Lingula* the shell material is a horny substance, and the two shell valves are connected only by ligaments; in a great majority of brachiopods, however, the shells are

120

hard and limy, and there is, as in a clam, a well-developed hinge connecting the two. There are strong muscles within which can clamp the two valves firmly together (they never do open at all widely).

The shell superficially resembles that of a clam or mussel. (The valves also resemble the shallow oil-filled vessels used as lamps by the Romans, hence the 'lamp shell' name.) But basically the situation is very different from that in pelecypods. Although a clam is not greatly concerned with symmetry, its two valves are left and right, with the opening at the bottom, the hinge at the top. A brachiopod may lie on the bottom in almost any position, but morphologically the two shells form on the upper and lower sides of the animal, the hinge at the back, the opening at the front.

Within the shell, the main fleshy part of the animal lies at the back, close to the stalk. Out from it, and occupying most of the cavity of the shell are two long coiled structures, bearing rows of little parallel tentacles, each vested with actively beating cilia. It is hardly necessary to say that here again we are meeting with the same type of food-gathering structure, the lophophore, which we have met with in the phoronids and bryozoans. Here, however, there is but a single pair of ciliated arms, which are much more expanded and complex than in moss animalcules or phoronids; the reason for existence of the shell is primarily the protection of these delicate objects.

Food particles present in water currents passing in and out through the shell opening are busily gathered up by the bands of cilia and, embedded in mucus, passed to the mouth. Beyond, there is a stomach and in *Lingula* a looped intestine, as in the two types described previously, and an anus opening back into the mantle cavity.

Here, however, there is a puzzling point. *Lingula* does have an anus; but in most brachiopods this is not the case; the intestine ends blindly, and waste materials must be passed back and out again through the mouth. This is, of course, the condition seen in lowly metazoans, such as the coelenterates and flatworms. At first one is led to the belief that perhaps the ancestral brachiopods were very primitive metazoans with a two-way digestive tube, and that development of an anus occurred within the evolutionary history of the group. But it is much more probable that the absence of an anus is due to loss and secondary simplification. After all, the amount of rough-waste in the tiny food particles upon which a brachiopod feeds is presumably small, and its re-passage via the mouth need not be particularly distressing.

We can reasonably assume that the brachiopods, like the bryozoans, evolved from small soft-bodied filter-feeders, and the major development which marked them off as proper brachiopods was the evolution of the characteristic shell. We would, hence, not expect to find them represented in the sedimentary record until a shell capable of preservation as a fossil came into existence. This took place at an early date. There are reports of some remains of brachiopod shells in the late Pre-Cambrian; and a variety of forms are found in early Cambrian deposits – most of them loosely hinged, but some with a good articulation between the valves already present.

It was, however, in the following Ordovician period that the great radiation of the group took place. The shell of such a form as *Lingula* is simple in structure and plain in appearance. The older brachiopods, however, developed a bewildering series of variations on this basic pattern, with complicated shell contours, varied ornamentation, spines and spicules. The old-fashioned crude methods of preparing fossil shell specimens by the use of hammer and chisel tended to chip off and ruin much of this ornamentation. In recent years, however, much better methods of preparation have been perfected. With the use of acids it is often possible to dissolve away the limestone in which a shell is embedded and leave its surface and ornamentation preserved in exquisite detail.

The varied brachiopod groups flourished greatly during the Palaeozoic. But decline set in, and beyond the Triassic there remained but a few of the once numerous brachiopod tribes, and these mainly in much diminished numbers. What caused this flourishing Palaeozoic group to meet their downfall in a fashion parallel to their contemporaries, the nautiloids? Competition, very probably. In the Palaeozoic, the brachiopods (barring the minor competition of bryozoans *et al.*) had more or less a monopoly of the ecological niche of filter-feeding. But a new group had entered the scene – the pelecypods, which, diverging from an active ancestral line, had adopted sedentary habits and a food-straining mode of life. Why the lowly clams and mussels should have been more successful in this mode of making a living than the once flourishing (and more interesting) brachiopods is none too clear. But they have done so.

Lingula is not merely a surviving brachiopod, but a survivor of the more primitive, hingeless subdivision of the group. Shells so similar in pattern to those of the living forms as often to be included in the same genus have been identified in the later Palaeozoic, and forms which, as far as can be judged from the shell, were very similar, are known not merely in the Cambrian but even in Pre-Cambrian rocks. *Lingula* is, like the nautilus, very much of a living fossil.

Echinoderms

We conclude this chapter on filter-feeders with an account of the phylum Echinodermata, the 'spiny-skinned' animals of which starfish and sea-urchins are the more generally familiar representatives. At first sight their inclusion in this chapter seems highly improper. These are highly organized animals, with numerous very specialized sorts of structures; the more familiar types are not sessile but free and capable of motion (of a sort); and, most especially, most members of the group are definitely not filter-feeders at all. But the evidence is reasonably clear that the most primitive of echinoderms *were* sessile and *were* filter-feeders. To show this as a possibility, we need not, for the time, resort to a description of ancient fossil echinoderms. Let us consider the living crinoids, 'lilies' of the sea bottoms.

The crinoids, or sea-lilies (figure 35), of which there are several hundreds of surviving species, are not as familiar to the visitor to the seashore as are other echinoderms, since they live in waters of at least respectable depth, rather than frequenting the shallows or the tideway. Typical crinoids are attached to the sea bottom by a slender stalk (for most of their lives, at least; the adults may eventually break free). Above is a compact body; above this a cluster of slender branching ciliated arms. The crinoid is complexly armoured and has various specialized internal structures. But if we, for the moment, disregard these, and ask ourselves what the basic pattern of a crinoid is, we come to an answer which is essentially similar to the one we would give for a brachiopod or a bryozoan. These other animals consist essentially of a stalk; a little compact body at the top of the stalk, with mouth and anus both opening on the upper surface; and above the body proper, tentacles armed with rows of cilia which filter food particles from the sea water and pass them down to the waiting mouth. The crinoid has various complicated trappings, but basically the same description will apply to this relatively primitive echinoderm and to a variety of early fossil members of the phylum. As in other cases, the early pedigree, before the acquisition of fossilizable armour, will probably remain forever unknown, but it is a reasonable assumption that the crinoids – and echinoderms as a whole – arose from the same array of small

123

soft-bodied little filter-feeders from which there also evolved the lamp shells and moss animalcules.

The presence of a complicated armour is, of course, one of the distinguishing features of a crinoid, as it is of all echinoderms. This is calcareous in nature, but differs from the shell structures of many invertebrates in the fact that, like vertebrate armour, it is laid down within the substance of the animal's tissues, rather than laid down exterior to the skin. Even the stalk is armoured, the living tissue in the centre being protected by a long series of skeletal rings. A further complex series of articulated plates ensheathes the body above the stalk. Above the body extend the long and branching arms which are the food-collectors. These are essentially comparable to the lophophores of a brachiopod or bryozoan or phoronid, but instead of fusing to form a single sheet of tissue at the base (as in a bryozoan) or a pair of arms (as in a brachiopod), there are five primary arms, which may branch and rebranch as we follow them outward.

The number 'five' brings to light a basic fact of echinoderm organization. To a sessile form (as discussed in connection with the coelenterates) symmetry of a bilateral type is meaningless; there is a top and bottom, but no left or right; almost everything is, or can be, just the same all the way round. There is thus a strong tendency for the development of radial symmetry. This most echinoderms acquired early in their history (although the little ciliated larvae from which the adult echinoderm develops is bilaterally symmetrical, and some early fossil echinoderms show traces of bilaterality). Early in their history they appear to have settled (for no readily determinable 'reason') upon five as the proper number of units into which to divide the circuit of the body, and with few exceptions all members of the group regard this number as sacrosanct.

But to return to the crinoid and its five arms. These, like stem and body, are sheathed in a multiplicity of tiny armour plates. But on the inner side of each arm and its branches is a lengthwise groove, leading downwards to the mouth – an ambulacral groove, to use a technical term. Here there is soft tissue rather than armour. All along the length of each groove are ranged, on either side, rows of little soft projecting 'feet'. These appear to serve in part for breathing, as a series of tiny gills. But they also bear cilia; these cilia set up water currents which, like those of the tentacles of a brachiopod or bryozoan lophophore, carry food particles down the grooves to the mouth.

In addition to the armour, echinoderms in general have a variety of complicated structural gadgets not found in other groups, and the crinoids are no exception to the rule. We may note particularly the unique echinoderm 'water-vascular' system. Pores on the upper surface of the body lead (indirectly) into a system of water-filled sacs and canals ringing round the mouth and sending a tubular canal down each arm. And within each arm, all the little 'tube feet' are hollow, their interiors occupied by water-filled branches of the arm canals.

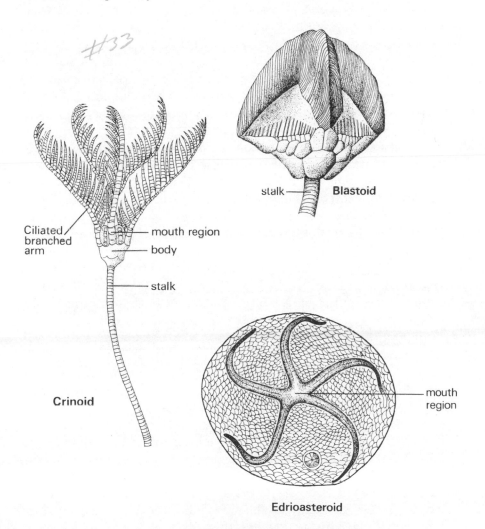

Figure 35. The earliest echinoderms were sessile and stalked, like the crinoids and blastoids. Some, at least, of the edrioasteroids were not attached, and these may be ancestral to the living, free-moving echinoderms.

125

The crinoids are of respectable antiquity, with a pedigree stretching back to the Ordovician. Proper crinoids are not found in the Cambrian; but in that period there were already present a considerable variety of echinoderm types of archaic nature, all pertaining to groups now long extinct. A few may have been truly free living, but this is dubious; most very definitely were stemmed forms, giving strong support to the belief that sedentary filter-feeding was the primitive echinoderm way of life. A few, the eocrinoids, seem quite generalized ancestral forms, resembling the crinoids in their general pattern, but with a simpler armour-plating and with little branching of the arms. Other members of this early radiation of Cambrian and Ordovician sessile echinoderms – carpoids, cystoids, blastoids, edrioasteroids (figure 35) – appear to have experimented with a variety of body forms. Some were for a time successful; but, of sedentary types, only the crinoids were a permanent success.

But as an amateur of nature knows, most of the echinoderms of today are not attached, and are capable of movement – to some degree, at least. Representatives of four classes of such echinoderms may be found on any seashore today (figure 36); these are (1) the typical starfishes, the Asteroidea; (2) the brittle stars, or Ophiuroidea; (3) the Echinoidea, the sea-urchins and sand dollars; and (4) less familiar, the Holothuroidea, or sea-cucumbers. The trend toward release from a stalk began at a respectably early stage in echinoderm history, for with the exception of the brittle stars (apparently a late side-branch from the orthodox starfish) representatives of all these groups had developed out of the rapid early radiation of echinoderms by the beginning of the Ordovician.

Basically it is easy to see how to transform a crinoid into a starfish – abolish the stalk, turn the animal over, top for bottom, and there you are! But the problem is still far from solved. The primitive starfish may have wished to travel. But how? No limbs were present, and since nearly the whole body was heavily armour-plated, the budding out of locomotor appendages would have been a difficult evolutionary process. But there was one recourse – use of the rows of tiny 'feet' lying along the arms (figure 36) and connected with the underlying water-vascular system already present. These are the structures by means of which the starfish makes his slow journeys over the bottom. A single tube foot is a feeble structure; but there are scores of them along each starfish arm. When internal pressure is applied to a little sac at the base, the tube foot expands, and a tiny sucker at its tip attaches to the

126

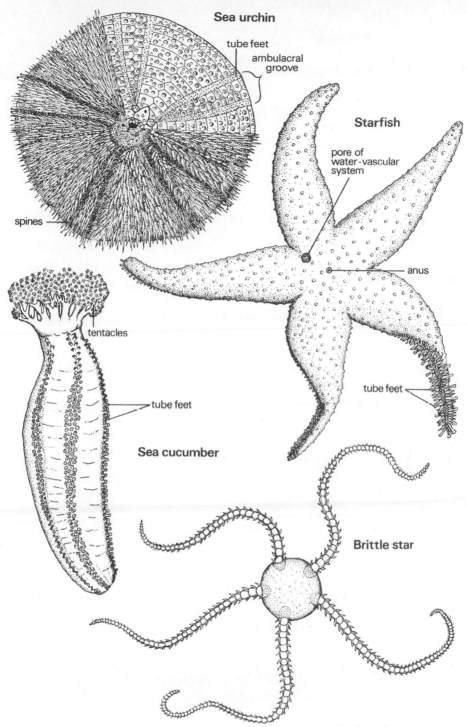

Sea urchin

tube feet
ambulacral groove

spines

Starfish

pore of water-vascular system

anus

tentacles

tube feet

Sea cucumber

tube feet

Brittle star

Figure 36. Living types of echinoderms. The spines and tube-feet have been removed from part of the sea-urchin to show the plates which make up the shell; the ambulacral groove with its two lines of holes for the tube-feet can also be seen. The mouth of the sea-cucumber is surrounded by mucous-covered tentacles, to which food particles adhere.

rock beneath; when the pressure on the foot is released, it contracts and the body is pulled toward the point of attachment. A single tug by a single footlet is of little effect; but given enough feet, enough time, and enough tugs, the starfish can move about, although at far from express speed.

Now for a second major problem: what to eat, and how? The crinoid-like ancestor was a filter-feeder. But, having turned itself over, the ciliated grooves which once strained food particles are underneath the animal, away from water currents. Furthermore, the tube feet, whose cilia did the job of food-collection, are used for a different purpose and are not available.

The starfish has made a major change in livelihood. It has become a predator, feeding on clams, oysters, and the like.

Did not observation show this to be true, it would be difficult to believe that a seemingly feeble starfish could prey upon a clam, which can, with powerful muscles, tightly close its hard shell and shut itself off, apparently very effectively, from any predator.

Steady persistence does it. Again, the tube feet perform the task. The starfish mounts upon the clam, attaches a series of tube feet suckers to each shell, and begins to pull. At long last the clam's muscles tire and relax; the shell opens, and the soft body of the clam is exposed.

But there is a further problem. The ancestral echinoderm's mouth was simply an opening through which microscopic particles could pass on their way to the stomach; there are no biting jaws, no beak. How to engulf the clam and get it into the stomach? The answer is a most unusual one: the clam is not taken into the starfish body to reach the stomach; the stomach goes out to the clam. The starfish turns the lower part of its stomach inside out; it extends outward through the mouth, and surrounds the clam's body and digests it on the spot. The starfish has had to resort to most unusual means to become an active predator; but unusual or not, the method works, as is shown by the abundance of starfish along the shores today, and by an abundance of fossil starfish in the sediments of every geological period since the Ordovician.

Present also in the Ordovician were the first sea-urchins. Some of the early Palaeozoic echinoderms had developed a rounded body in which there were no projecting arms; instead, the structure was such that the arms appeared to be, so to speak, plastered down on the surface of the spherical body, with a series of five ambulacral grooves radiating out from the mouth and converging toward the opposite 'pole' of the body. This seems to be basically the build of a sea-urchin; however, the simple body plan is disguised, through the fact that the creature's spherical surface is covered by a series of long protective spines, giving the sea-urchin somewhat the appearance of a tiny rolled-up hedgehog. (To an ancient Greek, by the way, the word 'echinos' meant, indifferently, either a sea-urchin or a hedgehog.) The five ambulacral grooves (figure 36) are furnished with tube feet and hence locomotion is possible to a sea-urchin; but since the feet must reach out beyond the spines, they are long slender structures, and sea-urchins are far from being notable as good travellers. They feed upon vegetable matter, rather than being predators like their starfish cousins. They lack the ability possessed by the starfish of everting their stomachs; they have, however, been able to evolve a series of tooth-like mouth structures to aid in the treatment of their tougher and less digestible food materials. The sand dollars are merely a flattened variant of the sea-urchin type.

Sea-urchins are known in strata of every geologic period since the time of their first appearance in the Ordovician; they appear in moderate abundance in some Mesozoic formations, but on the whole have been less successful than the starfishes. A cut below the sea-urchins, again, in degree of success as measured by numbers, in either living or fossil state, are the members of a final echinoderm group, the Holothuroidea or sea-cucumbers (figure 36). Their basic build appears to be somewhat similar to that of the echinoids. Like the echinoids, they are spine-covered, but in sea-cucumbers the armour between the spines is much reduced. Because of the lack of solid armour, the fossil record of the holothurians is none too good; however, they may be represented by a form in the Cambrian shales of British Columbia, and they are surely present from the Ordovician onward. Much as in echinoids, there are no free arms, and the ambulacral grooves lie along the surface of the body from the mouth at one end to the anus which here (and in echinoids as well) lies at the opposite body pole, in contrast to starfish and crinoids. Unlike the spherically-built echinoids, the body is rather elongated, with a large mouth at the front end. Curiously, there is a bit of bilaterality to the body; this, however, is probably secondary rather than primitive. The holothurians have yet another sort of diet; they are mud-eaters. As they progress sluggishly along, mud is taken in through the mouth; it travels along through the intestine, where any nutritious content is digested and absorbed, and the residue continues its travels onward and outward through the anus. A living, if a poor one.

This concludes a survey of a group of phyla which appear to be primitively filter-feeders. Many of them, once well established in this ecological niche, have continued in it, and have shown little evolutionary change over the ages. A majority of echinoderms have, it is true, abandoned filter-feeding for other modes of life; but on the whole, they seem to have entered side-eddies in the evolutionary stream, rather than advancing.

Looking at the filter-feeders as a whole, one tends to feel that this mode of life is a stultifying one, that no major progress is to be expected from a filter-feeding group; that they are essentially a dead-end type.

Not so. We have already noted a number of surprising reversals and changes in direction in the evolutionary history of one group or another. We are about to describe a further change of this sort, and one which, as vertebrates ourselves, is of personal interest.

Chapter 7

Whence the Vertebrates?

FOR all the rest of this volume, we shall be concerned with the vertebrates – the backboned animals, the group to which we ourselves belong. This may seem a rather unfair allotment of space. The vertebrates make up but part of one of over a dozen major phyla of the
animal kingdom; as to species, there are more species in a single
family of beetles alone than in all the backboned animals in the world;
and as to numbers of individuals, it needs no scientist to tell us that we
are vastly outnumbered by any one of a number of invertebrate
groups.

But, after all, there are legitimate arguments for concentrating a bit
on the vertebrates. From fish through amphibians and reptiles to
birds and mammals, the vertebrates include the great majority of
animals familiar and interesting to us. And a further legitimate, if
selfish, reason lies in the fact that we belong to this group, and in
studying vertebrates, we are studying our own relatives and may learn
something of our own antecedents.

Where did the vertebrates come from? Let us sort out the really
basic attributes of primitive vertebrates, the fishes, discarding all the
more advanced features, and see where among more lowly animals
these characters may be found. It is generally agreed that there are
three basic 'patents' found in fishes and present in but few animals not
members of the vertebrate series.

One: internal gills. All animals must breathe; must have some
method of taking in oxygen from the water or air surrounding them
and giving off waste carbon dioxide in return. In higher, land-dwelling
vertebrates lungs perform this function; but in fishes gills for water-
breathing are found. Many lower water-dwellers have gills; but, as
we have seen, these are generally feathery structures lying outside the
body. Fishes have a very different system – the gills are internal.
Water enters the throat, generally through the mouth, and passes out
to the surface of the 'neck' through slits or pouches in which are

situated the delicate gill membranes. This internal gill-pouch pattern is so deeply ingrained in vertebrate structure that we find that a typical fish series of gill pouches is present in every human embryo, even though it is probably close to 300 millions of years since they last functioned in a human ancestor.

Two: a dorsal hollow nerve cord. As we have seen, many invertebrates have a brain of sorts and, if they possess, in worms and arthropods, an elongate bilaterally symmetrical body, have one or more nerve cords running aft. Vertebrates have such a cord – the spinal cord. But this has two characters not ordinarily found in other groups. Typical invertebrate nerve cords are solid structures; the vertebrate cord is hollow, filled with spinal fluid. Further, it runs down the back of the body, in contrast to typical invertebrates.

Three: an internal skeleton. Many invertebrates have some sort of skeletal 'stiffening' in their make-up, but such supporting structures are generally surface structures, as the shell of a mollusc or the 'shell' of a lobster. Vertebrates, too, may have an external armour of scales or bones, but in addition there is always present an internal skeleton of bone or cartilage. Basic in this is the backbone, the vertebral column from which the group gets its name, consisting of a long jointed series of elements running the length of the body.

But preceding the backbone in development of the individual and in evolution of the group is a more basic structure, termed the notochord. In the embryo of every vertebrate there early develops a long tubular structure running from head to tail along the back just below the nerve cord. Inside the tube are soft, cellular materials; but they are enclosed in a stout sheath, giving the whole the general picture of long, slender sausages, flexible but stoutly built, which can do a respectable job in holding together the structures of a small marine animal. In most vertebrates the notochord dwindles and disappears as the individual grows, to be replaced by the stronger, if less flexible, bony backbone; but in such lowly forms as lampreys and hagfishes there is little development of vertebrae, and the notochord is still prominent in the adult animal. Further, there are, as will be seen presently, some small marine animals which are unquestionably related to the vertebrates but of more primitive nature, which have no vertebrae at all, but do have a prominent notochord. We cannot, of course, properly call such animals vertebrates; what is done by professional zoologists is to consider these lowly animals plus the vertebrates as making up, together, a major division of the animal kingdom, the phylum Chordata. (For purposes of discussion, our more primitive chordate relatives are generally lumped as 'lower chordates'. We will describe them a few pages on.)

We have, now, outlined some of the key basic characters which are present in vertebrates, and are ready to explore among lower animal groups for vertebrate relatives – forms in which some of these characters might, hopefully, be found. Such quests have been pursued with zest ever since the general acceptance of the evolutionary theory a century ago. And in most cases they have ended in blind alleys.

Vertebrates are bilaterally symmetrical animals, with a segmental arrangement and active in nature; hence in this quest it was but natural that attention was long focused on active, bilaterally symmetrical types of invertebrates as possible relatives – the various worm groups, for example. For several decades a major theory was that the backboned animals were related to the annelid worms – not so much the inhabitants of our gardens as the more highly organized marine members of the group. Here are active, bilaterally symmetrical, segmented animals, with a bit of brain and with a nerve cord running the length of the body. These are some of the features expected in a vertebrate ancestor. But beyond this, the theory falls flat. What about a notochord? Despite forlorn attempts, no one has ever found anything much like a notochord in the body of even the best of the annelid worms. And of internal gills there is no trace. Worse yet, the supposed resemblances in segmentation and nerve cord are not all they might be. Among vertebrates the muscles and skeleton are segmented, but neither the skin on the outside nor the digestive tube on the inside show the slightest evidence of segmentation; in the annelids, in contrast, every organ system is segmented, from surface to gut. The annelid has, as we have said, a single nerve cord running the length of the body. But it is a solid tube, in contrast to the hollow spinal cord of vertebrates. Most especially, the annelid nerve cord runs along the ventral side – the belly side of the worm; that of the vertebrate runs down the back. Learned writers hopefully suggested that maybe, in a transition from worm to vertebrate, the animal had turned over. (After all, one would tend to think that it would not make much difference to a worm which side was up.) However, this made for further complications. The worm's mouth was on the under side of its snout; so is a vertebrate's. But if the worm turned over, the mouth would be on the top of the head; in the transition a new mouth would have to be developed on the new lower side and the old one closed.

One would think that the transitional stages would have been puzzling ones for the worm. And they certainly proved puzzling to scientists. It can be readily understood that, after having tried out this seemingly simple and attractive theory of annelid origins for vertebrates, scientists gradually abandoned it and sought other fields.

For a time an alternative theory of arthropod origins proved of interest. Why not this group of highly organized invertebrates – crustaceans, arachnids, insects and so on – as ancestors? To be sure, they are characterized by the presence of jointed appendages, often quite numerous, with external skeletons, quite different from the paired fins or limbs of vertebrates. But these might have been lost, to be later replaced by appendages of vertebrate type, and the presence here of bilateral symmetry, segmentation, and a single nerve cord (as in annelids) are points in their favour. In early days of the study of animal anatomy comparison was made between vertebrates and insects. But the comparison is not too close. (And, anyway, insects are a relatively modern group; vertebrates are much older.) More popular as possible ancestors were the arachnids, particularly the ancient water-dwelling relatives of the scorpions, termed eurypterids, which were described in Chapter 4. These had good external armour. So did many early fish-like vertebrates, and (except for the presence in eurypterids of numerous jointed legs) the top view of an eurypterid has considerable resemblance to that of such an ancient vertebrate as *Hemicyclaspis* (figure 39).

So far so good. But this comparison breaks down for the same reason as the theory of annelid ancestry. Like annelids, arthropods have a fine nerve cord; but in arthropods as in annelids, it lies on the under side of the animal. Like an annelid, the arthropod must be turned over to turn into a vertebrate. It is the under side of a primitive vertebrate that should look like the top side of an eurypterid. But it does not look like it at all. And I doubt if, today, any active worker would still advocate our descent from arthropods.

But if neither annelids nor arthropods are our ancestors, where should we look? Other groups have been suggested – roundworms, even (rather implausibly) molluscs; some, despairingly, have suggested that we do not have any relatives among the more advanced invertebrates, and that vertebrates probably evolved quite independently from very lowly metazoans.

In recent decades those interested in vertebrate ancestry have tried a different approach. Instead of dashing wildly off into a comparison with members of other phyla, they have tended to stick closer to home base – to examine carefully the evidence furnished by a study of our closest relatives, the 'lower chordates', and see in what direction it leads. Let us review this evidence. But since this is not a detective story, let me in advance mention one startling conclusion to which it leads – namely that close relatives amongst invertebrates are, of all unlikely choices, the sessile filter-feeders and echinoderms described in the last chapter.

Most highly organized of our lower chordate relatives is the small marine animal known to every student of elementary zoology as *Amphioxus*, the lancelet (figure 37). Tiny, translucent, and looking like a small minnow, *Amphioxus* is common in shallow marine waters in many regions. It is not a proper vertebrate, for it not only lacks any trace of backbone, but it is lacking in many other features of that group. There is, for example, nothing that can be called a brain; almost nothing of sense organs for smell, sight and hearing. But when it comes to the three basic structures by which, we said above, a vertebrate relative can be recognized, *Amphioxus* passes a perfect test. Although there is no developed brain, there is a well-developed hollow dorsal nerve cord. Although there are no vertebrae, there is a well-developed notochord extending the length of the animal, literally from stem to stern. And as to gill slits, *Amphioxus*, as if to emphasize its claim to recognition, has not the five or six pairs present in most fish, but half a hundred or so doubled pairs, running half the length of the body. The habits of this little creature are significant. *Amphioxus* is capable of swimming, like a tiny minnow, and sometimes does swim. But most of the time it is found burrowed, in sessile fashion, tail down in the sand, with only its mouth and snout exposed. It makes its living by running a stream of water in through its mouth, into its throat and out through its many gill slits. As the water passes through the gills, food particles are filtered out, collected, and passed back into the digestive tract. *Amphioxus*, thus, is not an animal which seeks its food; it is essentially a sessile filter-feeder.

This mode of feeding suggests a reconsideration of the primary function of the internal gills which are such a basic feature of primitive water-dwelling vertebrates. In fishes they are almost exclusively breathing organs. In *Amphioxus* food-filtering seems to be much more important, and internal gills may have originated as filter-feeding devices, breathing coming more and more into the picture as evolution progressed to higher – and bigger – forms (most small soft-bodied animals can 'breathe' rather effectively through their skin). *Amphioxus* is hardly to be considered as directly on the trunk of the family tree leading to vertebrates, for it has at least a few special features of its own. But most students of the field would agree that it represents a stage of evolution through which the vertebrate ancestors

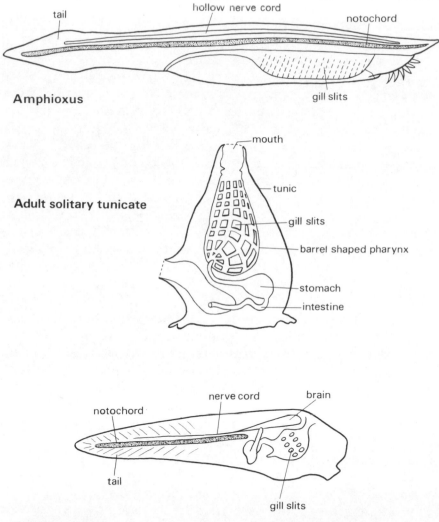

Figure 37. Two types of lower chordate. Several vertebrate features, including a muscular tail used for swimming, can be seen in *Amphioxus*. They appear more clearly in the young tadpole of the tunicate than in the bottom-dwelling adult.

passed half a thousand million or so years ago. There is thus much justification for the song (to the tune of 'Tipperary'), once popular among young zoologists, of which the chorus runs:

> It's a long way from Amphioxus,
> It's a long way to us;
> It's a long way from Amphioxus
> To the meanest human cuss.
> Good-bye fins and gill slits,
> Welcome teeth and hair;
> It's a long, long way from Amphioxus,
> But we came from there.

A step down from *Amphioxus* is a varied group of small and inconspicuous marine animals variously known as tunicates, ascidians or sea-squirts. None are active swimmers to any great degree, although some float freely in surface waters; a majority are bottom-dwellers, some forming branched colonies, others living solitary lives, attached to hard substances on the sea bottom. We shall not take the time (or rather, space) to describe all the various forms in detail, but look only at a typical solitary tunicate. Looked at from without, no creature could look less like a vertebrate relative (figure 37). Covered with a leathery tunic (whence the name) it looks like a small blob of nothing in particular, just sitting there and spending its life pulling in a current of water through a hole in the top and passing it out through another hole on one side. Even when dissected, obvious chordate characters are few. There is no notochord; no nerve cord; almost nothing in the way of a nervous system. But in one feature the adult shows clearly its relationship to *Amphioxus* and the vertebrates. Most of the interior of the animal consists of a structure roughly comparable to a barrel with part of its staves pulled off. The water current entering through the hole at the top – really its mouth – reaches this 'barrel' and passes out through the slits in its sides. Food particles filtered from the water pass down through the 'barrel' and into a stomach and intestine and form the animal's nourishment. It is obvious that the 'barrel' is a highly complex set of gill slits; we are dealing with a filter-feeder, like *Amphioxus*, but one more simply built.

Many tunicates develop into adults more or less directly from the egg, or may bud off from their parents. In some forms, however, the embryonic story is more complex. There first develops a larva, in appearance much like a tiny frog tadpole (figure 37). In the large head

137

of the larva there is developing the 'barrel' which is to constitute most of the bulk of the mature tunicate. But other structures not present in the adult are there as well. There are definite sense organs and a tiny brain in the 'tadpole' head. And behind this structure is a well-developed swimming tail, in which there is a typical nerve cord and, beneath, a good notochord. The larva is able to swim about for a time, until there is located a suitable place for attachment. Once this takes place, the tail is resorbed; notochord, nerve cord, brain and sense organs disappear, and the animal becomes its simple, sessile adult self.

This story is often regarded as one of degeneration, on the assumption that the ancestral tunicate had a tail and other advanced features in the adult and that the simple condition seen in the adult tunicate is due to loss. Stemming from this belief, many a biological sermon has been preached, warning that slothfulness leads to degeneration. But, as we shall see, the story probably reads the other way. Very likely, I think, the tunicate ancestor was much like the modern adult, and developed directly from the egg. Only late in the story did the 'tadpole' develop, as a highly useful larval adaptation, greatly helping the young animal to find a suitable home. Once this home was found, the swimming tail had no further use for existence and, sensibly, was resorbed.

We do not have living today any direct ancestors to the tunicates, but we do have forms related to these ancestors, although a bit off on a side track, in the group termed the acorn worms, *Balanoglossus* and its relatives. The acorn worms are called worms, and superficially they look something like annelid worms; but in actual structure they are not at all like these true worms, and further, despite their appearance, are quite inactive in their habits. Much like *Amphioxus*, they spend most of their lives in burrows in the mud, subsisting on food particles which come to them from the water about them. But while their habits may be similar to those of *Amphioxus*, they are much simpler in build and, while it is agreed that they are related to the vertebrates and other chordates, they are so far removed from them in their simplicity of structure that many scientists who study them suggest that they be classed in a separate major subdivision (phylum) of animal life, as the Hemichordata.

There are three parts to an acorn worm's body (figure 38). At the front is a stout proboscis, which appears to be useful in burrow-digging. Behind this is a ring-shaped collar (proboscis and collar together look a bit like an acorn in its cup, hence the popular name). Behind the collar is a long body; this, however, shows no sign of the segmentation characteristic of a true worm. If you were to dissect an acorn worm to look for structures basic to the chordate pattern, you would in great measure meet with disappointment. A notochord, that structure which gives its name to the chordate group? There is a little pouch at the base of the probóscis which has been compared to a vestigial notochord; but the comparison is a dubious one. A dorsal hollow nerve cord? There is a trace of such a structure in the collar region, but that is all.

But gill slits? *That* is a different story. There is a long series of such gill slits, stretching far down the body. Here is one good basic feature which ties these animals in closely to the other chordates. Just as in *Amphioxus* or a tunicate, the acorn worm draws in a current of water through the mouth, filters its contents as the current passes through the gills, and subsists on the food particles filtered out. This suggests that we really should consider internal gills, rather than the nerve cord or even the notochord, as the one really basic clue to identification of our lowly relatives.

Unlike the case of the tunicates, the developing acorn worm shows no advanced characters lacking in the adult. But the young do give us some suggestive clues as to chordate relationships. In many cases the egg develops into a tiny ciliated larva before assuming adult shape (figure 38). This little larval type is very similar to the larvae of some of the echinoderms, and when first found was actually thought to be the larva of a sea-urchin. However, many years ago a zoologist working in the marine station at Naples reared some of these larvae in the laboratory, and found that, contrary to his expectations, they developed into acorn worms!

This unexpected development suggested, improbable as it then seemed, that chordates were in some fashion related to echinoderms. In later years other lines of evidence tended to reinforce this belief. Apart from the special nature of this little larva, the general pattern of embryonic development of acorn worms resembles that of echinoderms. Further, certain biochemical resemblances suggest a chordate-echinoderm connection. But this sounds like nonsense. Surely we vertebrates do not derive from echinoderms?

If we descend one further final stage into the underworld of primitive chordates or chordate relatives, we finally come to some tiny simply-built creatures which at long last shed light, not only on this

139

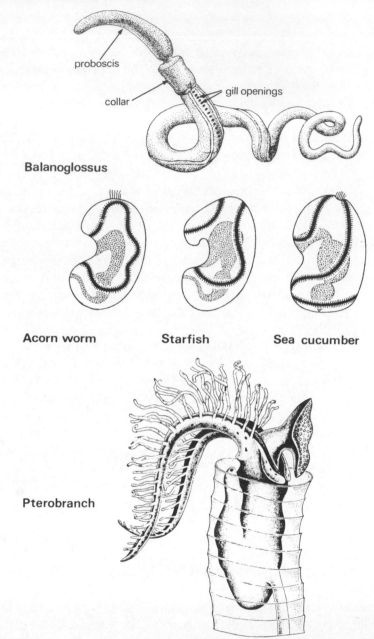

Balanoglossus

proboscis

collar

gill openings

Acorn worm   **Starfish**   **Sea cucumber**

Pterobranch

Figure 38. More evidence of the ancestry of the vertebrates. While the adult acorn-worm has gill-slits of vertebrate type (top) its larva is very like that found in some echinoderms (middle). The pterobranch provides another link between the acorn-worms and the invertebrates.

140

puzzle but on the whole picture of chordate origins. These are the pterobranchs – little forms which are so poorly known that there is no popular name for them, and so rare that we only know them from specimens dredged up from the deep ocean by a few marine expeditions. The pterobranchs are tiny animals, only a fraction of an inch in size, living in colonial fashion within branching tubes, with, superficially, the appearance of tiny stemmed flowers. The 'petals' of the flower are feathery arms, below which is a blob of a body and, below this, a stalk which may connect the individual with the other members of the colony (figure 38). At the base of the arms there is a somewhat swollen region which corresponds to the 'collar' of the acorn worm and, above this and within the circle of the arms, a projecting bit of tissue corresponding to the proboscis. These structures tend, then, to show that these little forms are related to acorn worms and, through them, to other lower chordates and the vertebrates. But in these tiny deep-sea dwellers almost no trace of the key features of a chordate are to be found. There is not a trace of a notochord, nor of a hollow nerve cord. Tunicates and even acorn worms, however, still proudly showed an abundance of gill slits. But here? Of the only two pterobranchs of which we have much knowledge, one has a single pair of gill slits; the other none at all. Like the higher chordates, they gain their nourishment from food particles in the waters about them, but gain it in a different fashion. Each arm stretching out above the body bears, on its inner side, a band of cilia; food particles caught by these bands are carried down the arms to the mouth and on into the digestive tract.

We have now, in good detective fashion, faithfully followed the clues that lead from the vertebrates down through simpler and simpler chordates to a point where we can, at long last, tie in to invertebrate types with which we became familiar earlier in this book. The description of a pterobranch given just above corresponds almost exactly to that which we gave in the last chapter for some of the lowly filter-feeding invertebrates such as moss animalcules, brachiopods, and primitive echinoderms – sessile forms with, on top of a stalk, a compact little body from which stretch out ciliated arms as food-collectors. Surely, of course, the chordates are not direct descendants of any one of these living groups of filter-feeders; but it appears highly probable that the chordates originated, like brachiopods and echinoderms, from an ancestral filter-feeding stock. But in our own evolutionary progression from such primitive ancestors there has been a startling shift in form and structure and mode of life. The ptero-branch is still at a very primitive stage, hardly at all removed from a simple type which could have given rise to a brachiopod or echino-derm as well as to a chordate. Two major changes are needed to evolve a primitive vertebrate from a lowly sessile ancestor. The first is a change in the method of filter-feeding; the shift from arm-gathering of food particles to one of straining out food particles from a water current passing into the 'throat' and out through gill slits. With this shift, we are on the level of an acorn worm or tunicate – forms which, with developed gill slits, have acquired a basic chordate character, but forms which are still sedentary in their mode of life.

The major advance appears to have been the development of a swimming larva, such as that which we see today in many tunicates. Here are present the basic patents which are needed for future advance toward the vertebrate level; an active swimming form, fur-nished not only with gill slits but with a vertebrate type of nervous system and sense organs, and a notochord to support the muscular structures of a tail capable of active swimming.

This new addition – one might almost say a new, second body fused on to the original sessile one – was, at first, merely a larval adaptation, useful in bringing the young tunicate – or pre-tunicate – to a place advantageous for his future sessile station. But if, as appears to be the case, some ancient chordates with this type of larval structure re-tained this new, active body into the adult stage, there would open out before them a new type of existence as active animals. They were ready to begin a new series of evolutionary adventures, and, presently, a new type of life – that of vertebrates. Higher members of the verte-brate series (such as ourselves) have advanced far and changed greatly in structure from primitive types; but we owe our existence, it would seem, to the fortunate development of an active swimming larva by our sessile lower chordate ancestors.

A note here on neoteny and its general implications regarding evo-lutionary processes. The term refers to a situation in which an animal long remains youthful, and refuses, à la Peter Pan, to grow up, and may reproduce while in an immature state. Among the salamanders, as we shall note later, a number of types remain larval and customarily breed as such, and in some the ancestral adult stage is completely eliminated. We customarily think of evolutionary advances as pro-ceeding from one adult type on to another. But, on reflection, there is no real reason why a neotenic animal, its original adult stage 'forgotten', may not evolve – and possibly evolve in a quite different direction. That, we have seen, is probably true of the neotenic tadpole larva of lower chordates – a fresh start in an entirely new direction. And not improbably neoteny has been an important factor in other evolutionary lines as well.

Chapter 8

Fishes

HAVING looked into the question of vertebrate origins, as far as the clues from lower chordates enable us to go, let us now begin an account of the evolution of the vertebrates themselves. Here we are on much more solid ground, for almost all vertebrates have hard skeletal structures which can be preserved in the fossil record. Most have bone in their skeletons, and even those – such as sharks – which lack bone, generally have such structures as teeth and spines which are capable of preservation. Over the course of the past century and a half, palaeontologists have gradually accumulated a body of evidence which, while far from complete, gives a reasonably coherent story of the rise of the great group of backboned animals, up through the various stages in fish evolution, on to land in the story of amphibian and reptilian evolution, and finally, with the development of birds and mammals from reptiles, brings us to the present stage of vertebrate history.

First, the evolution of fishes. To such land vertebrates as ourselves, this would seem a prosaic story. Fish, you might be inclined to say, are all very much alike; they all swim about in the water with fins instead of legs, and breathe with gills instead of lungs. Fish are fish; let's mention them briefly and have done with them, and get on to more interesting animals.

But, dear reader, may I plead with you to be more broad-minded about the matter? Might I ask you to try to look at it from the fish's point of view? Fish vary greatly from one group to another, and show, from primitive to advanced types, a number of major evolutionary stages. Much of the structural pattern which we have today in our own bodies was developed, step by step, in the evolution of fishes, over a history of, certainly, well over one hundred million years before even the initial stages of land life appeared. The fish (if he could) might argue that it is land animals, not fishes, that are monotonously uniform. To him land vertebrates, whether frog or man, look very

144

much the same; they all walk about on land with legs, and all breathe air with lungs. It is the fishes, he would say, which show real diversification.

Jawless Vertebrates

One of the most important features of vertebrates generally is the presence of good biting jaws. These have enabled many backboned animals to become aggressive, flesh-eating predators. And they have further made it possible for them to cope with various other types of food, and hence to take up the highly varied modes of life followed by vertebrates today. As we pointed out in the last chapter, the ancestors of the vertebrates had no such structures, but were lowly filter-feeders. When did jaws first appear in this evolutionary series? *A priori*, one might have assumed that jaws came into existence at the time and stage when ancestral lower chordates first took on the characters of vertebrates and could be classed as fishes, even if fishes of a lowly sort. But the evidence, both from living vertebrates and from the fossil record, shows that this was not the case. Jaws came later; the earliest vertebrates were jawless.

If we survey the fishes of today, we find that the great majority of them are of an advanced type, with good bony skeletons and many highly developed structures. A cut below them are such forms as the sharks and skates; however, these, too, are good jaw-possessing forms. But below the shark stage we find living fishes which lack jaws – the cyclostomes, or 'round-mouths', the lampreys and their slimy cousins, the hagfishes. The hags are marine; some of the lampreys are purely freshwater. Best known and typical of this lowly group is the so-called sea lamprey, which spends most of its adult life in salt water, but its youth in inland streams. This lamprey is a fish of respectable proportions, reaching about two feet in length (figure 39). It has a long slender body, like that of an eel, and in fact is sometimes called a 'lamper eel'. But this resemblance is purely superficial; a true eel is an advanced bony fish, and the lamprey shows many primitive, as well as specialized, features. The most obvious characteristic is that to which the group name refers. The lamprey is truly primitive in that it lacks jaws. But it is, nevertheless, able to lead a predacious life. The round mouth forms an adhesive sucker, by which the lamprey can attach itself to its prey – some other fish. Within the mouth is a curious tongue-like structure, tipped with sharp horny 'teeth' (figure 39); this apparatus enables the lamprey, once attached, to rasp away the skin of its prey and suck its blood. (The hagfishes have a similar tongue-structure, but are less aggressive, preying on dead or dying fishes.)

There are various other special features of lamprey anatomy. More advanced fishes have two pairs of paired fins, primarily useful as stabilizing or steering structures. Lampreys and hagfishes completely lack them. The skeleton is poorly developed in lampreys, and what there is of it consists only of cartilage, a relatively feeble material compared with the bony structure of a majority of fishes and all land vertebrates. This absence of bone was long thought to be a primitive feature. Lampreys and hags have but a single nostril, lying in the mid-line of the snout in a hagfish and high up on top of the head in lampreys. All other vertebrates have a normal pair of these olfactory structures. And, finally, a curious item is that in the internal ear all other vertebrates have three little semicircular liquid-filled canals which give them a sense of balance, whereas the lampreys have but two, a hagfish only one.

Here then, is an odd combination of features – some certainly primitive, others perhaps degenerate, still others surely specialized. The lampreys and hagfishes represent a primitive jawless stage in vertebrate history. But certainly the living cyclostomes are not, in themselves, the actual ancestors of higher vertebrates. This is apparent from the fact that they prey on other fishes. Obviously the first fishes did not prey upon themselves; this would be as poor an economy as that of the legendary community where everyone makes a living by doing his neighbour's washing. The sucking mouth and rasping tongue are specialized acquisitions.

How, then, did the ancient true ancestors live? Our discussion of vertebrate ancestry gives us the clue, which receives ample confirmation when we turn from the adult lamprey to the young one.

Mature sea lampreys leave the sea and ascend coastal streams for reproduction. The egg develops into a small larva which, before maturing into adult form, lies buried for several years in the sands or muds of its natal stream, with only the head projecting. In the larva there is no sucking disc or rasping tongue. In strong contrast to the adult, it makes its living as a filter-feeder, bringing a water current into its throat and out through the gills, straining out food particles in passing. Here, in the larval lamprey, we have retention in a true vertebrate of the mode of life which, we have seen, was that of their lowly ancestors of early chordate or pre-chordate stages.

146

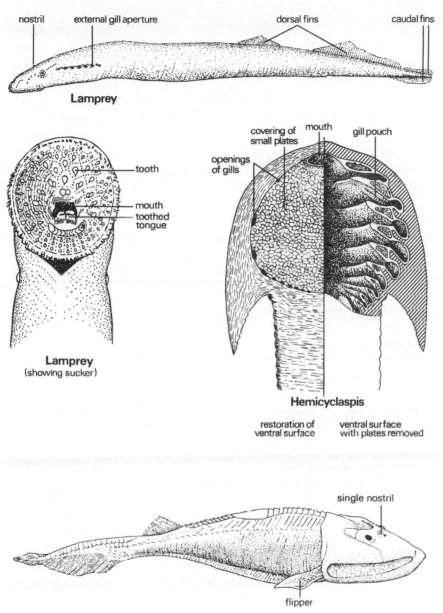

Figure 39. Living and fossil jawless fish. The lamprey uses its round mouth to attach itself to other fish. *Hemicyclaspis*, only a few inches long, lived on the bottom of Devonian streams. The gills open into the flattened lower surface of the head, while the eyes and single nostril open upwards.

147

Surely, then, the first vertebrates, with which the whole line began, should have been ancient filter-feeding fishes. We have long known such forms, usually called ostracoderms, but it is only in recent decades that we have gained any adequate knowledge of them. Although possibly the chordates as a whole are probably as ancient an animal phylum as the more highly organized invertebrate types, the vertebrates themselves are rather slower in making their appearance. There are no known Cambrian vertebrates. In the rocks of the latter part of the following Ordovician period there have been found fragmentary remains of ostracoderms. Then a gap in the fossil record. In the late Silurian and early Devonian, ostracoderms are numerous and frequently found in well-preserved form. But by that time higher fish types descended from the ostracoderm stock were already evolving; in the later Devonian ostracoderms are rare, and no fossil jawless fish is known from any later period.

The ostracoderms were in general no larger than minnows, few of them reaching more than a few inches in length. Quite in contrast with the modern cyclostomes, they were invariably covered, as their name implies, with bony armour, and in some there was bone in the internal skeleton as well. In their general appearance, too, most of these ancient forms contrast strongly with the lampreys and hags. But when the structure of an ostracoderm is studied, it is seen that these ancient forms have basic resemblances to the modern jawless forms (figure 39). Some time past a distinguished Swedish palaeontologist, Stensiö, made careful studies of one group of early Devonian ostracoderms, including *Hemicyclaspis* and its close relatives, particularly the head structure. The head is often no larger than a postage stamp; but under a binocular microscope, the bones of the skull could be 'dissected' with fine needles, and specimens could be cut into slices by grinding at very thin intervals, so that details of internal structure could be reconstructed and interpreted. Despite the differences in appearance, there are surprising similarities to modern lampreys in such features as, for example, a single nostril placed high up on top of the head and a lamprey-like internal ear. As expected, there is no development of jaws. Most of the space in the 'head' of the fish is occupied by a set of large gill pouches for straining out food particles. We are dealing with a primitive vertebrate that is still a filter-feeder, as were the fishes' lower chordate ancestors, and as the larval lamprey still is today. From one point of view we can conceive of a *Hemicyclaspis* as consisting primarily of a large food-straining device, but with a well-developed fish trunk and tail attached, which carries this structure about from place to place in search of nutritious muds to filter.

Our recent acquisition of adequate knowledge of these ancient fishes has raised many interesting problems as to the early history of our vertebrate stock. The skeleton, for example. Most vertebrates, we have said, have a good bony skeleton; but lower fish types today – not merely cyclostomes but the sharks and skates – lack bone and have only cartilage (gristle). In higher vertebrates the skeleton – the internal parts of it, at least – first appears in the embryo in the form of cartilage, which is replaced by bone as the animal grows. It was reasonable to believe that ancestral vertebrates had a purely cartilaginous skeleton, and only later in fish evolution did bone appear. The embryological story – first cartilage, then bone – seemed to be a recapitulation of the presumed phylogenetic story.

Study of the ostracoderms gave a rude shock to complacent holders of this belief. Here we have the oldest known vertebrates – and here is a highly developed bony armour! What does this signify?

The answer seems, quite clearly, that we must radically revise our ideas as to skeletal evolution. We have, in a previous chapter, discussed the 'reason' for the development of bony armour in early vertebrates, as a defence against eurypterid predation. It is clear that the ancestral vertebrates had bony skeletons, at least as far as surface armour was concerned, and that the cartilaginous condition of the skeleton of a lamprey or shark is not a primitive one, but degenerate; these forms have secondarily lost ancestral armour, and have slumped back to an embryonic condition of the skeleton. Quite surely the cyclostomes are descended from once armoured ostracoderms. We do not have a complete series of connecting links; but amongst known ostracoderms, various of the later types appear to show a lesser development of bony armour than do their predecessors; slight further loss, and descendants, as cyclostome ancestors, would lack bone and hence fail to appear in the fossil record.

Another problem of interest, but one to which there is not a universally accepted answer, is that of the environment in which the ancestral vertebrates lived. Quite surely the sea was the original home of life, and the home of the lower chordate ancestors of the vertebrates, and hence it was early assumed that the earliest fishes, also, were marine forms, which only later invaded fresh-water streams and ponds. But many of our fossil records of early vertebrates are from rocks which were laid down in inland waters, and there is evidence which strongly indicates that certain basic elements in the physiological patterns of all vertebrates can only be explained by their having been established in ancient days by ancestral types living in fresh, rather than salt, water. The fossil evidence is far from conclusive, but there is a strong case for the belief that the ancestral vertebrates were among the first of early animal forms to leave the sea and explore the possibilities of life in inland waters.

Shark-like Fishes

Among living vertebrates an evolutionary stage above that of the cyclostomes is that shown by the sharks and such related fishes as the skates, rays, and chimaeras. In these forms, and all higher types, there are present biting jaws and paired fins. With the evolution of jaws, and of teeth to arm them, vertebrates could leave the bottoms, abandon lowly mud-grubbing as a mode of life, and become predacious forms, living on larger living things. In this more active type of life, better locomotion was highly desirable, and good paired fins for stabilization and steering developed.

The origin of jaws, which revolutionized vertebrate existence, can be readily deduced from anatomical consideration of a shark skeleton and from embryological studies. In all fishes (and in the embryos of all higher types, as well), bars of cartilage or bone are present between successive pairs of gill openings and aid in the pumping of water currents. Each bar includes two main elements, upper and lower. It is certain that the primary jaw structures are a pair of such gill bars which lay behind the originally small mouth and were pressed into service for this new function. The origin of teeth appears to be another example of a change of function. The skin of sharks is covered with a shagreen of hard spiny denticles, and the armour of many of the ancient ostracoderms had similar structures as surface 'ornaments'. Denticles and teeth have similar structure, and teeth appear to have been developed from denticles lying along the margins of the developing jaws, and pressed into service as biting structures.

All ostracoderms had a powerful tail for propulsive purposes, but some were destitute of 'accessories' to aid in steering and to prevent pitching or rolling. Such forms must have swum in rather erratic tadpole fashion. In other ostracoderms, however, there are the beginnings of regulatory devices – stabilizing keels in the form of fore-and-aft folds of skin and scales, and paddle-like flaps in the shoulder

1 The jackal, coyote (left and right background), wolf and dog (left and right foreground) are all different species of the single genus *Canis*.

2 The skate is flattened and dwells on the sea bottom.

3 Chimaera.

4 Labyrinthodont amphibians. *Ichthyostega* (lower right) was mainly aquatic and had a tail fin, and *Eryops* (top left) was probably rather crocodile-like in its habits. Both *Cacops* (lower left) and *Seymouria* (top right) were fully terrestrial.

5 This slab of rock, about 6 ft. long and 4 ft. high, contains the bones of many specimens of the labyrinthodont *Metoposaurus*, which apparently died as the Triassic river they lived in dried up.

6 The larvae of this Mexican Salamander, *Ambystoma*, may breed before they lose their gills.

7 Two early reptiles. *Pareiasaurus*, such as that shown (above), was a large herbivore, while little *Captorhinus* (below) was like a lizard in habits and appearance.

8 Both the ichthyosaurs (top) and the mosasaurs (middle) were marine reptiles up to 30 ft. long. *Mesosaurus* (bottom) was only about 3 ft. long and lived in rivers.

9 Triassic relatives of the lizards. The habits of long-necked *Tanystropheus* are uncertain, but *Rhynchosaurus* (right) was herbivorous.

10 From such Jurassic types as *Rhamphorhynchus* (top right) evolved forms such as little *Pterodactylus* (lower right) and *Pteranodon* (left) whose wingspread was 27 ft.

11 Bipedal saurischian carnivores. *Tyrannosaurus* (right) of the late Cretaceous,
19 ft. high, evolved from a form like the rather smaller *Antrodemus* (top left)
of the Jurassic. His eggs may have been stolen by ostrich-sized *Ornithomimus*
(lower left).

12 Quadrupedal saurischian herbivores. *Brachiosaurus* (left) is the largest land animal known, and may have weighed 50 tons. *Diplodocus*, nearly 100 ft. long, is the longest reptile known.

13 Bipedal ornithischians. *Iguanodon* (left) and one of the peculiarly crested hadrosaurs (right).

14 Armoured ornithischians. *Stegosaurus* (top left), *Ankylosaurus* (lower left) and *Triceratops* (right).

15 (*opposite* top) *Archaeopteryx*, the Jurassic link between reptiles and birds. *Ichthyornis* (middle) and flightless *Hesperornis* (bottom) are Cretaceous sea-going birds.

16 Flightless birds. The kiwi of New Zealand (middle) is still alive and the dodo of Mauritius (lower left) died out only in the 18th century. Eocene *Diatryma* (background, left) was 7 ft. high, and *Phororhachos* of the Miocene (right) was 5 ft. high.

17 Platypus.

18 Spiny anteater, *Echidna*.

19 Opossum.

20 Wombat.

21 Shrew.

22 Phcnacodus.

23　*Baluchitherium* (left), *Brontotherium* (top right), *Moropus* (lower right).

24 Peccary.

25 Llama.

26 Chevrotain, or mouse deer.

27 Okapi.

28 Prongbuck.

29 The coney, *Hyrax*.

30 Archaic ungulates. *Arsinoitherium* (left), *Coryphodon* (lower right) and *Uintatherium* (top right).

32 The living dugong (below) and *Desmostylus* of the Miocene (above).

31 (*opposite*) The earliest elephant, pig-sized *Moeritherium* of the Upper Eocene (below) and the last mastodon, *M. americanus* of the Pleistocene.

33 South American ungulates. *Toxodon* (left), *Thoatherium* (middle background), *Typotherium* (right) and *Pyrotherium* (foreground).

35 Tree sloth.

34 (*opposite*) The South American anteater, *Tamandua*.

36 South American Pleistocene
edentates. A glyptodont (left) and
the 20-ft.-long ground-sloth
Megatherium (right).

38 Pangolin.

37 Aardvark.

39 Kangaroo rat.

40 The capybara,
Hydrochoerus.

41 Tree Shrew.

42 Lemur.

43 *Tarsius.*

44 *Proconsul.*

45 *Australopithecus.*

46 *Homo erectus*.
47 Neanderthal man.

48 Cro-Magnon man.

region of some members of the *Hemicyclaspis* group. In the shark-like fishes and higher types there have definitely developed, in addition to median fins, two pairs of paired fins, pectoral (shoulder) and pelvic (hip) in position. These structures are small in fishes, but generally capable of movement and useful in steering. And they are, of course, of the utmost evolutionary importance in that they are the structures from which grew the limbs of land vertebrates.

Sharks today constitute a modest proportion of the fish faunas of the seas; there are some dozens of different genera, ranging in size from small dogfish to the great basking shark and whale shark, with lengths ranging upwards to forty-five or fifty feet and weights up to a dozen tons. These large sharks are inoffensive plankton feeders. Most sharks, however, are aggressive predators, although fortunately most confine their attention to fishes as a food supply, the great white shark being the only member of the tribe for which there are numerous records of attacks on man. Closely related to the sharks are the skates and rays (plate 2), forms which feed on 'shellfish' – molluscs and crustaceans. This diet is mainly available on the ocean bottoms, and the rays are specialized for bottom-dwelling. They have a broad flat-tened body and enormously expanded pectoral fins; unlike the sharks and most other fishes, which swim by means of lateral movements of body and tail, these depressed forms progress along the bottom by rippling motions of the great pectoral fins. In adaptation to shelled food, the teeth, sharp-pointed in sharks, are here developed into a battery of flat crushing plates.

The skates and rays are clearly a flattened derivative of the shark type. Very different, however, are the members of a group of living fishes termed technically the chimaeras, or rat-fishes. They are gener-ally brigaded with the sharks and skates to form the vertebrate class Chondrichthyes, or cartilaginous jawed fishes, since, like the sharks, they have no bone in their skeleton and since they share reproduc-tive habits and a number of other characters with the sharks and rays.

In other ways, however, they differ markedly. These fishes are poorly known to scientists and general public alike, since they are relatively rare and mainly high-seas and deep-water forms, appearing in shallow coastal waters in only a few regions. The chimaeras are small fishes, but of unusual appearance – hence their name, although they are far less grotesque than the fire-spouting chimaeras of legend. There is a large head and large eyes, behind which the body tapers away to a slender, rat-like tail (plate 3). Chimaeras, it appears, are not too restrictive in diet, and may eat anything which comes to hand but are, basically, 'shellfish'-eaters like their distant relatives, the skates and rays. Their adaptations are to some degree parallel to those of the skates; their short but powerful jaws are armed with stout plates for shell-crushing and their pectoral fins are expanded, although not to the extent seen in the skates.

A fair amount of fossil evidence is available for tracing back the history of these cartilaginous jawed fish types. Despite the lack of bone for preservation, sharks' teeth of essentially modern types are found every here and there in marine formations of every age back to the Jurassic period, perhaps 150 million or so years ago, and even forms nearly identical with living species were in existence in the Cretaceous, before the time of dinosaur extinction. The skates and rays have a parallel history; they are, quite surely, an offshoot from the sharks, and the first relatively unspecialized skates are found in Jurassic deposits. Parallel, too, is the story of the chimaeras. They were apparently rather more numerous and more varied in the later Mesozoic than they are today, and can be also traced back to the Jurassic.

Before the Jurassic the known story is a more restricted one. As we might expect, skates and rays are not found; they had presumably not yet begun to differentiate from shark ancestors. There is no definite proof of the presence of chimaeras in older formations, although certain types of crushing tooth-plates in the late Palaeozoic are possibly those of chimaera ancestors. The shark pedigree, however, can be carried back much further.

Today in the Pacific Ocean we find, as well as the more characteristic modern types of sharks, the Port Jackson shark (which gets its name from the Australian harbour where it was first found). This has a dentition quite different from that of other living members of the group in that the front teeth are sharp-pointed, the more posterior ones flattened crushers; the Port Jackson shark can thus amiably adapt himself to any type of food he encounters, fish, flesh, or shellfish. He appears to be a relict survivor of a type of ancestral shark from which more modern sharks are derived; this type has numerous representatives in late Palaeozoic days, notably in the marine beds of the Carboniferous period.

We can trace shark lineage back one further step, into the late Devonian. At this time there lived the most primitive of known sharks, *Cladoselache* (figure 40). This form was world-wide in distribution in marine waters, but the best remains are in beds in the region of Cleveland, Ohio. Here, in the shales, are found hardened nodules which, when split, sometimes will expose the complete body of one of these ancient sharks, a foot or two in length. The preservation is remarkable; owing to some freakish situation in the waters in which the Cleveland shales were deposited, putrefying bacteria were apparently absent, and some of these *Cladoselache* specimens show not merely skeletal structures, but even musculature. *Cladoselache* is a trim little shark, rather primitive in some regards, particularly in its broad-based fins, but still a typical shark in all respects, giving no clue to the earlier ancestry of the group.

Placoderms

In older decades the then prevalent ideas of vertebrate phylogeny led to the assumption that primitive sharks, possessing jaws but without a bone in their body, were derived from some sort of primitive vertebrates which would have lacked jaws but would, like the sharks, have been boneless, purely cartilaginous forms as regards skeletal development. But what we have already learned about the history of bone among jawless vertebrates would lead us to suspect that the story of shark ancestry is more complex and rather different. This appears to be the case. Although connecting links are not well established, it is probable that the sharks, which appear relatively late in the story of fish evolution, were derived from a much older group of jaw-possessing, bone-armoured forms, the Placodermi, or plated-skinned fishes. They appeared at the dawn of the Devonian 'Age of Fishes', and flourished greatly during that period but became extinct (except for some possible late stragglers) at its close. Many of these placoderms were forms of grotesque appearance and unusual structure. All had jaws and paired appendages; but these structures were in general of 'unorthodox' structure. One gets the feeling that the placoderms were, so to speak, a series of nature's 'experimental models' in the evolution of jaw and fin structures.

A majority of known placoderms belonged to a sub-group termed arthrodires ('jointed-necked fishes'). Late and advanced members of this group survived to the end of the Devonian period, and are found in great numbers in the same Cleveland shales in which *Cladoselache* is found. Arthrodires appear to have been highly predacious. One of the Cleveland Shale forms, generally described under the name of

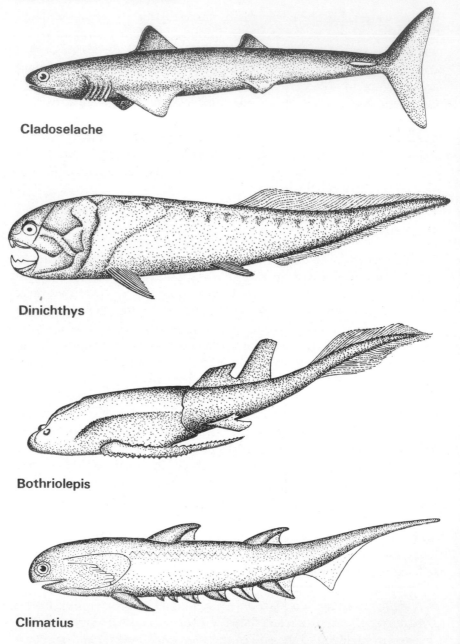

Cladoselache

Dinichthys

Bothriolepis

Climatius

Figure 40. Archaic fish of the Devonian. Both *Dinichthys* and *Bothriolepis* were heavily armoured. More active *Cladoselache* is ancestral to the living cartilaginous fish, while *Climatius* may be related to the higher bony fish.

154

Dinichthys (figure 40), may have reached thirty feet in length; *Cladoselache* may have been a staple in his diet. In arthrodires the head and gill region was covered by a great bony shield, and a ring of armour behind this sheathed much of the trunk; the two sets of armour plating were connected by a pair of movable joints (hence the group name). Peculiar bony plates served the functions of jaws and teeth. We cannot, of course, be sure just how the jaws operated, but the movable joint between head and trunk made it possible for an arthrodire to open and close its mouth by raising and lowering the head – quite the reverse of normal procedure. Paired fins are rarely preserved, but are definitely known to be present in advanced arthrodires. In front of the pectoral fins of even many advanced arthrodires the shoulder armour sends out a tiny spine. As we trace the arthrodires back through the Devonian, we find that in somewhat earlier forms the paired fins are smaller and the shoulder spines more prominent. And in the oldest arthrodires of the earliest Devonian there is little trace of fin structure, while on the other hand, the pectoral spines are enormous fixed structures, curving far out and back from the shoulder region. We cannot be sure, but we get the impression that in the arthrodire group the shoulder spines were 'invented' first as locomotor aids of some sort, the development of movable fins an afterthought.

The arthrodires are the most common of placoderms, but they are quite surely not direct ancestors of any later fish types. The same was surely true of a still more curiously built series of small placoderms called the antiarchs. These were immensely abundant in late Devonian fresh waters; at such a famous fossil locality as the Hugh Miller Cliffs of Scaumenac Bay in eastern Canada, perhaps 80 per cent of all fossil finds are those of an antiarch named *Bothriolepis* (figure 40). The geologists who first discovered this locality thought that they were dealing with fossil turtles, and superficially they do have such an appearance, for much of the broad body of these odd little fishes was covered, above and below, by a stout bony shell. In front of this shell is a small bone-covered head, and although the proportions are different, we are dealing basically with the same two-piece jointed set of armour plating that we saw in the arthrodires. But the oddest feature of these odd little creatures is that at the sides of the shoulder region we find not normal fins nor the fixed spines of primitive arthrodires, but long bone-covered appendages which were movably connected with the shoulder by a complex joint and have much the appearance

155

of appendages of crustaceans. It is difficult to imagine any major use to which these curious structures may have been put, other than to enable the antiarch to resist currents in the streams in which they may have dwelt. But, useful or not, they were certainly no bar to antiarch success, for although, like other placoderms, they became extinct at the end of that period, the antiarchs were amongst the most flourishing of Devonian fishes.

Although arthrodires and antiarchs must be ruled out of the direct line of descent of later fishes, there were still other placoderms which were relatively little specialized and which include, in all probability, the ancestors of both sharks and chimaeras. We have relatively few specimens of such forms, and our knowledge of them is much less complete than in the case of the arthrodires and antiarchs. Like their cousins, these forms have a double set of head-plus-trunk armour, and there may be short shoulder spines. But in them there seems to be going on a development of typical paired fish fins and, most significantly, they seem to show during the Devonian a degeneration of the armour, which is becoming thinner and breaking up into small fragments. With a bit further reduction, one would expect that their descendants would then appear as true cartilaginous fishes, ready to take up life as ancestral sharks or ancestral chimaeras. The story is, today, far from complete, but one may confidently predict that future finds will round out the story of the descent of the modern cartilaginous jawed fishes from armoured placoderm ancestors.

We cannot leave this 'underworld' of curious armoured jawed fishes without mention of an extremely puzzling ancient group known as the acanthodians (e.g. *Climatius*, figure 40). These were small fishes which first appeared during the course of the Silurian (which makes them the oldest of jawed vertebrates) and persisted in modest numbers and variety until the Permian. They are sometimes called the 'spiny sharks', but, except that the tail fin tilted up sharply at the tip as it does in sharks, there are no reasons to connect them with sharks. They had good bony skeletons, including in some cases considerable internal ossification as well as on the surface. But despite their antiquity, their bony skeleton and their possession of jaws – in this case typical fish jaws – the acanthodians show no evidences of relationship to the partially contemporary placoderms. The whole body and tail was solidly covered by a set of diamond-shaped scales which in their structure show a curious similarity to those of some of the higher bony fishes. The most striking feature of these little ancient forms, however,

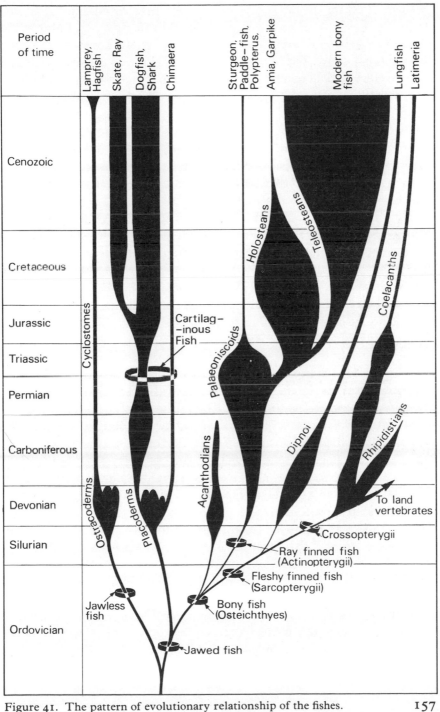

Figure 41. The pattern of evolutionary relationship of the fishes.

is that except for the tail every one of their fins, paired or median, was supported by a stout bony spine; indeed, in many cases, as far as the evidence goes, the spine constituted the whole fin structure, and only seldom do we find traces of the web of skin and deeper structures present in a normal fish fin. In every case there are stout paired spines representing the normal pectoral and pelvic fins; but in some cases there are extra pairs of finlets, up to the number of half a dozen. Nature had not, so to speak, 'decided' how many pairs of fins gave the best results, and was here in an experimental mood. It is amusing, but fruitless, to speculate as to what the later course of vertebrate evolution might have been had the fishes ancestral to land vertebrates retained a higher number of paired appendages.

How these little acanthodians fit into the general evolutionary picture we do not know. They show no evidence of relationship to sharks. There are some features suggestive of the higher bony fishes that we are about to discuss, but the spiny nature of the acanthodian fins is a stumbling block. Quite possibly they represent a short, dead-end sideline of the fish family tree; one of nature's unsuccessful experiments.

Higher bony fishes

In earlier days students of fishes could distinguish, amongst jaw-bearing forms, two main groups: one, including the sharks, skates and chimaeras, seemed comparatively primitive; a second, including all other familiar fish types, seemed more advanced. Since the sharks and their relatives lacked bone, they were termed the class Chondrichthyes, or cartilaginous fishes; since, in contrast, all the advanced forms had bony skeletons, they were reasonably called the bony fishes, the class Osteichthyes. Now that we know the true early history of fishes, and the prominence of bone amongst ancient and primitive forms, this term is not too meaningful. But, nevertheless, it remains true that the higher fish types have all retained bone, and in most cases have attained even more completely ossified skeletons than were to be found in ancient bony types. Bone is utilized in efficient fashion.

Higher bony fishes appear in the geologic record fairly early in the Devonian period. They are hence, as we would expect, much later in appearance than the jawless ostracoderms; but they are but little younger than the placoderms and definitely older than the sharks. Although many modern bony fishes are marine, the older types were almost entirely inhabitants of fresh waters, and in that habitat they rose almost immediately to a position of prominence. In ancient bony fishes the body was completely enclosed in bony scales, primitively with a shiny enamel-like covering, and the head, gill and shoulder regions covered by stout bony plates. Internally, too, most early bony fishes show a highly ossified skeleton. In some of the oldest bony fishes we find a pattern of bone arrangement (quite different from that of placoderms) that can be traced, with modifications, not only into later fish types, but into land forms as well. For example, a number of the bones of the human skull can be identified with confidence in the skull pattern of some of the most ancient bony fishes of the Devonian.

A further characteristic feature of the higher bony fishes is that it is highly probable that, to begin with, all had lungs or lung-like structures. All fishes have gills, for water-breathing purposes; very few (only five genera, to be precise) have lungs today. But the fact that they still persist in members of both of the major bony fish stocks is strong evidence for the belief that they were an attribute of the ancestral forms. The functional reason for their presence in early members of the group has to do with Devonian climatic conditions. Seasonal drought appears to be the key. The nature of Devonian continental sediments suggests that at that time vast regions of the earth had a climate which today is generally restricted to some tropical areas – a climate with annual alternations of wet and dry seasons. During the wet seasons, gills would suffice to obtain an oxygen supply for breathing purposes; with drought and water stagnation, ability to utilize atmospheric oxygen would be highly useful and might make all the difference between survival and death. In later periods, it would seem, such violent alternations of wet and dry seasons became in general less marked and less widespread. The only fish which have retained lungs live in tropical regions in the southern continents where seasonal droughts are present today. In most modern fishes we find that the original lungs have apparently been modified into a sac, termed the air bladder, which seldom has retained any breathing function. It has, instead, become a structure which can be emptied of air or gas and refilled when needed, forming a hydrostatic organ which enables a fish to float higher or lower in the water.

Ray-finned fishes

Although the bony fishes do not appear in the geologic record until the Devonian (and few until the middle part of that period), they must

159

have originated in fresh waters of some region unknown to us, rather earlier – perhaps in the late Silurian. For they were already diversified at their earliest appearance and distinctly separable into two major groups – the Actinopterygii, or ray-finned forms, and the Sarcopterygii, or fleshy-finned fishes (figure 41). The former group includes the vast majority of all living fish species and a great proportion of known fossils as well. The sarcopterygians are – and were – much fewer in numbers, but of major evolutionary importance, for they include not only the lungfishes, the Dipnoi, but also a nearly extinct group, the Crossopterygii, which gave rise to land vertebrates.

The two groups can be clearly separated, even at their earliest appearance, by a number of features, some of them readily seen on many a fossil specimen. The group names are indicative of one such diagnostic character. In actinopterygians the paired fins mainly consist of a web of skin, supported by horny rays, and only at the very base do we find a scaly lobe containing a fin skeleton and muscles. In fleshy-finned forms, quite in contrast, the scale-covered lobe, containing flesh and bone, extends well out into the fin. Other features include differences in scale structure, differences in skull patterns, the fact that some sarcopterygians have internal nostrils as do land vertebrates, and so on. One obvious difference by which early members of the two groups can be readily separated is that primitive ray-fins had a single dorsal fin; primitive fleshy-finned forms had two; however, later members of both groups vary greatly in dorsal fin patterns.

Let us first consider the history of the Actinopterygii, the ray-finned fishes. They have no descendants, had nothing to do with the origin of land vertebrates; but, as fishes, they have been outstandingly successful. For most of the Devonian period, when they first appeared, the ray-finned forms were rare. But in every subsequent period, actinopterygians were the most common of fresh-water fishes, and since early Mesozoic times, at least, they have likewise swarmed the seas in vast numbers. The factors responsible for their outstanding success are difficult to determine. A difference – possibly significant – between typical ray-fins and most other fishes has to do with sense organs. For most fishes the nose is highly important as a source of information about the surrounding world. In ray-fins smell appears to be little developed, and the eyes are generally large and apparently the dominant sense organs; this contrast is reflected in brain organization. The transformation of the lung, when no longer needed, into a hydrostatic organ may have been advantageous for advanced members of the ray-finned group. Perhaps the most important factor in the rise of the ray-fins may have been mere force of numbers. In other groups of fishes the number of eggs laid is relatively small, generally but a few dozen to, at most, a few hundreds. But here – particularly in advanced ray-fins – the eggs are small in size, but often enormous in numbers, sometimes several millions being laid by a single fish. In other groups, individuals must be conserved; amongst the ray-fins, shoals of individuals may perish, but unrivalled fecundity will soon make up the loss.

There are, at a guess, perhaps 30,000 different species of ray-finned fishes alive today; did we know (which, perhaps fortunately, we do not) all the extinct forms which lived in earlier geologic periods, the totals probably would reach several hundreds of thousands. The attempt to classify the ray-finned fishes and arrange them in proper categories is the despair of those who work on fish systematics; and to attempt to give any comprehensive account of the evolution of this group would drive me to despair. I will not attempt to do the ray-fins justice, but will briefly outline a few major features of their history.

On the whole, they may be divided into three main evolutionary stages, which were successively prominent in Palaeozoic, Mesozoic, and Cenozoic times. The principal Palaeozoic group is that of forms frequently termed palaeoniscoids (after one of the better-known genera). A typical palaeoniscoid was a small, well-streamlined little fish, with thick shiny scales, long jaws with a powerful gape, and with, as a readily picked-out feature, a tail in which the fleshy, scale-covered tip of the body extends upward and backward to the tip of the fin – the so-called heterocercal tail type, probably primitive in most fish groups and characteristically exhibited in the sharks. The oldest ray-fins, of the Devonian, were palaeoniscoids of this sort; their descendants were highly numerous – and rather varied, in the Carboniferous and Permian. During the Triassic, however, the palaeoniscoids diminished in number, giving place to higher forms descended from them, and today there survive only two small groups of palaeoniscoid descendants, both highly modified in certain regards.

One of these two groups includes the sturgeons and the paddlefishes or spoonbills of the Mississippi and Yangtse rivers (figure 42 A). In these forms the old shark-like tail is still present, but they are modified and degenerate in other regards. The snout is developed into a long rostrum (and broadened, as well, in the spoonbills), and the skeleton is quite degenerate. Of the originally complete covering of

161

thick scales, almost nothing remains in the paddlefishes, and in the sturgeons scales are represented only by a few rows of plates. The internal skeleton, too, is very much reduced; very few of the elements ossify; most remain in an embryonic, cartilaginous condition, and did we not know their fossil pedigree, we would have little idea that the sturgeons and paddlefishes were derived from palaeoniscoid ancestors with a highly ossified skeleton.

A second archaic surviving type is represented by two tropical African fish, *Polypterus* (figure 42 B) and an elongate cousin. Here the fins are much modified; instead of a single dorsal fin there is a whole row of little dorsal 'sails', the tail fin has become symmetrical, and *Polypterus* has developed a fleshy lobe in his pectoral fins. But despite such alterations (irritating to those of us who make group definitions to which animals will not adhere), *Polypterus*, in his general organization, is clearly a palaeoniscoid in basic characters and is quite primitive in many regards. Most notable is the fact that he and his elongate cousin are the only ray-finned fish which have retained to the present day the true lungs which we believe to have been present in all primitive bony fishes. Their presence is correlated with the fact that *Polypterus* lives today in regions of tropical Africa where seasonal droughts persist; lungs have undoubtedly been useful in the survival of this archaic type.

A second, typically Mesozoic stage in ray-finned evolution began in the late Permian with the development from palaeoniscoids, probably along a number of independent lines, of fishes of more advanced nature, in which the jaws shortened and gained new types of supporting structures, apparently of greater efficiency, and the heterocercal tail had been abbreviated; the scale-covered lobe extending into the fin is reduced to a short stub, at the most. Before the end of the Triassic these progressive types, known as holosteans, become dominant, and the greater part of the Jurassic bony fish fauna consists of forms of this sort. But although I have characterized this intermediate stage in ray-finned evolution as 'Mesozoic', its importance diminished greatly in the Cretaceous, and in modern times this group, like its Palaeozoic predecessors, has dwindled to insignificance. The only two survivors are North American types. The gar-pike, *Lepisosteus* (figure 42 D), is persistently primitive in retaining the thick, shiny scales of ancestral actinopterygians, but specialized in his long predacious jaws, and the bowfin or fresh-water dogfish (*Amia*) is less specialized but less primitive (figure 42 C).

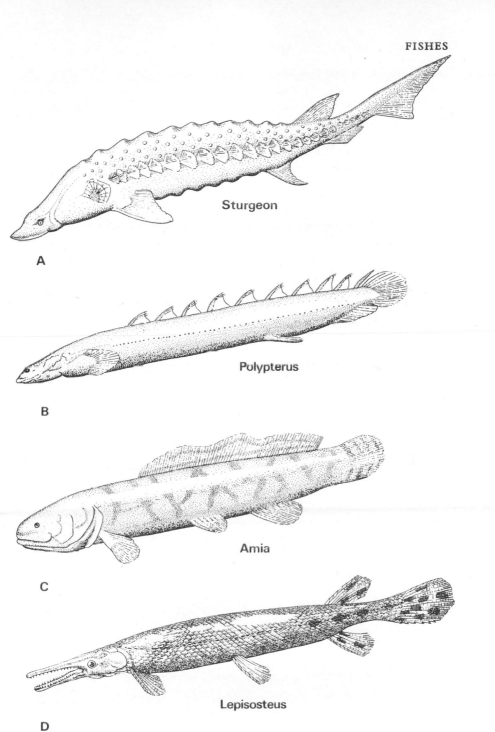

Sturgeon

A

Polypterus

B

Amia

C

Lepisosteus

D

Figure 42. Living fresh-water relics of earlier stages in the history of the higher bony fish.

163

The third major stage in actinopterygian evolution is that seen about us today in the form of the teleosts, the appropriately named end forms of the ray-finned bony fish series. In these fishes the old shark-like tail has been completely reduced to a superficially symmetrical, so-called homocercal fin type (in which, however, there are internal traces of its heterocercal origin), and in which the scales have lost all trace of their original shiny surface and are (if not lost altogether) thin, flexible structures. To attempt to name all the types of fishes included in this group would be endless – and unnecessary, for, except for types already named, all known fishes are teleosts. Of living forms, it is generally agreed that the tarpon is the most primitive, but that the herrings and their numerous relatives are almost equally close to the basic stock. The salmon-trout group is relatively primitive, and (except for the development of some peculiar ossicles which aid in hearing) the carp and catfishes and numerous related fresh-water minnow-like forms are not far divergent. The eels are highly divergent, but divergent from a primitive point on the teleost family tree. A high stage in teleost evolution is reached in the spiny-finned teleosts, in which stout horny spines appear in the fins, notably in the dorsal fin. Here the sea bass represents a central type, from which have radiated a host of advanced, mainly marine, members of the teleosts.

Traces of teleost or pre-teleost forms appear before the end of the Triassic, and in the late Jurassic a limited number of small and primitive teleosts, that superficially resemble modern herrings, put in their appearance. During the Cretaceous, primitive teleosts rapidly increased in numbers and variety, and gradually superseded their more primitive predecessors. And at the end of the Cretaceous there come into sight the first of the advanced spiny-finned teleosts, which were to assume an important position in Cenozoic times and in modern seas.

Lung fishes

Let us now turn from a description of these remarkably successful fishes to the sarcopterygians, the fleshy-finned fishes, which were, except in early days, none too successful in their own right, but are of extreme evolutionary interest as including the ancestors of all land vertebrates. The membership of the group includes the Dipnoi, or lungfishes, and the Crossopterygii.

Fin structure, as the group name indicates, is the most obvious, as

well as one of the most important diagnostic features of the sarcopterygians. With but few exceptions, the fins of actinopterygians consist
mainly of a web of skin stiffened by horny rays. A few small teleosts,
with stout rays in the fins, are able to clamber about on beaches and in
swamps; but never could a limb stout enough to have supported
proper land animals have evolved from a fin of this sort. In sarcopterygians, on the other hand, the fin contains a stout lobe of flesh and bone
(albeit fringed by a ray-finned web) from which the evolution of a land
limb was possible. In the most primitive fleshy-finned forms the fins
are leaf-shaped, with the skeleton within taking the form of a long
axis with short side branches. This pattern persists in dipnoans
generally, but in most crossopterygians there is a trend for the abbreviation of the fin axis and the development of a shorter but stout lobe.

When the sarcopterygians first come clearly into view in mid-
Devonian times, lungfishes and crossopterygians were already clearly
distinguishable. Both were at this time among the commonest of all
fresh-water fishes. Primitive lungfishes and the most primitive crossopterygians were then quite similar in general appearance, with a
stout scaly covering, an uptilted heterocercal tail, stout paired fins,
and two dorsal fins along the back. They could, however, be told apart
on closer study by variations in the skull patterns and, particularly, by
the initiation of the specialized dentition that is a dipnoan 'trademark'.
The lungfish tended to lose rapidly the marginal row of teeth that are
the main reliance of most vertebrates, and to concentrate on the
formation of a pair of large, compound toothplates on the palate
above and a similar pair on the lower jaws. Typically such plates are
fan-shaped structures, with a series of radiating ridges, each ridge
including a row of small teeth. Upper and lower plates interdigitate,
and the upper plates are solidly supported by a fusion of upper jaw to
braincase. The whole makes an excellent apparatus for dealing with
small fresh-water 'shellfish' which appear to have been, throughout, a
staple in the lungfish dietary.

The dipnoans owe their popular name of lungfishes to the fact that,
except for two ray-finned fishes already described, they are the only
living fishes which possess these air-breathing structures. We have
pointed out earlier that lungs appear to have been common amongst
early bony fishes; the fact that both lungfishes and crossopterygians
were abundant in the Devonian was presumably due to the prevalence
in that period of seasonal drought conditions under which lungs would
have a high survival value. Up to the end of the Palaeozoic, lungfishes

remained moderately common, but show some evolutionary changes, such as a trend for a straightening out of the tail and a fusion of the other median fins with it to form a smoothly symmetrical terminus to the body. By the Triassic the main evolutionary line of lungfishes had reached a point where the common lungfish of that time, *Ceratodus*, had reached a form and structure which can hardly be told from that of the living Australian lungfish, *Epiceratodus* (figure 43).

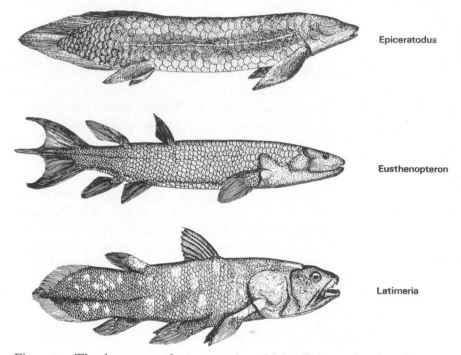

Epiceratodus

Eusthenopteron

Latimeria

Figure 43. The three types of sarcopterygians. Living *Epiceratodus*, three feet long, is a lungfish. *Eusthenopteron* of the Devonian, one to two feet long, is a rhipidistian. *Latimeria*, about five feet long, is the last surviving coelacanth.

Lungfishes remained fairly common in the Triassic, but in later geologic periods they are rarely found as fossils. The reason appears to be a climatic one. Beyond the Triassic, few known deposits give much indication of the continuation of seasonal drought conditions under which lungfishes would have marked advantages over other, lungless, fish types. Lungfishes became reduced in numbers and in territory. Today *Epiceratodus*, the sole representative of the main lungfish evolutionary series, is restricted in range to a relatively small territory, subject to drought, in Australia.

There are two other living lungfishes, one in central Africa, the other in the Gran Chaco region of Paraguay – persistent regions of seasonal drought. These forms, with an elongate and rather eel-like body, represent a side-line of the dipnoan stock, of which the history is poorly known. They have evolved an additional adaptation for drought survival. If the pool in which the Australian lungfish lives dries up completely, he is stranded in the mud and generally does not long survive. But the slender-bodied African and South American forms dig vertical burrows into which they can retreat and 'aestivate', with life processes going on at a low level, until the waters return. A recent discovery has recently shed light on the history of this useful adaptation. In the early Permian redbeds of Texas there have been found vertical cylinders of clay. These appear to be lungfish aestivating burrows which filled with mud when the wet-season floods arrived. Most are empty, for most lungfish presumably swam away when the waters returned. A few contain lungfish skeletons – those of the unfortunates which did not survive the drought.

Crossopterygians

Contemporary with the oldest lungfishes were their cousins, primitive crossopterygians. Typical members of the group were, like the dipnoans, abundant in the Devonian, but, unlike them, became rare in the Carboniferous and are not found beyond the early Permian. Quite surely these ancient forms, such as *Eusthenopteron* (figure 43), were similar in the anatomy of their 'soft' organs to their lungfish cousins, which in many features resemble the amphibians; but these crossopterygians avoided the specialized tooth and jaw structures which definitely eliminate the dipnoans from any possible position as actual ancestors of land vertebrates. The pectoral fins of most of these older crossopterygians have a simple skeleton, but one which has just the basic pattern from which a land limb could be, and was, derived. At the near end of the fin is a single bone articulating with the shoulder skeleton; in the next segment two bones are present; beyond this an irregular branching arrangement. This is a structure essentially similar to, say, a human arm, with one bone in the first segment to the elbow, two bones in the forearm, and beyond this a branching series of bones in the wrist and fingers. In the skull, too, there is a bony pattern which is closely comparable to that seen in early land vertebrates and comparable, in a broad way, with that of our own bodies. Even certain

167

braincase peculiarities which were once thought to debar these forms from a position directly ancestral to land forms are now known to be present in the oldest of fossil amphibians. Although no specific species or genus can be pointed to with assurance, we are definitely dealing with a type of fish directly ancestral to land animals (and ourselves). The primitive crossopterygians, termed the rhipidistians, died out, as we have said, in the early Permian, due, probably, to their inability to cope with the contemporary amphibians which were their descendants and were, in many cases, living similar lives in the same water bodies. It is unfortunate that (unlike the lungfishes) there are no survivors, for scientists would be vastly interested, could it be done, in studying the structures of such truly ancestral types.

There is, however, a peculiar quirk to the crossopterygian story. The typical members of the group, as was said earlier, have been extinct since the end of the Palaeozoic era, more than 200 million years ago. But early in their career, the crossopterygians gave off a rather specialized side-branch of fishes termed the coelacanths. These shifted from fresh water, the original crossopterygian habitat, to the seas, obviously changed considerably in their skeletons (as can be told from the fossil specimens) and, quite surely, we thought, had changed as well in other anatomical features in their new mode of life. We have long known that they persisted far later than their more typical relatives, for fossil coelacanths are not uncommon in marine rocks of the Mesozoic, the Age of Reptiles. But no trace of a fossil coelacanth has ever been found in any rocks younger than those of the close of the Mesozoic, about seventy million years ago, and so lecturers on the subject (like myself) always stated with emphasis that '*there are no living crossopterygians*'.

About three decades ago, however, came a discovery that confounded us, and added weight to the truism that one should never make a positive statement on negative evidence. A commercial fisherman, operating in the Indian Ocean out of East London, South Africa, cast his nets a bit deeper than usual, and brought up a strapping five-foot fish, the like of which he had never seen before (figure 43). Ashore, he presented it to Miss Latimer, who ran the local museum; she, equally at a loss, sent a photo to Dr J. L. B. Smith, South African fish expert. One may imagine his astonishment, for without question this photograph of a living (or rather, recently living) fish was that of a coelacanth, supposedly extinct since the days of the dinosaurs! Dr Smith described this sensational fish, which he named *Latimeria* in honour of Miss Latimer, and instigated a search for the 'home' of these fishes, from which the one caught in South African waters had presumably strayed. That home was presently found in deep waters off the Comoro Islands in the Indian Ocean, and a fair number have now been obtained. The shift in the habitat of the coelacanths from fresh waters, not merely to salt, but to the deep ocean, explains why the fossil record of coelacanths ceased with the Cretaceous; our marine fossils, almost without exception, come from beds laid down in shallow coastal waters, and almost nothing is known in fossil form of deep-water dwellers of the past. The anatomy of the coelacanths is being studied by competent workers in Paris, and publication, from time to time, of their results is awaited with deep interest. As had been expected, the living coelacanths have departed considerably in structure from that presumed present in their Palaeozoic ancestors; but even so, they give us the only opportunity we have of gaining an insight into the morphology of our ancient water-dwelling ancestors.

Chapter 9

Towards the Land – The Amphibians

WE have seen that the vertebrates have been highly successful as water-dwellers. The fishes – particularly the teleosts – have adapted themselves to every watery environment – fresh or salt, from polar regions to equator, from mountain streams to the deepest ocean depths. But beyond this stage of their development lay the greatest vertebrate adventure of all – the invasion of the land. First were to come the amphibians – today a poor group, with only such forms as frogs, toads, and salamanders as representatives, but vitally important in earlier periods as having taken the first steps out of the water and towards dry land. From them were to come the reptiles, who fast became fairly competent in a terrestrial existence and from them, still later, the birds and mammals. In this chapter we shall discuss the early stages in the conquest of this new environment, the development of the most primitive of four-footed animals, the tetrapods.

The story of the amphibians can be divided into two almost completely separate chapters. The first is the history of a great ancient group, the Labyrinthodontia, which arose from fish ancestors, flourished greatly during the late Palaeozoic, gave origin to the reptiles (and hence to all higher land types), but became extinct by the end of the Triassic period. The second chapter is that of the modern orders, flourishing today in modest fashion. They have a fossil record stretching back into the Mesozoic; but, curiously, there is almost no evidence as to their earlier history, and no connecting links between them and the ancient Labyrinthodontia.

Fish ancestors

We have, in our last chapter, hinted at the nature of the fish ancestors of land forms. It has long been agreed that, of the two great groups of bony fishes, it is amongst the fleshy-finned forms, the Sarcopterygii, rather than the ray-finned types, that the ancestry of the amphibians

170

must lie; the actinopterygian fin lacks the basic structural features necessary to develop a land appendage – a tetrapod limb.

Of the two sarcopterygian groups, the Dipnoi were long favoured by many workers as tetrapod ancestors. The presence of lungs in this group is no argument in favour of them, of course, since, we have noted, lungs were apparently widespread in early bony fishes. But, it was pointed out, the lungfishes showed in their soft anatomy a much closer resemblance to amphibians than did any other fishes. Further, the embryo and larva of a lungfish show remarkable similarities to those of frogs and salamanders.

But there are obvious stumbling blocks, notably in the specialized nature of the head skeleton and the peculiar nature of the dentition of lungfishes, on which we commented in the last chapter. We must regretfully exclude the lungfishes from the direct line of ancestry. As sarcopterygians, they are quite surely related to the ancestors of land vertebrates; but they must be regarded as, so to speak, the uncles, rather than the actual progenitors of the four-footed land vertebrates, the tetrapods.

It is to the other major group of sarcopterygians, the order Crossopterygii, now entirely extinct except for one aberrant form, that we must turn to find the actual ancestors. We have already noted that the typical crossopterygians of the Palaeozoic possessed paired fins with a structure basically similar to that found in land limbs. Skull structure is generally considered of crucial importance in palaeontological work. Study of crossopterygian skulls reveals a pattern which is very close indeed to that of the most primitive land animals; many of the individual elements of these fishes' skulls can be matched, bone for bone, with those of even mammalian and human skulls. The structure of the braincase, buried deep in the skull, is regarded as especially significant in determining relationships. It is difficult to prepare a fossil of this sort – the size of a person's thumb in a typical crossopterygian – by using ordinary palaeontological methods of chisel and drill. Some years ago, by appropriate technical means, I was able to 'slice' such a braincase into some 300 or so serial sections, each only a fraction of a millimetre thick, and reconstruct it much enlarged. I found, to my delight, that in many of its details, such as the numerous tiny openings for the entrance and exit of nerves and blood vessels, it was basically similar to what could be expected in an amphibian ancestor. Typical crossopterygians have been extinct since the close of the Palaeozoic, so that we cannot, except by inference, tell much about the soft tissues

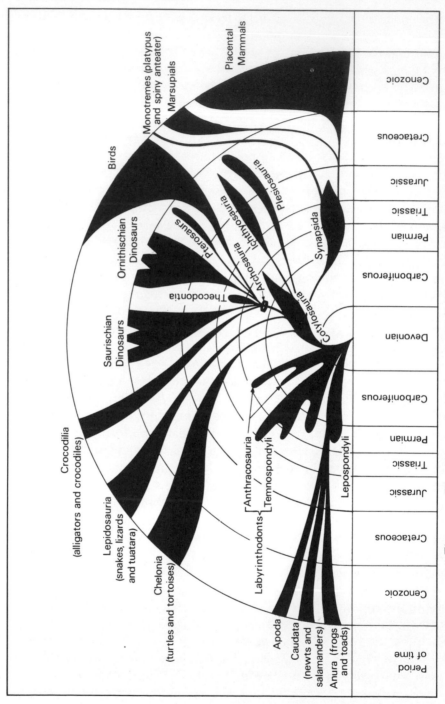

Figure 44. The pattern of evolutionary relationship of the land vertebrates.

of these ancient fishes, but there is no reason to doubt that the fringe-finned forms of the Devonian, like their dipnoan cousins, fore-shadowed the amphibians in reproductive processes and in their internal organs, including the presence of lungs. All in all, there is little question but that it was from these typical ancient crossopterygians that land animals descended.

Labyrinthodonts

The ancestral amphibians, from which rather surely all land verte-brates have descended, are the numerous and varied members of a great group, long since entirely extinct, known to palaeontologists as the Labyrinthodontia. The name, given to this basic tetrapod group by the distinguished English palaeontologist of the last century, Sir Richard Owen, is one that is not particularly significant. It simply refers to the fact that in ancient tetrapods the tooth enamel was greatly folded inward in complicated fashion so that, when a tooth is sectioned, it has a pattern like a Cretan labyrinth. Unimportant as this feature is, however, it does call attention to the fact that crossopterygians and early amphibians are closely comparable not only in major structural patterns, but also in a long series of lesser features; the teeth of crossopterygians, as an example, were built in the selfsame labyrinthine way.

An 'average' labyrinthodont — not especially early nor especially late, not especially primitive nor especially advanced nor specialized — was *Eryops* (plate 4), of the early Permian. Remains of this animal are not uncommon in Texas redbeds of that age; skeletons of *Eryops* are to be found in a number of American and European museums. This rather large member of the group, running to half a dozen feet in length, would have appeared in life something like a snub-nosed, short-bodied alligator, and — although being, of course, a true amphibian, whereas a 'gator is a proper reptile — probably led a similar amphibious existence. There is a well-developed tail; the limbs are short but rather sturdily built. As tracks of amphibians of this sort show, the body cleared the ground, although as low-slung as that of a modern car; the trackway was broad, the walk a rather clumsy waddle. The head was large, broad, and rather low, and solidly roofed by bone, except for sockets for the paired eyes, looking as much up-ward as outward on either side, and for a smaller third eye in the middle of the forehead. Beneath the skull roof, and the casing for a small brain, was a large mouth cavity with a long gape, the jaws armed with extensive rows of sharp teeth; it could, like Alice in Wonderland's crocodile, 'welcome little fishes in with gently smiling jaws'. The remains of *Eryops* are most common in what appear to be bog and pond deposits, so that, despite its ability to get about on land, it presumably spent most of its existence in the water.

Eryops, as we have said, was fairly representative of the group, except for its large size; a few labyrinthodonts were larger, but others were of much smaller size, down to forms a foot or less in length – tail and all. Forms with a build rather comparable to that of *Eryops* are not uncommon in the Permian. In the coal swamps of somewhat earlier times the record shows the presence of an abundance of other labyrinthodonts, variable in size and structure, but on the whole rather more primitive than *Eryops*, and for the most part with feebler limbs and less ability to get about on land. For a long time, Carboniferous amphibians were the oldest known. Recently, however, there have been found very ancient labyrinthodonts from rocks on the bleak coasts of eastern Greenland which date from the end of the Devonian – a time when the ancestral crossopterygians were at the peak of their development. These oldest four-footed animals, known as the ichthyostegids (plate 4), have not as yet been fully described. They are, however, of great interest. They are definitely amphibians rather than fishes, for the typical tetrapod limb pattern is already present in their stubby appendages. But they approach their fish ancestors more closely than such a form as *Eryops* in various ways, such as a number of skull features and the persistence of a remnant, at least, of the fish type of swimming tail.

Starting thus in the late Devonian, the ancient labyrinthodonts flourished in the Carboniferous, and the main line of their development, of which *Eryops* is representative, persisted not only through the Permian but the Triassic as well. The members of this most abundant group of labyrinthodonts are included in the order Temnospondyli. Carboniferous temnospondyls generally had small limbs and appear to have been mainly pond-dwellers. In the Permian, however, many forms, such as *Eryops*, gained stouter legs and better ability to venture onto land. The strongest trend toward terrestrial existence among early amphibians is seen in a group of early Permian temnospondyls of which *Cacops* (literally 'funny-face') is representative. This was a form of modest size – not more than a foot or two in length, tail and all – with sturdy and obviously effective legs (plate 4).

174

Life on land, however, had its dangers, for by that time predacious reptiles were abroad. In relation to this menace, *Cacops* and his relatives had developed stout bony armour over the body in the fashion of an amphibian armadillo.

But even protection of this sort did not suffice to keep the temnospondyls ashore in the face of continually increasing competition from their more advanced reptilian contemporaries. By the later Permian temnospondyls appear to have abandoned any major effort to emerge onto the land.

The last Triassic survivors of this main evolutionary line were curious degenerate forms. Often of large size, they had slumped back to a purely aquatic mode of life. The body and head were greatly flattened, the limbs tiny. Obviously animals of this sort could never have left the water. Confirmation of this fact was made by a discovery of a Harvard collecting party in New Mexico a number of years ago. Exposed along the foot of a small hill, formed by Triassic shales and sands and apparently extending clear through it was a layer, less than a foot thick, densely filled by a host of skulls and skeletal bones of *Metoposaurus*, one of the last of the labyrinthodonts (plate 5). It can be estimated that remains of at least a thousand individuals were present in this layer as preserved, and it is impossible to guess how much farther it may have extended before it was eroded to its present condition. The story seems fairly clear. It is probable that these flatheaded and weak-legged amphibians inhabited a series of lagoons that may have spread over a considerable area in this part of what is now New Mexico. There is reason to believe that the region was subject to droughts. During a major drought, one may believe, the lagoons gradually dried up, one after another; their amphibian inhabitants, unable to emerge onto land, became increasingly confined to smaller and smaller areas, and finally into one remaining pond. Even this, however, eventually dried up completely, and the entire concentrated host of amphibians suffered a mass death.

This temnospondyl line, then, of labyrinthodonts was doomed to extinction after a long career. Less abundant and earlier extinct, but vastly more important from an evolutionary point of view was a second line of labyrinthodonts, the Anthracosauria. The Carboniferous members of the group were in the main rather primitive water-dwellers, but a number of diagnostic features in the skull indicate that they were approaching a reptilian condition in their structure. No anthracosaurian persisted beyond the Permian, but in that period and in the

175

latter part of the preceding Carboniferous period there appeared a type of anthracosaur of which a typical representative is *Seymouria* (named after a town in the Texas Permian redbeds region). Here the anatomical build of skull and skeleton is almost exactly intermediate between that of a labyrinthodont and that of a primitive reptile (plate 4).

It is easy enough to tell a modern reptile from a modern amphibian from its anatomical structure; numerous features, for example, are present by which we can distinguish a turtle, lizard or snake from a frog, toad, or salamander. But, as discussed later, the crucial difference between these two classes of vertebrates lies in the mode of reproduction. If reptiles are descended from the ancient labyrinthodont amphibians, we would logically expect to find, if our fossil record is at all adequate, extinct transitional forms which, in default of a knowledge of their reproductive habits, we would have difficulty in assigning to one side or the other of the boundary between the two classes. This is the case with *Seymouria*.

We have, above, given an outline of the factual story of the labyrinthodonts, first of vertebrates to walk upon the land. But we have not discussed the 'why?' of this radical advance in the direction of vertebrate evolution. The ancient crossopterygians, the fossil record appears to tell us, were leading a successful life in the Devonian streams and lakes. What caused certain of their descendants to start this evolutionary development and begin the great adventure of walking out onto the land?

Various suggestions have been offered, but most of them have little validity. That the 'lure of atmospheric oxygen' was the stimulus gives us a fine phrase; but it has no meaning. Crossopterygians, like many other early fishes, had lungs, and could obtain all the atmospheric oxygen they wished by merely sticking their heads out of water; emerging onto land for it was not at all necessary.

That they were, so to speak, pushed out onto land because of enemies in the water is equally out of the question. The crossopterygians were, as far as we can determine, aggressive predators, and except for some fresh-water sharks, were dominant among the stream and lake fishes of the Palaeozoic.

The opportunity of acquiring new food sources available on land? No solution here, either. As was just said, fringe-finned fishes were carnivores, eaters of animal food; and when amphibians began their careers in the late Devonian, there was precious little animal food on land for them to eat. At a somewhat later time, insects and their larvae and grubs may have afforded a basal food supply. But amphibians were well along on their careers before insects appear in the fossil record. Scorpions, it is said, had reached land by the late Devonian. But it is hard to believe that scorpions could have furnished an attractive source of food for the ancestral amphibians.

Faced with these seeming difficulties in finding any reasonable scientific solution for the phenomenon of amphibian evolution, some thinkers on the subject have abandoned natural explanations, and gone in for more mystical, supernatural explanations. Such features as lungs and land limbs, developed by the amphibians, they have argued, are of little account to a fish as a fish; their evolutionary development cannot be explained by the theory of natural selection, for they would be useless and of no selective value until the land had been attained. The evolutionary trend to land, they say, can only be explained if there were some mystical 'inner urge' within the animals, or if there lay behind it a planned, determined evolutionary course directed by some supernatural power or deity.

As scientists we cannot, of course, deny the possibility of such mystic urges or directives. But, as scientists, we should not have recourse, in despair, to mystical or supernatural explanations of natural phenomena if a natural explanation, based on known principles, can be found. Can such an explanation be found for the development in fishes of such terrestrially useful structures as lungs and legs?

Yes. Under special conditions, such features could be of high and immediate selective value for survival of an ancient fish purely as a water-dweller, without reference to their potential utility for a future life on land. These special conditions were climatic – seasonal drought. As we have mentioned earlier, such conditions appear to have been widespread in the Devonian period, during which the first amphibians evolved.

Lungs? We have already pointed out that these structures could be – and were – of immediate use to a fish under seasonal drought conditions, adding greatly to the chances of survival of a fresh-water dweller. No mystic pre-adaptation for future land life need be put in the picture.

But what of legs? Of what use could such structures be to a fish? Here again, seasonal drought appears to give the reason for their selective development.

Let us picture a time in the late Devonian, when both crossopterygians and early amphibians were present together in some body of fresh water. The early amphibians, like their crossopterygian relatives, were essentially water-dwellers, despite the presence of primitive legs. As long as the pool in which they lived was full and the water well aerated in a wet season, the amphibian had no advantage; in fact, his limbs might have made him a less efficient swimmer. Then picture the oncoming of a drought, with the water of the pool becoming stagnant. Still the amphibian had no advantage, for the crossopterygian could come to the surface for atmospheric oxygen as well as he.

But suppose the pool dried up completely? Then a sharp contrast as to survival shows up in favour of the amphibian. The crossopterygian would be, literally, stuck in the mud, and destined for death if the water did not promptly return. But the primitive amphibian, with short but sturdy legs developed from the fleshy fins of his ancestors, could leave the drying pool and – probably very slowly and painfully in the earliest stages of amphibian development – crawl up or down the river bed, find a pool which still had water in it; enter it, and resume his life in the water. Limbs, it would seem, were not evolved in some mystic drive or urge toward a career on land; they arose, like lungs, as structures useful in enabling a water-dweller to survive as a water-dweller. These structures went far toward making terrestrial existence possible, but this potentiality was not due to design but was, essentially, the result of a happy accident.

The modern orders

Let us now turn from the story of the first land animals to that of the living groups of amphibians – a series of forms very different from the ancient labyrinthodonts.

Of the three orders in existence today, the Anura, the tailless forms including the frogs and toads, are the most flourishing. They are, however, the most specialized of amphibians, and, in many ways, are amongst the most specialized of tetrapods. Their specializations are in great measure associated with their hopping mode of locomotion. The backbone is extremely short; a primitive land animal had as many as thirty or more joints in its back, not including the tail, while a frog has not merely lost its tail (except for a short fused rod in the hip region) but may have as few as eight vertebrae in its back. The hip girdle is much specialized in relation to hopping, and there are also peculiar modifications in the shoulder to break the shock of landing. Most especially the hind legs are much elongated, with the development of an extra, third joint in the ankle region to give better leverage in jumping. It is probably their hopping specializations which have enabled the frogs and toads to continue to the present day in a reasonably flourishing condition.

The basic structural pattern is nearly uniform in all members of the order, but there is considerable diversification in habits and anatomical details. Most familiar of anurans are the typical frogs, almost world-wide in distribution, and the common toads, most purely terrestrial members of the order, equally widespread except that they never reached Australia. Among the numerous anuran variants we will mention only the tree frogs, widespread but most common in America. Although called 'frogs' they are actually closer to the toads than to the common frogs in structural features. Generally of small size, they are aided in their tree-dwelling mode of life by the development of expanded adhesive pads on the toes, as well as clawlike toe tips.

More generalized in proportions are the salamanders and newts constituting the order Caudata ('tailed' amphibians, in contrast to the 'tailless' Anura). Their general appearance is not dissimilar to that which we imagine to have been true of many of the ancient labyrinthodonts. But in many features of the skull and skeleton they are very degenerate. There is much less ossification of the skeleton than in the older amphibians; there is here the beginning of a 'relapse' toward an embryonic cartilaginous condition of the internal skeleton, although this degeneration has not gone as far as it has in many fishes. Here (and in the anurans as well) the ancient scaly covering of the body present in the fish ancestors has disappeared, leaving them with a soft and moist skin. This functions as a useful accessory breathing organ, but on the other hand, leaves the animals vulnerable to desiccation, so that when not in the water they are mostly found in moist woodland areas or sheltered under stones or logs. Salamanders are mainly dwellers in the more humid regions of the North Temperate zone, and are not adapted to life in the tropics. There are several families of typical salamanders and newts in Eurasia and North America, but in addition there are various aberrant forms.

Most salamanders are small, but the 'mud-puppy' of the American Midwest attains two feet in length. Still larger is the 'hell-bender' of the Allegheny River (*Cryptobranchus*), and a related Japanese form may exceed five feet. A close relative is known from mid-Tertiary

179

rocks in Europe; this was, when first discovered, called '*Homo diluvii testis*', and thought to be the remains of a poor sinner drowned in the Noachian flood. Other salamander variants include blind cave-dwelling types, and forms which are purely water-dwellers, never emerging onto land, which tend to lose their limbs and swim in eel-like fashion by body undulations.

A third and final order of modern amphibians is that of a group variously termed the Apoda or Gymnophiona. As was the trend in the salamanders just mentioned, the apodans have lost their limbs. They are small creatures, worm-like in appearance, and they are also worm-like in habits, for they are tropical burrowing forms.

Although amphibians (degenerate forms apart) possess limbs and are thus able to walk upon the land, they have in general retained the old fish-like mode of reproduction. In typical cases, frogs or toads or salamanders, even if they live ashore for much of their lives, return each spring to lay eggs in the water as did their fish ancestors, and the young spend the first stages of their lives as water-dwelling, gill-breathing larvae. In the case of the frogs, the young, as tadpoles, are radically different in structure and mode of life from the adults. Finally, after a period which ranges from weeks to years (in the bull-frog), there is a radical change in the animal's structure – a metamorphosis. Gills and tail are resorbed, lungs and legs develop. In the salamanders there are similar modifications from larva to adult, but the changes take place more gradually.

Because of the necessity of an animal to return to the pond for reproductive purposes, the amphibians, despite their general ability to walk forth upon the land, are still chained to the water, and cannot become true terrestrial animals. Since several hundred million years have elapsed since the time of origin of the amphibians, one might expect that evolutionary processes might have occurred amongst the modern forms tending to free them from this major handicap. Such is the case; a variety of frogs and salamanders have, in one way or another, eliminated partially or altogether their inherited method of reproduction of laying eggs in the water, fish-fashion. No method found amongst modern amphibians, however, has been as successful as that devised by the reptiles far back in Carboniferous days – the development of a new egg type, described in the next chapter. The amphibians are, in consequence, a defeated group, insignificant today amongst tetrapods.

As if in acknowledgement of defeat, we find among some salamanders a trend toward abandonment of any attempt to live a terrestrial life, and an evolutionary 'relapse' toward a purely aquatic, gill-breathing existence. A famous example is the axolotl.

Over much of North America there ranges an amphibian known as the spotted salamander (plate 6). In most areas, after an early life passed as a gilled aquatic larval form, it metamorphoses into an air-breathing adult. In certain western highlands, notably in Mexico, this is not the case; this salamander spends its entire life in the water and breeds while still a gill-breathing larva. The Mexican form was once believed to be a distinct species, termed the axolotl. But it has been found that, if experimentally treated in various ways, it can be caused to change markedly, lose its gills, develop lungs, and come ashore as a typical spotted salamander.

The axolotl has begun a process of evolutionary degeneration, but has not lost the potentiality of reversing the degenerative process. Certain other salamanders, however, have completely lost the ability to attain the ancestral adult condition. Examples are the mud-puppy, mentioned above, and the siren, an eel-like aquatic form from the United States. These always remain life long gill-breathers; they have completely lost the ability to metamorphose.

As to the ancestry of the modern amphibian orders, nothing is known of the worm-like Apoda in the fossil record. Amongst the salamanders, a pedigree can be traced back to the Lower Cretaceous; but the one form of that antiquity is already modern in type and shows no transition toward any more primitive tetrapod type. With the frog group our knowledge is somewhat greater. Typical frogs, essentially modern except in detail, are present in the Jurassic. From deposits of the preceding Triassic period in Madagascar, there has been re-covered a specimen of a form known as *Protobatrachus*. This has a skull of definitely frog-like build, but although the backbone is somewhat shortened, it is still considerably longer than that of a frog, and there is no development of the hopping structure of the hind legs.

There our attempt to trace the pedigree of the modern orders ends. Presumably their ultimate tetrapod ancestors were labyrinthodonts, since we believe members of that ancient group to have been the basic tetrapod stock. But there are no definite links between the oldest sala-manders and frogs and any known labyrinthodont forms. In the late Palaeozoic, contemporary with the labyrinthodonts, there were pre-sent a number of small amphibians, known as the lepospondyls, which differ from labyrinthodonts in various features, and which may possibly be related to the ancestry of the modern types. But at present we are unable to tie these forms in with the labyrinthodonts, on the one hand, or with the frogs and salamanders, on the other. The greatest current gap in our knowledge of the evolution of land vertebrates is the absence of a pedigree for the living amphibian orders.

Chapter 10

The Triumph of the Egg – The Reptiles

THE amphibians, to be sure, are of importance as giving us the first stages in tetrapod evolution. But in the long run their role has proved to be a minor one. Numerous and prosperous in the late Palaeozoic era, they presently shrank to insignificance. It was the reptiles developed from them who, well before the close of the Palaeozoic, took over the main stream of vertebrate evolution and completed the conquest of the land.

Although as reptiles advanced they came to show numerous and varied features progressive over those found in amphibians, the basic difference between the two classes lies in the mode of reproduction. As was said in the last chapter, the typical frogs and salamanders with which those of us in northern clime are familiar breed in the very same way that their fish forebears did. The eggs are laid in the water, are fertilized there, and the young lead an essentially fish-like life before their eventual emergence as four-footed animals. The amphibian must lead two lives in succession, and must compromise by never being fully adapted to either. Willy-nilly, he is bound by strong ties to the ancestral waters.

The reptile is freed – freed through the fact that in this class a new type of egg has developed, by means of which the necessity of water breeding is absolutely done away with. This type of egg – termed the amniote egg, from one of the membranes found within it during development – was evolved by the primitive reptiles and retained in birds and the most primitive mammals.

This egg type is, to us, a familiar and hence seemingly prosaic structure, suitable for the breakfast table. It is, in reality, the most marvellous single 'invention' in the whole history of vertebrate life (figure 45). A shell surrounding it protects the developing embryo from mechanical injury. A bountiful supply of yolk makes it possible for the young to have a modest growth before it becomes necessary for

183

it to seek its own living – quite in contrast to a tadpole, which must begin to forage before it has reached (in some cases) the size of a pin. As the embryo develops, there forms about it a series of highly useful membranes. The amphibian embryo developed in water; in the reptile egg a membrane termed the amnion, water filled, gives a miniature reproduction of the ancestral pond, and, surrounding the youngster,

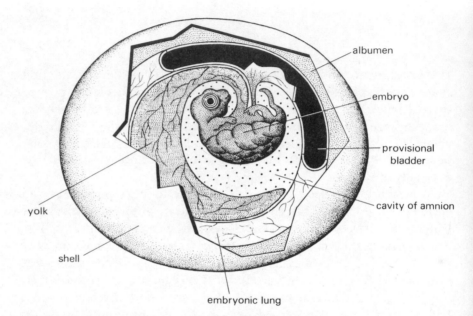

albumen

embryo

provisional bladder

cavity of amnion

yolk

shell

embryonic lung

Figure 45. Semi-diagrammatic view of a turtle's egg.

prevents desiccation. The kidneys begin to function actively in a growing embryo and, with resulting tidiness within the egg shell, a further membrane forms a sac-like provisional bladder. An embryo must breathe; this membrane extends out and around beneath the porous shell and its surface functions as an embryonic lung. Thus fortified and aided by a whole series of adaptive structures, the young reptile is able to grow to a respectable miniature of the adult before hatching, and emerge as a purely terrestrial type. The ties with the water were broken, and the earth lay open to full conquest by reptiles.

Some of the ancient amphibians, such as *Eryops*, had already developed very sturdy legs and, had it not been for the handicap of old-fashioned development, looked as if they were ready for a truly terrestrial career. In my earlier days of lecturing, I used to paint, before

184

classes, a dramatic picture of such forms, eager to conquer the land and already prepared for this conquest except that (a striking phrase) they were, lamentably, 'chained to the water' by their archaic methods of reproduction. At long last came the final step in their release – the development of the new land egg. Now the bonds were broken, and these amphibian descendants burst eagerly out to populate the earth!

A pretty story. But, I now realize, not the real one. It seems probable that the new egg type did not develop as the last step in terrestrial adaptation, but appeared well before early four-footed forms were otherwise prepared for true land life. It is probable that the egg came ashore before the adult was ready to follow it.

My doubts about the reality of the picture I had painted were aroused when I came to study the anatomy of some of the more ancient fossil reptiles. These were forms that, from the nature of their adult structure, were truly reptilian, rather than transitional types, and surely laid eggs of the land type. But certain of them showed strong indications that they were, as adults, still water-dwellers, spending much of their lives in ponds and streams. Why should such forms have developed a land type of egg, if they were still water-dwellers themselves? What was the value of this adaptation?

The clue may be found if one broadly considers the reproductive habits of modern amphibians. As I said before, various of the frogs, toads, and salamanders with which one is most familiar do follow the ancestral pattern of laying eggs in ponds. But a very large proportion of modern amphibians do nothing of the sort. Among newts and tropical frogs and toads, the supposedly 'normal' practice is actually the exception. The eggs may be laid under logs, in the stumps of trees, even in nests of cemented leaves in trees; they may be carried about by one or other parent, in pockets on the back of the toad or, in the case of the 'obstetrical toad', wrapped around the hind legs of the father, who occasionally 'dunks' them in water to prevent drying. The general objective seems to be to put them anywhere *but* in the water!

Why? There are, when one stops to consider it, good reasons why the water should, if possible, be avoided, even in the case of an animal which lives in that environment in adult life. One factor is that a mass of eggs in a pond presents a tempting supply of food – an amphibian caviar, so to speak – which may attract the attention of a variety of voracious animals, ranging from insects to other vertebrates. This is probably the main deterrent today to aquatic egg-laying. In Palaeozoic days, when there evolved the amniote egg, furnishing the best solution to the problem, dangers of this sort were probably less marked than is now the case. But a second factor was then more prominent – the threat proffered by seasonal drought. This climatic condition, then widespread, was, we have seen, responsible for the development of other adaptations for land life, such as lungs and limbs, and it may have also played a major part in the variation and selective processes which resulted in this last major change necessary for the future de-development of terrestrial existence. If eggs are deposited in a pond, the continued presence of water in it must be guaranteed for a considerable time, since the young must not only go through the embryonic period, but also the 'tadpole' larval period – often a long one. With the threat of drought, a high premium would be placed on any reproductive process which would avoid this danger. Various amphibians, it would appear, have tried varied means of countering the dangers of water development. Most have met with indifferent success. The one conspicuously successful solution was the development of the amniote egg – whose possessors, through this achievement, raised themselves as reptiles to a new level of evolutionary potential.

We saw earlier that other major features which were eventually to make terrestrial life possible came about not through any mysterious 'urge' toward such an existence, but as adaptations immediately useful to the water-dwelling animals which developed them. The final major adaptation, the new egg type, likewise appears not to have evolved with any 'thought' of its use in land life but, again, as something immediately useful and of survival value to an ancient water-dwelling animal. Once all these major changes and adaptations had appeared, the way onto the land was open, whenever the time was ripe.

The time *was* ripe toward the end of the Carboniferous period, some 300 million years ago. Like other members of the evolutionary 'main line' of vertebrates, the ancestral reptiles were eaters of animal food. During the time of the Coal Swamps there appeared, for the first time, an abundance of primitive insects – some, for example, much like modern cockroaches in general build and appearance, others rather like dragonflies. Such forms and their larvae and grubs gave for the first time a basic supply of food on land for small early reptiles. After a bit some of the reptile types which had come ashore became converted to plant feeding. And, with numerous small or inoffensive relatives already present, the opportunity arose for true flesh-eaters to walk the land. Thus, before the Permian period succeeding the Coal Measures had advanced far, a flourishing land fauna was set up. It would appear, however, that higher vertebrates owe a major debt of gratitude to the insects. Had they not arisen, it is doubtful when, if ever, vertebrates would have ventured from the ancestral waters.

The oldest reptiles are considered by scientists as making up a stem group, now long extinct, of the class Reptilia termed the Cotylosauria. In general, these archaic terrestrial explorers still walked about with the old-fashioned sprawled gait which was the best that their amphibian progenitors had been able to do in the way of locomotion. Among such forms one group, the pareiasaurs (plate 7), grew to considerable size in the Permian, and are abundant in fossil beds of that age in South Africa and Russia. They are notable as the first major set of reptiles to adapt themselves to a plant-feeding diet (as indicated by their dentition). For this mode of life, a waddling gait was no handicap (plants will not run away). In South Africa skeletons of pareiasaurs are frequently found in the 'mudstones' of the Karroo deserts, invariably right-side up, with their legs beneath them, preserved to this day in the position in which they met death by being bogged down in the ancient swamps where they sought their food. The pareiasaurs, however, were but one of a number of branches into which the cotylosaurs diverged. Much more important, from an evolutionary point of view, was a group of forms of which little *Captorhinus* of the American early Permian is best known (plate 7). These were, on the whole, small (*Captorhinus* but a foot or so in length), rather more agile, and, unlike the pareiasaurs, still flesh-eaters — although insects were probably the only 'flesh' to which these little if ambitious animals could aspire. It is generally agreed that *Captorhinus* and his relatives were ancestral to at least part of the later reptile orders, and it is not improbable that nearly all later land animals may trace their pedigree to *Captorhinus*-like progenitors.

The Mesozoic era, including three successive periods — Triassic, Jurassic, and Cretaceous — is popularly called the 'Age of Reptiles' because of the abundance of major reptile groups which then dominated the world. But the cotylosaurs were already well established by the beginning of the Permian preceding the Mesozoic and the true reptilian age began with that period — to last over a vast stretch of time of close to 150 million years.

We may now begin to search out the origin of the wildly varied reptiles that soon appeared on the evolutionary scene. In this chapter we will note the development of some of the groups which have survived to the present, reserving for later chapters some of the more spectacular members of the class.

Among reptiles still with us today, the turtles (order Chelonia) are probably the earliest to have begun a distinctive evolutionary history. Familiarity does not necessarily breed contempt, but does make one blasé. One tends to think of these animals as very prosaic; but if turtles were extinct, we would probably gaze on them with wonderment, for they have evolved the best system of armament ever produced by any vertebrate. Over the back is a solidly built bowl of bone, covered by horny scutes – the carapace; over the belly, a similar shield – the plastron. The two plates are firmly bound together on either side; at the front a broad gap allows space for head and front legs to be drawn into safety; at the back there is a similar opening into which hind legs and stub tail can be tucked. The shell evolved at an early time when the old-fashioned sprawled pose of the legs was still the fashion, and once the armour was evolved, it was impossible to improve the locomotor pattern; the turtle, on land, is as slow and clumsy in locomotion as was his cotylosaurian ancestor. But lack of speed is of no concern to him. If danger approaches, there is no need for him to run from it; he simply withdraws into himself, to become a seemingly inanimate lump until he is convinced that the 'all clear' has sounded.

We are, as yet, none too certain as to the course of the early stages of turtle evolution, but before the end of the Triassic, first of the three periods of the 'Age of Reptiles', full-fledged turtles, with complete armour, appear. Once this pattern had been evolved, the further course of chelonian history was relatively uneventful. There has, to be sure, been a bit of spreading out of the group into a number of discrete families, varying, on the one hand, from the presumably primitive marsh-dwellers to the purely terrestrial true tortoises, on the other, to marine types such as a number of extinct and surviving turtles which may reach considerable proportions. But apart from such improvements as in the methods of pulling their heads into the shell, there has been no major modification in the structure of turtles since their first appearance. The turtles appeared at about the same time as the dinosaurs. The dinosaurs and other spectacular reptile groups ran their course and became extinct. The turtles continued on, undisturbed. Mammals now dominate the scene. The turtles have taken no notice of us. And one may, not unreasonably, suspect that, in the far distant future, when mammals (and man) have become as extinct as the dinosaurs, the turtles will still be plodding stolidly and conservatively along the corridors of time.

A second group of reptiles which are still well represented today likewise come into view in the Triassic period. These are forms known as the Lepidosauria – the 'scaled reptiles' (in contrast to the plated skin of the crocodilians and the armour of the turtles). The primitive pattern of this group is preserved today in the lizards. This modern group, which, together with their snake descendants, makes up the order Squamata, is somewhat specialized and advanced in technical characters of the skull, teeth, and so on, which were not present in most of the small ancestral forms of the late Permian and Triassic. But before the Triassic had ended there had appeared various little reptiles which are certainly close to the true lizards in structure. In the Cretaceous, before the reign of the dinosaurs had been concluded, the fossil record shows the presence of a considerable variety of lizards of which many appear to be close to the pattern of modern forms. Today lizards, with little control over their body temperatures and unable to withstand cold winter weather, are almost entirely confined to the tropics, where they still flourish in modest if rather varied fashion. Apart from an extinct marine group (described in the next chapter) few lizards are of any great size. Largest are some of the monitor lizards (*Varanus*) of the Old World tropics. Members of this group found on the East Indian island of Komodo were once reputed to be 'dragons' reaching twenty-eight or thirty feet in length. When subjected to scientific scrutiny, they shrank (alas!) to about ten feet as a maximum (tail included). Even so, this makes for an animal with considerable bulk and dangerousness, particularly if, as is said to be the case, they are poorly endowed with brains and well-endowed with nasty dispositions.

Last of any reptile groups to appear in the fossil record, and the only ones which appear to be still progressing on an evolutionary course, are the snakes. They have, quite surely, evolved from lizards – perhaps from forms related to the monitor lizards. Transitional forms were present in the Cretaceous, but it was only in the Tertiary, after most other reptile groups had become extinct, that the great development of the ophidians took place. Most obvious of snake characteristics is the loss of limbs. The snakes have abandoned the clumsy four-footed method of locomotion of their ancestors, and progress by an undulatory motion of their elongate bodies, the well-developed horny scales preventing back-slipping. But loss of limbs is not a unique character; a large number of lizards have tended toward limb reduction or loss. Although only a small percentage of modern snakes lead subterranean lives, there is considerable reason to believe that loss of limbs in snakes is, as in many lizards, due to a burrowing stage in early snake evolution. More definitely characteristic are their skull and jaw structures. The two halves of the snake lower jaw are connected with one another by elastic materials and

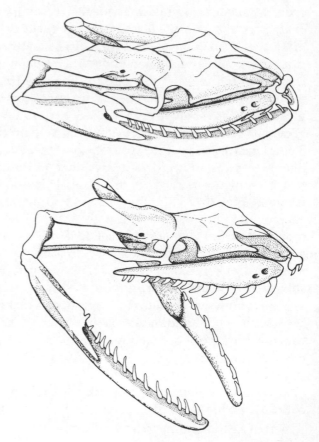

Figure 46. The jaws of a python can be widely opened and the two halves of the lower jaw separated from one another, so that large prey can be swallowed.

can be widely separated (figure 46). In addition, there is a joint part way along each jaw half as well as the orthodox joint between jaw and skull; still further, the supports propping the upper jaw on the skull are movable, and the skull itself is flexibly built. All these features, put together, allow the snake to distend its mouth to a remarkable degree, and swallow large prey whole; a snake of modest size can, with a bit of strain, engulf, for example, a full-grown rabbit.

Apart from some small and archaic burrowing forms, the boas and pythons, large and small, are representative of a primitive stage in snake evolution, to be followed by the numerous types of harmless snakes common in almost every part of the world. A final evolutionary development among ophidians was the coming of poisonous types; our fossil record of snakes is none too perfect, but it appears that venomous forms did not appear until far along in the Cenozoic. The mechanism includes the transformation of mouth glands, which in ordinary vertebrates secrete harmless mucus, into poison sacs, and the development of specialized fangs for poison injection. The simplest fangs are teeth which have a lengthwise groove down which poison may trickle into the victim's flesh; more highly developed are the fangs of the vipers, built like a hypodermic needle for poison injection. Poison fangs would appear to have developed, quite independently, in several different snake families. Related to the harmless grass snakes and their kin of the northern tropics are a series of tropical types which are inoffensive in appearance and habits, but are known to possess, toward the back of their jaws, poison fangs capable of seriously affecting – and even killing – creatures as large as a man. A second venomous group is that of the cobras and their relatives, such as the deadly mambas of Africa and the little coral snakes of the tropics. Third are the vipers, which include not only the Old World vipers, but such American forms as the flourishing rattlesnakes and even larger and more deadly forms in the New World tropics. And, finally, a family of sea-snakes which will be mentioned in the next chapter.

The lizards and snakes constitute the greater part of the 'scaled reptiles'. But we cannot complete the roster of the Lepidosauria without mention of one reptile of modest size which is the sole representative of a quite distinct order of its own. This is the tuatara, *Sphenodon*, of New Zealand. This island group is so far removed from the rest of the terrestrial world that very few land vertebrates of any sort have been able to reach it. The tuatara looks very much like a lizard and, in fact, does resemble the lizards in many structural features. But when studied scientifically well back in the last century, it was discovered that it is basically different from the lizards in important features of its skull and is the sole living representative of a group of reptiles related to the lizards and snakes, but constituting a distinct order with the imposing name of the Rhynchocephalia. Forms not very different from the tuatara are known from fossil beds dating from the very beginning of the Age of Reptiles, and members of the order played a modest role in early Mesozoic times. The group, however, is unknown in late deposits in other parts of the world. The persistence of the tuatara in New Zealand is a good example of the fashion in which geographical isolation may allow the survival of primitive forms in the absence of competition. In other regions the rhynchocephalians failed in competition with more progressive animals – notably mammals. But no land mammal ever reached New Zealand before the coming of man, and here alone this inoffensive little animal has persisted for many millions of years after his kin failed elsewhere. Even so, the tuatara is close to the end of its tether. Seemingly because of the introduction by man of potential mammalian enemies, the tuatara, once widespread in New Zealand, is today found only on a few small coastal islands; even there its survival seems guaranteed only by government protection.

We have above given a brief account of the evolution of the living reptile groups (apart from the crocodilians, to be considered later with their more spectacular archosaur cousins). The story is, on the whole, a prosaic one. But the history of reptiles in the Mesozoic, the Age of Reptiles, is quite another story. In early days even the lepidosaurs put out some weirdly experimental side-branches. For example, in the Triassic, there developed among the oldest lizards 'flying' forms, recently discovered both in Europe and North America, in which long ribs along the trunk extended outward to simulate aeroplane wings, and another form, possibly (but not surely) a lizard offshoot, *Tanystropheus*, was a reptilian 'super-giraffe', with an absurdly elongate neck stretching forward from a normally shaped body (plate 9). The animal was, it appears, a shore-dweller; but what it stretched for we do not know. In the Triassic even the modest tuatara's relatives attained prominence for a short time. In that period, particularly in the Middle Triassic, this group attained a temporary prominence with a development of forms termed *Rhynchosaurus* (plate 9). About the size of a pig, these reptiles developed a parrot-like beak and a powerful chopping dentition, probably used for cracking nutritious 'pits' of plant fruits of that day; for a time the rhynchosaurs became, in South America and Africa, the commonest of peaceful herbivorous animals.

But flying and giraffe-lizards and rhynchosaurs were but minor elements in the great panorama of Mesozoic reptile history. In succeeding chapters we shall talk of some of the varied Mesozoic marine reptiles; of the archosaurs, or Ruling Reptiles, including the dinosaurian hosts of the past and the ancestors of the birds; of still other reptiles destined to give rise to the mammals which now dominate the surface of the globe.

Chapter 11

Water Reptiles

IN the last chapter we pointed out the advance in reproductive methods whereby the reptiles finally triumphed in attaining the possibility of becoming true terrestrial animals. But many reptiles, even though capable of being land-dwellers, reversed the process, and turned back to the water, to become not only inhabitants again of the fresh waters that their ancestors had inhabited, but, further, to become dwellers on the high seas. A long series of forms, extinct and living, shared in this trend.

Turtles, for example (figure 47A). The chelonians probably evolved their shell and other peculiarities at a time when the ancestral reptiles were still more or less amphibious in habits, and a large proportion of turtles are still marsh- and pond-dwellers. From this condition, we can readily see, a shift toward purely aquatic life is not too difficult, and there evolved, well before the close of the Age of Reptiles, a goodly assortment of marine turtles, several of which are still extant. The usual turtle has limbs capable of taking him about on land; in the truly marine forms, however, the limbs have been transformed into paddle-like flippers, and these water-dwellers' only contacts with the land are short excursions onto the shore for egg-laying by the lady members.

The Squamata, the lizards and snakes, show today relatively little interest in water-dwelling. Of living lizards the only one which more than dips his toes is a Galapagos species which feeds along the coasts of these islands, where there is little to eat ashore. Snakes are more venturesome. A few of the typical harmless types are found in freshwater ponds and streams, swimming in eel-like fashion. And there is one striking group of purely marine snakes – the family Hydrophidae, literally 'water snakes' – which are present in the warmer parts of the Indian and Pacific oceans, where 'population explosions' sometimes cause them to be present over large areas in loathsome abundance. They are fish-eating forms of modest size, which are, however, highly poisonous.

194

Although modern lizards show little inclination toward a watery career, the picture in the Cretaceous period was a very different one. Developing from forms similar to the modern Monitor lizards, with transitional types earlier in the period, giant lizards termed mosasaurs became abundant in late Cretaceous seas (plate 8). Numerous skeletons of these forms have been found in Cretaceous chalk rocks of England, the Low countries, Kansas, and even far-away New Zealand. (The name is due to the fact that the first good specimen found came from the banks of the Meuse – the Mosa, in Latin.) These marine fish-eaters grew to considerable size, reaching lengths of thirty to forty feet. The turtles, with a rigid body and no tail to speak of, had to depend for swimming on their limbs, turned into oars. The mosasaurs, in contrast, had a long, flexible trunk and a highly developed tail, and hence were able to use body and tail undulation for forward progression in somewhat fish-like fashion; the legs are short; the feet, rather large and webbed, were probably efficient steering organs.

The marine forms mentioned so far are allies of familiar reptile groups. More spectacular were two wholly extinct orders of marine reptiles, the plesiosaurs and ichthyosaurs. Common in marine deposits of both Jurassic and Cretaceous periods were the plesiosaurs. In contrast to most water-dwellers, which swim by undulatory motions of trunk and tail, the plesiosaurs had a stout, compact body, firmly welded into a unit, and very little tail. In this they resembled the turtles, and, indeed, one older writer described a plesiosaur as 'a snake threaded through the body of a turtle'. Because of this build the plesiosaurs had to depend, like the marine turtles, upon limbs developed as oars to 'row' them through the water. The feet, which formed much of the length of the limbs, were highly developed. The normal number of five toes was present, but in each toe the number of joints, never more than five in any normal reptile, was greatly increased, so that well over a dozen are sometimes found. Some plesiosaurs were of modest size, but on the average they were of considerable bulk, and included the largest of known reptiles, apart from some of the dinosaurs. The known maximum size is that of *Kronosaurus* (figure 47B), a Cretaceous form from Australia, which measures nearly fifty feet from the snout to the tip of the stubby tail.

Plesiosaurs appear to have made a living on the numerous bony fishes present in the Mesozoic seas. With powerful limbs, they could probably get up considerable speed. But the stiffly built body was a

195

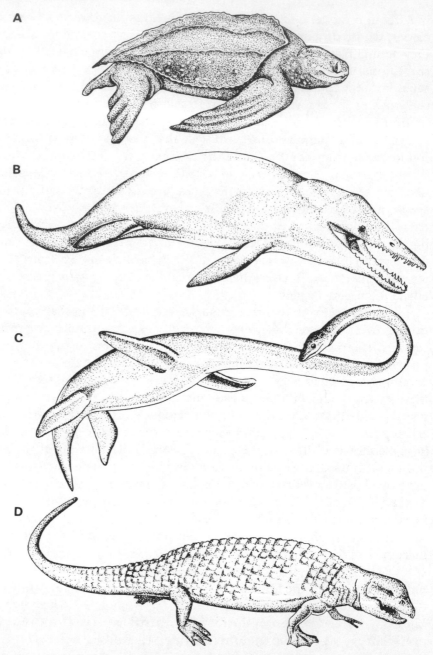

Figure 47. Some aquatic reptiles which paddle themselves along. A, turtle. Both short-necked *Kronosaurus* (B) and long-necked *Elasmosaurus* (C) are forty- to fifty-feet-long plesiosaurs. D, *Placodus*, a mollusc-eating placodont.

196

handicap in pursuit of elusive fishes; sharp turns and delicate steering were out of the question. In compensation, there developed in many of these forms a long and surely flexible neck, with as many as seventy-two neck vertebrae in one case (figure 47C). If a fish tried to escape the onrush of its pursuer by an agile sideways turn, the plesiosaur could swing its neck sideways and nip the fish as it passed. In a second plesiosaur type, the neck was short, but the head greatly elongated in compensation.

The plesiosaurs had no close relatives of any sort among land reptiles. In the earlier Triassic period there have been found primitive relatives, the nothosaurs, as well as some specialized cousins termed placodonts (figure 47D), which, with teeth developed as broad, flattened crushing plates, made their living from beds of molluscs along the shores. The nothosaurs – reptiles of modest size – show the beginnings of the specializations perfected in the plesiosaurs. But these were much less developed at that time; the limbs, for example, had not departed far from the normal land pattern, and nothosaurs presumably led more or less amphibious lives in estuarine and coastal waters. Before the nothosaur stage, however, the pedigree of the plesiosaurs is a blank; they cannot be tied in with other major reptile groups, and their mode of origin from the ancestral cotylosaur stock is quite unknown.

Still more completely adapted for marine existence were the members of a further major group of ocean-dwelling reptiles, the ichthyosaurs. Their name, 'fish reptiles', was happily chosen, for these forms were almost ideally fitted to take up again a fish-like life in the waters. In early Jurassic deposits at Boll, in southern Germany, numerous slabs of hard black shale have been found in which are present splendid specimens of ichthyosaurs, showing not only the skeleton but, in carbonized form, the complete body outline. The body was beautifully streamlined (plate 8); the neck was essentially done away with, so that the body had a torpedo-like shape for cleaving the water efficiently, increasing in depth backwards from snout to 'shoulder' region, and then gradually tapering toward the tail. Fish-like, too, was a development of fins. Typical fishes have a dorsal fin projecting upward along the back. Such structures had long since been lost by ancestral tetrapods, but slab specimens show that such a structure had redeveloped in ichthyosaurs, although there are no skeletal elements to support it. Well-preserved specimens of ichthyosaurs had long been known to exhibit, apparently, a sharp 'break' near the base

197

of the tail, the tip running downward. This was at first thought to be an accidental, post-mortem break, and older restorations of ichthyosaurs show the tail straightened in proper reptile fashion. But certain of the slab specimens, with body outlines preserved, prove that this 'break' is not a break at all, but a perfectly natural condition. The ichthyosaurs had redeveloped an excellent tail resembling that of a shark. But whereas the shark tail is stiffened by the backbone continuing on into the upper lobe of the fin, the ichthyosaurs have developed the reverse of this structure; the backbone turns sharply downward to stiffen the lower lobe.

With this type of body and tail, swimming in ichthyosaurs was obviously fish-like, and there was no need for the paired limbs to become great oar-like structures, as in the stiff-bodied plesiosaurs. In correlation, they have been reduced to small steering structures. They are, however, even more highly modified than in plesiosaurs, for not only has there been, as in that group, a notable increase in the number of short joints in each toe, but in some cases, most unorthodoxly, an increase from the proper number of five toes to six or seven. Fish, we believe, were the food supply of plesiosaurs. Squids, on the other hand, seem to have been a major source of nourishment for ichthyosaurs, for in some cases considerable numbers of indigestible squid 'pens' have been found within the body region of ichthyosaurs preserved in slab form.

Reproduction in reptiles is, of course, generally of an egg-laying type, although in some snakes and lizards the eggs hatch within the mother's body. Marine turtles come ashore and lay eggs in the sand, and very probably plesiosaurs, with powerful flippers, could do the same. But it seems improbable that ichthyosaurs, with limbs reduced to small fins, could do this. Surely they must have borne their young alive? Confirmation of this supposition comes from a number of specimens in which the skeleton of a small and obviously young ichthyosaur has been preserved with the body cavity of an adult. We are here surely dealing with mothers and their unborn young.

The ichthyosaurs were on the whole a more ancient group than the plesiosaurs. True plesiosaurs are unknown until the opening of the middle period of the Age of Reptiles, the Jurassic. Ichthyosaurs, however, were already flourishing in the latter part of the preceding period, the Triassic. Members of the group in general are of modest size, one or a very few yards long – but in the Triassic some early forms were relative giants, thirty feet and more in length. In Nevada there was recently discovered the graveyard of a whole 'school' of such giants: this has become a state park. The peak of ichthyosaur development appears to have been at the beginning of the Jurassic, and in rocks of this age numerous specimens are to be found, notably in the Lyme Regis district of England and in southern Germany. Beyond this period, the ichthyosaurs waned and, unlike the plesiosaurs, few are known to have survived into the Cretaceous.

We shall conclude our review of the evolution of water-dwelling forms with mention of a little reptile which is by far the oldest known of all aquatic representatives of the class, *Mesosaurus* (plate 8), which flourished briefly at about the beginning of the Permian period. We might well omit mention of this animal (it has no known relatives) if it were not for the fact that its distribution forms an appropriate introduction to a series of vexing problems concerning the geography of the world in ancient geological times.

Mesosaurus lived in fresh waters – not the ocean. It is present, in abundance, in early Permian fresh-water deposits of just two areas – South Africa and south-eastern Brazil. There is not a trace of it in any other part of the world, although fossil-bearing beds of the same age are plentiful elsewhere. How did it manage to be present in these two places, which by land (and fresh-water) routes are 20,000 miles or so apart, and these two alone? There is, of course, a chance that, although *Mesosaurus* was normally a fresh-water dweller, a few individuals might have somehow crossed the South Atlantic. But this is very much of an outside chance; it is hard to believe that this rather feeble little fellow could have breasted the waves of the 3,000-mile crossing of this ocean waste. Again, might not the mesosaurs have made the trip from South Africa to Brazil (or vice versa) via the fresh waters of the continents as they now exist? But it is a very long trip – up Africa, across Asia, down North and much of South America. Again, it is pretty much of an outside chance that this could have happened and that no trace of this great trek would have been preserved in our abundant fossil record of the Permian. But if these ideas do not hold, we are driven to the conclusion that in those ancient days South Africa and South America were not as remote from one another as they are today. Was there not some direct way in which the one continent could have been reached from the other?

Many puzzling problems of this sort have beset students of the geographical distribution of animals. In the last century, the favourite solution was the assumption that there have existed in the past various

199

'land bridges' – usually thought of as relatively long and narrow strips of terra firma – connecting continental regions now widely separated. Did a fossil horse from Florida appear to resemble one from western Europe? The solution is simple; build a land bridge from Florida to Spain. Does a fossil wolf-like pouched mammal from South America closely resemble the pouched Tasmanian 'wolf'? The answer is easy; a land bridge (a really long one, this) from Patagonia to Australia. And so on, and so on. If all the land bridges proposed by one author and another during the past century were to be plotted on a single map, the present oceans would, I suspect, have the appearance of a spider web of interlacing bridges. It is difficult to imagine the physical forces that would have caused this multiplicity of bridges to keep popping up and down from time to time, and disappear leaving little or no trace in the ocean bottoms. Worse still are the potential traffic problems on these imaginary bridges. Each was made to solve the distributional problem of some one specific type of animal. But each proposed bridge generally opened up the question as to why other animals, not present on both sides of the bridge, did not cross as well. All in all, the whole bridge complex tended to crash (scientifically) under its own weight. Land bridges are now out of fashion, and it is rather generally agreed that for at least the Cenozoic – the last seventy million years or so – the continents have kept essentially their present relations to one another, although with some ups and downs, sinkings and risings, of the connections or narrow gaps obvious at the present time.

But for the older ages of the earth the picture is not so clear. And there are strong suggestions that there were then connections between continents not found today – these not as slender bridges, but as actual juxtaposition of continents now widely separated (figure 48).

One suggestion, which has long had strong support, is that there once existed a great southern continent, Gondwanaland, which included much of present South America and Africa and peninsular India and Australia as well, the whole separated from the main northern continental areas by a broad sea where the Alps and Himalayas now rise. (The name of Gondwanaland comes from a region in the part of India included.) This was supposed to have been in existence in the late Palaeozoic and early Mesozoic, and to have later split up into its scattered present components. A major argument for belief in Gondwanaland lies in the fact that in Permian and Triassic times the plants of these regions were almost identical, and made up a flora very different from those of northern regions. Then, too, many of the geologic formations of these ages in South America and South Africa are very similar to one another. Again, the faunas of South America and Africa in ancient times are in many regards very similar – so similar that it is difficult to believe that their only contacts were by way of the remote north. And, of course, little *Mesosaurus* fits in nicely to this scheme; if South Africa and South America were once check by jowl, the two areas of his occurrence lie side by side.

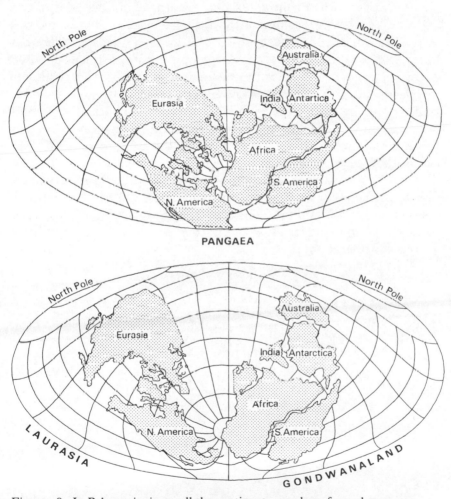

Figure 48. In Palaeozoic times, all the continents may have formed one mass, called Pangaea (above), this later splitting to form two super-continents, Gondwanaland and Laurasia (below). The continents, under this theory, probably moved to their present positions during the late Mesozoic.

201

A still more radical proposal of this general sort was the theory of continental drift put forth half a century ago by a German, Alfred Wegener. His belief was that, in the early days of the earth, not merely the southern continents but *all* the land surfaces of the earth were one connected mass, and that, as geological periods went by, they slowly separated, drifted apart, and eventually reached their present positions. When first proposed, this scheme of things was looked upon with horror by most right-thinking geologists. The physicists were shocked at the idea of continents gaily floating about over the earth's bedrock, and, indeed, as first advanced by Wegener, the scheme was too radical for anyone's acceptance. But in recent decades there has been a noticeable shift in views. The geophysicists are not as opposed as they once were, and as for the palaeontologists, many are willing to accede to the drift theory for the older periods, although they are positive that by the Cenozoic the picture was much like the present one. Particularly obvious and fascinating is the situation as regards the Atlantic Ocean. If we mentally close the continents of the two sides up on each other, they fit excellently, and it is easy to believe that the two hemispheres were apposed to one another in ancient days, only to drift slowly apart as geologic ages passed. The hypothesis of continental drift is still far from general acceptance, but such bits of evidence as that of *Mesosaurus* indicate that it is worthy of very serious consideration.

Chapter 12

Ruling Reptiles

ONE of the most spectacular events of animal evolution was the rise and dominance, during the Mesozoic era, of the major reptilian group known as the Archosauria, or ruling reptiles. Included among their numbers were, amongst others, all of the dinosaurs, great and small. The crocodilians alone remain today as relics of this once great group, but the archosaurs have been of lasting importance as the progenitors of the birds.

The origin and rise of the ruling reptiles was associated with improvements in locomotion. As told above, primitive tetrapods came onto the land with all four limbs sprawled far out to the sides; this same type of gait was present in the ancestral reptiles. It is preserved to this day by the turtles, who encased themselves in their shells in this pattern. This is a very inefficient, slow, clumsy way of waddling about the countryside; so much of the available muscular effort must be spent in keeping the body off the ground that little is available for forward progression. The lizards show a little improvement, but not much; the snakes have given up completely. If a terrestrial reptile were really to get ahead in the world, something needed to be done to evolve a new pattern of locomotion.

As we shall see later, the reptiles which were to give rise to mammals remained four-footed runners – quadrupeds, that is – but improved the stance of both front and hind legs. Another mode of improvement was, however, possible; and this was the pattern which gave rise to the archosaurs. In early but progressive members of this group possible improvement of the front legs was given up as a bad job. These were left to wither or be used for other purposes than terrestrial locomotion; major attention was given to the hind legs. The knees were turned forward, close beneath the body. In this new pose a longer stride was possible; further, the leg-bones could directly support the weight, relieving the musculature of much of its former work. The front end of the body was tilted up into a bipedal pose, the front legs free of the ground; the body was counterbalanced on the hind legs by a long if slender tail. So rebuilt, the animal could become an effective running type, greatly improved for offence or defence.

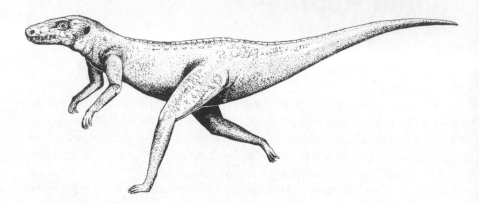

Figure 49. *Euparkeria* running, using its hind limbs alone.

The oldest archosaurs, constituting a basal order, the Thecodontia, appeared early in the Triassic period, at the very dawn of the Mesozoic Age of Reptiles. Representative of an early stage is *Euparkeria*, whose skeleton has been recovered from South African deposits of this age. This was a fairly small animal, with a length of about a yard, tail and all; in appearance it would have looked somewhat like a lizard, except that the hind legs were already noticeably longer than the fore, and drawn in closer to the body. For part of the time, when not hurried, it would have ambled about the countryside, we feel sure, in a four-footed fashion, for the front legs were still quite usable. But when hurried, as when in pursuit of prey (for *Euparkeria* was a predator), the animal could rear up on its hind legs and run rapidly in bipedal fashion (figure 49).

A great variety of thecodonts are known from the Triassic. Many tended to continue in great measure as quadrupeds, frequently developing a cover of armour-plate, presumably in protection against larger and more predacious thecodont cousins; some, the phytosaurs (figure 50), took up an amphibious life in the water, paralleling the later crocodilians which were to spring likewise from this thecodont base. Still others, however, persisted in the development of bipedal habits, and some of the more advanced thecodonts show transitions to the true dinosaurian condition.

But before going on to describe the evolution of the dinosaurs, let us first mention some other lines which the archosaurs developed from the ancestral thecodont stock. To begin with, the least spectacular of Ruling Reptile groups, the order Crocodilia. In some senses of the word, the crocodiles and alligators may be called degenerate, for the members of this order have not followed out the promise of 'higher things', in the way of spectacular bipedalism, implied by the

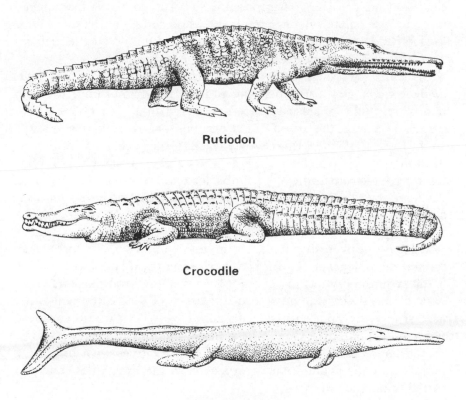

Rutiodon

Crocodile

Metriorhynchus

Figure 50. The phytosaurs, such as *Rutiodon*, were very like the crocodiles but their nostrils lay farther back, between their eyes. *Metriorhynchus*, nearly fifteen feet long, is a Jurassic marine crocodile which had developed a fish-like tail fin.

trend in this direction among many thecodonts. Instead, these creatures slumped back to a quadrupedal gait (figure 50) and became essentially water-dwellers, whose excursions onto or beyond the river banks are rare. Even in the Triassic there have been found forms transitional between thecodonts and proper crocodilians, and by the beginning of the Jurassic there appear reptiles which in all basic features are not too far from the conditions seen in modern crocodiles and alligators. The only unique feature in which members of this group differ from the run of reptiles is a neat nasal structure which enables them to breathe readily in the water even with the mouth open in seizing prey. In a typical reptile, the nostrils open directly down into the roof of the mouth, so that when the mouth is open in the water air-breathing is impossible. The crocodilians have developed a 'false palate' which extends the whole length of the roof of the long muzzle, so that as long as the tip of the snout is above the surface, breathing can continue even with a wide-open mouth.

Since the Jurassic, members of the main line of crocodilians have made few changes in structure except for some further improvement in this breathing apparatus, and some modification in backbone structure. To be sure, the group did at one point show some originality. In the late Jurassic seas there were present some purely marine crocodiles (figure 50), which to some degree paralleled the ichthyosaurs, for they had transformed the limbs into steering paddles and had developed a fish-like tail of modest size. But these forms soon disappeared, and the later history of the group is one of continued monotony.

We have spoken disparagingly of these unlovely creatures, and termed them degenerate. But is this treatment truly deserved? What is the evolutionary test of success? Survival. Other archosaurs went on to found successful 'advanced' dynasties of dinosaurs, which we gaze at in awe (if not entirely with admiration). But where are these noble monsters now? Gone, these many millions of years. And the crocodilians? Still with us. If human conservatives wish to draw a moral from the evolutionary story, it is to the crocodiles (and the turtles) that they may turn.

Before proceeding to the dinosaurs, let us treat of another very divergent group of thecodont descendants which progressed on into a purely bipedal mode of life, in which the front legs persisted despite their lack of use in locomotion. Here were these structures, which we might now call arms rather than front legs, still with the animal and available for some new use. Use in flight is (or rather was) one such possibility. Twice, among thecodont descendants, there took place the modification of the arms into wing structures. One very successful modification in this direction led to the evolution of birds, of which we shall treat in the following chapter. A second, and apparently earlier trend in this direction, but one taken up in quite another fashion and quite independently of the avian line, resulted in the evolution of flying reptiles, the order Pterosauria. The pterosaurs appeared in the early Jurassic and persisted until close to the end of the Age of Reptiles. Best known of relatively primitive Jurassic forms is *Rhamphorhynchus* (plate 10). This animal, of quite modest size (perhaps a yard, at the most, from snout to tail tip), had a compact body, feeble hind legs, a long tail bearing a steering rudder, and highly developed arms in which three fingers were short and clawed but the fourth greatly elongated and supporting a wing which, like that of modern bats but in contrast to birds, was a broad flap of skin. The name 'prow beak' is not inappropriate, for the jaws are long and slender, but armed with powerful pointed teeth. Very likely *Rhamphorhynchus*, like some modern sea-birds, lived on little fishes, for which it dived out of the air.

The pterosaurs flourished to a considerable degree for much of the Age of Reptiles, and developed a number of variant types. In the late Jurassic there abounded smaller forms, such as *Pterodactylus* (plate 10), some specimens of which were no bigger than a sparrow, in which the tail was only a stub and the teeth reduced, probably with the beginning development of a horny bird-like bill. In the late Cretaceous there developed giant types, such as *Pteranodon*, one specimen of which appears to have had a wing spread of some twenty-seven feet (plate 10).

Like many other reptile groups, the pterosaurs did not survive the end of the Cretaceous. It is reasonable to assume that their lack of success was due to an inability to compete with their distant cousins, the birds, likewise developed from the early archosaur stock. If we consider the structure of pterosaurs, it is easy to imagine why they failed. The wing, for example, is an exceedingly awkward structure – merely a single expanse of 'sail' with no supports except attachment to the wing-finger at the front and the body flanks at the back, quite in contrast, for example, to the bat wing, in which four fingers were involved. The 'sail' had little possibility for adjustment and manœuvrability, and probably the pterosaurs were for the most part restricted to a soaring type of flight with the wings in fixed position. Seemingly troublesome, too, was the odd structure of the hind legs. Presumably the pterosaur ancestor was a biped, capable of running on its hind legs. But by the time the pterosaurs come into the known geological record the hind legs had become weak and highly specialized, and it would seem impossible for a pterosaur to have stood erect on them; probably they were mainly used to suspend the resting bird, head down, from a branch, like a bat. But if, by chance, a pterosaur landed on the ground how could it take off again? For a little pterodactyl the problem may not have been too great; but as regards a giant *Pteranodon*, it is difficult for us to imagine how it managed to exist at all.

A great part of the evolutionary story of the archosaurs is, of course, that which tells of the rise, and eventual fall, of the hosts of dinosaurs, many of which are so well known today that they are almost as familiar to schoolboys as to scientists. The popular conception of the dinosaurs is that of a single great group of giant reptiles. But this concept needs a degree of qualification. Many dinosaurs were large, but others were of very modest size. Further, there were two quite distinct groups of dinosaurs, related, it is true, but no more closely related to one another than they were to their cousins the pterosaurs and crocodilians. The two groups are ranked as orders, termed the Saurischia and Ornithischia. Key diagnostic characters, to which these names refer, can be readily seen, by even the most casual visitor to museum exhibition galleries, in the hip-bones – the pelvis – of any mounted dinosaur skeleton (figure 51). Both dinosaur groups are descended from primitive thecodont ancestors which had become bipeds. With the changed posture of the hind legs, the structure of the pelvic girdles – to which the legs were attached and from which many of the muscles operating the legs sprang – was likewise modified. One major group had a triradiate pelvic structure, with one bone, termed the ilium, lying above the hip socket; a second, the pubis, running down and forward; a third, the ischium, running down and back. Forms with this type of pelvis, which did not depart far from the hip structure of normal reptiles, are the Saurischia, the term meaning essentially 'reptile-like pelvis', and we may call them the reptile-like dinosaurs. In a second group, the pelvis is built more like that of birds, in tetraradiate fashion, in that the lower front bone, the pubis, had two prongs in primitive members of the group, a main branch (sometimes reduced) swinging back parallel to the ischium and, in addition, a prominent rod running forward and acting, it would seem, as a needed support for the animal's belly in an upright pose. Dinosaurs with this pelvis type form the order Ornithischia, and we may call them the bird-like dinosaurs (keeping in mind, however, that it is only in hip structure that they closely resemble their avian cousins).

Of the two groups, the saurischians, the reptile-like dinosaurs, were

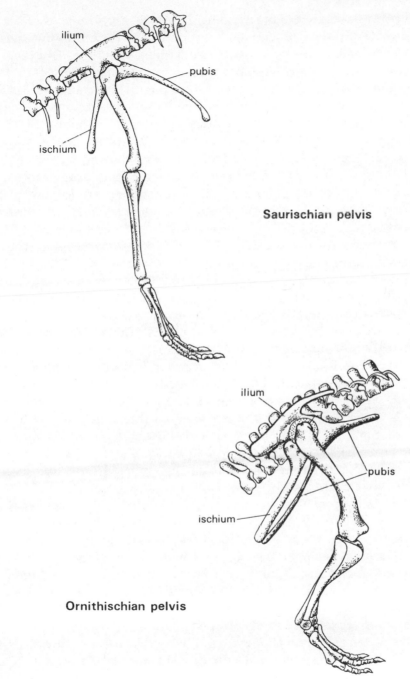

Figure 51. The types of pelvis, diagnostic of the two types of dinosaur.

the first to become prominent. There are numerous remains of such forms even in the late Triassic, at a time when their primitive relatives, the thecodonts, were still in flourishing condition. Even then, however, several divergent lines were becoming apparent within the saurischian order. Primitive forms were bipeds, or tending, at least, toward a two-footed gait, and, further, the ancestral stocks, with powerful pointed teeth, were obviously predacious in habits. In later periods of the Age of Reptiles two lines of predators can be distinguished. One of these lines tended to remain relatively small, and in the Jurassic period produced swift and agile little forms, some no larger than a rooster or turkey, which probably preyed upon small lizards and the like. In the late Cretaceous some end members of this line were of the type of *Ornithomimus* (plate 11), found in beds of this age in western North America. This animal is sometimes called the 'ostrich-like dinosaur'; for not only was it about the size of an ostrich, but the resemblances extended to the small head, toothless and with a bird-like bill, a long slender neck, and powerful hind legs capable of making considerable speed; the arms were persistently long, and of the three fingers retained by this animal, the 'thumb' could be apposed to the other two, giving the animal clutching powers. How did a reptile with these varied adaptations make its living? This question was long debated. The best suggestion is that it was an egg stealer, robbing the nests of other dinosaurs. Teeth are not needed, but a good beak to break the egg shell is; the 'clutch' of the hand would be useful in grasping eggs; running ability would enable the thief to evade an outraged parent (not always successfully, however; for in Mongolia the crushed remains of a related form have been found close to the nest of a dinosaur of another type).

A second group of reptile-like dinosaurs were bipeds which tended to grow to larger size, with massive skulls and highly-developed, sabre-like teeth. These were the major flesh-eaters amongst dinosaurs, and surely preyed upon the variety of harmless herbivores described later in this chapter. Carnivores of this sort by the end of the Jurassic had reached considerable size. Best known of Jurassic forms is *Allosaurus* (or *Antrodemus*), with a yard-long skull and measuring about thirty feet from nose to tail (plate 11). The hind legs were sturdily built, as befits an animal of this size, but *Allosaurus* was obviously a speedy and agile reptile, well suited for the pursuit of prey. In these big carnivores, the front legs were much shortened; we are dealing with purely bipedal types. Three fingers only remained in the *Allosaurus* hand; these, however, bore powerful claws, and the hands were no doubt useful in seizing and rending the prey.

A continuation of this evolutionary line led, in the late Cretaceous, to the development of such giant carnivores as the 'tyrant reptile' *Tyrannosaurus*, the largest flesh-eater ever to walk the land (plate 11). *Tyrannosaurus* stood some nineteen feet high in his semi-erect pose, with a five-foot skull and sharp shearing tooth blades, some of which were close to a foot in length. In contrast to the massive hind legs were the rudimentary arms, in which only two tiny and seemingly useless fingers remained.

A third line of saurischians evolved along a strongly contrasting path, leading to the great amphibious dinosaurs, technically termed the Sauropoda. The ancestors of this group appeared in the middle to late Triassic, together with early members of the carnivorous saurischian lines described above. But they were more heavily built than the ancestral carnivores, and the front legs showed relatively little tendency toward reduction; probably these pro-sauropods were only partially bipedal, and were slumping back toward a purely four-footed pose. Correlated with this, the head was small, and the teeth relatively small and blunt pegs. These animals were, it seems, taking up a vegetarian existence, in which haste in pursuit of food was not a necessity.

From such forms came the giant amphibious dinosaurs, familiar to all visitors to the great museums of the world. Although some persisted on into the Cretaceous period, their remains are most abundant in late Jurassic deposits in the western United States and Tanganyika. Perhaps best known is *Diplodocus* (plate 12), since skeletons or replicas are widespread in museum exhibition halls.[1] This animal has the reptilian world's record for length, a specimen with an unusually well-preserved tail measuring 97½ feet overall; the weight has been reasonably estimated at about twenty-five tons. The head was tiny, the dentition very feeble for an animal of this size; presumably the fodder was some sort of soft water vegetation. The neck was long, the trunk broad-barrelled for the temporary storage of the presumably pulpy food materials. The legs were massive and the hind legs were heavy pillars, as they must needs be to support such an enormous

[1] For an amusing reason. A skeleton of one species of *Diplodocus* was excavated by the staff of a Pittsburgh museum founded by the millionaire Andrew Carnegie. The wily museum director had the species named *Diplodocus carnegiei*, and the old gentleman, highly pleased, had plaster casts made for presentation to a number of other museums.

weight. The problems of weight support of an animal's body increase disproportionately with increase in size and weight. In an animal of this gigantic size it is, in fact, hard to see how even these great limbs could have sufficed for walking on land, and it is generally believed that these giants were mainly water-dwellers, inhabitants of the swamps and lagoons in which lay their food supply. Lending support to this assumption is the fact that the nostrils are located high up in the skull; the animal could breathe if almost completely submerged.

Diplodocus is only one of a considerable series of the great reptiles. Almost equally well-known is *Brontosaurus*, the 'thunder-lizard' which, not as elongate as *Diplodocus*, was more massively built, with an estimated weight of thirty-seven tons or so. The weight record, however, goes to a further member of the group, *Brachiosaurus*, which probably weighed about fifty tons. In most sauropods the front legs were considerably shorter than the hind – a reminiscence of the fact that bipedal tendencies with a trend toward 'arm' reduction may have been present in the ancestors. *Brachiosaurus* is an exception to this rule, for the front legs are long, and the long neck tilted strongly upward from the shoulders (plate 12). As mounted in the Berlin museum, the height is so great that *Brachiosaurus*, were he able to stroll about the streets, could look over the top of a three-storey building.

The saurischian dinosaurs, thus, produced some spectacular types of ancient reptiles. Their cousins, the bird-like dinosaurs, never rivalled the larger reptile-like dinosaurs in absolute size, but developed types more bizarre in many ways. We have already noted the technical difference between the two dinosaur orders as regards hip-bone structure. There are further contrasts. The reptile-like forms began as carnivores, and except for the sauropods, continued as such. The bird-like forms were vegetarians from the beginning, with never a flesh-eater among their numbers. Related to these habits, it would appear, nearly all members of this order lost the teeth from the front of the mouth, developing here instead a horny bill, and the cheek teeth tended to develop a characteristic leaf-like shape. As in the saurischians, the primitive members of the bird-like group were more or less bipedal. Here, however, the bipedal trend was much less emphasized, and three of four major sub-groups of the bird-like forms had reverted to quadrupedal locomotion.

The reptile-like forms, we have noted, had already become abundant in the Triassic. Development of the bird-like forms appears to have been much slower, for we as yet have found very few remains of ornithischians in the rocks of that period, and seemingly primitive members of the order still flourished in the Jurassic and even the Cretaceous. *Hypsilophodon*, for example, whose remains are found in the Lower Cretaceous Wealden beds of southern England and the Isle of Wight, was a slender biped only about a yard in height in upright pose.

Some of these relatively primitive ornithischians followed the general dinosaur trend toward increased size. A contemporary of little *Hypsilophodon* in the Wealden beds of southern England and Belgium was *Iguanodon*, a rather heavily built bipedal herbivore standing some dozen feet or so high (plate 13). At this time there were already present giant dinosaur predators for whom such an animal would furnish a splendid meal. *Iguanodon's* bipedal gait would probably enable him to escape this fate on many an occasion, but if cornered he was armed for defence. On each hand the 'thumb' terminated in a sharply pointed cone-shaped bone, presumably sheathed in life by an equally sharp-tipped horny covering. This pair of weapons could, one may believe, be effectively wielded as stilettos if the worst came to the worst.

Bipedal bird-like dinosaurs flourished even in the closing stages of the Cretaceous – in fact, remains of the hadrosaurs, or duck-billed dinosaurs of those days, are more numerous than those of all other known ornithischians put together. The typical hadrosaurs were rather good-sized forms, averaging about sixteen feet high in upright pose (plate 13). They could, quite surely, run about on their hind legs. They were, however, rather heavily built, and one may doubt if they were very speedy. The front legs are persistently long and well developed, and it seems certain that when in leisure mood they strolled about on all fours in ancestral fashion. (That this was the case is suggested by the fact that the front toes as well as the hind were tipped by small hooves.) But in addition to these two types of terrestrial locomotion, the duckbills were swimmers. There is nothing in the skeleton particularly to suggest this, but in a number of cases skeletons have been found with which skin impressions were preserved, and the toes are seen to have been webbed. Very probably the duckbills were amphibious, feeding largely on water vegetation, and, in addition, finding in the water a habitat into which carnivorous enemies could not follow them.

The popular name of 'duckbills' is due to the fact that the front of the toothless jaws was greatly widened and presumably covered by a broad, duck-like bill. It was mentioned above that the ornithischian teeth were simple leaf-shaped structures. Such teeth were competent to deal with soft vegetable materials. In the late Cretaceous, however, new plant types, more difficult to crop and chew, seem to have been making their appearance, and a simple row of leaf-shaped teeth would not be up to the task. Among mammals, as we shall see, individual teeth may be elaborated into complex grinding molars for tasks of this sort. The dinosaurs never succeeded in developing such structures. Nature, however, solved the problem for the hadrosaurs in another fashion. In the duckbills each tooth remained simple in structure, but the number was vastly increased. In each branch of both upper and lower jaws we see, instead of a single row of teeth, a number of rows side by side, and, further, beneath each row, a number of rows of would-be successors. The battery of teeth in each jaw was cemented together into a solid structure as a very effective grinding device. It has been estimated that the four great tooth plates present in a duckbill's mouth might, together, include well over a thousand individual teeth.

A curious trend in duckbill evolution was the development of crested types. In structurally primitive forms there was a slit-like nasal opening above the bill. In one form, which shows the first trend toward a crest, the bones which normally surround this opening are somewhat expanded above, giving a 'Roman nose' appearance. Further along this structural sequence, there appears a crest above the top of the head, rounded in outline as seen in lateral view, rather thin from side to side. This, one would think, was an upward growth from the bones roofing the skull. It is not; it is the same two bones which normally surround the nostril extended upward and backward. In a further stage the dorsal crest is still present, but a stout bony prong extends backward from it. And in an extreme development the crest has vanished and instead there is a long curved prong extending far back over the neck. Here again, it is the same two bones that should surround the nose that form this 'horn'. It is as if mother nature had, so to speak, taken a firm grasp of the duckbill's nose and yanked it strongly up and back over the animal's head.

The function of these curious crest structures is none too clear. As might have been surmised to be the case, investigation of internal structure shows that in the crested forms the air passage from the external nostril, instead of leading directly to mouth and throat, runs upward into the crest and then doubles back downward into the roof of the mouth. Since the duckbills were amphibious, it is natural to think that perhaps this structure had to do with under-water breathing.[1] But there is little capacity for air storage in the tubes. A heightened sense of olfaction is an alternative suggestion.

Even more strongly than in the reptile-like dinosaurs, members of the ornithischian group tended, whenever the occasion offered, to abandon bipedal running and plant themselves again on four feet. After all, they were feeders on vegetation, and vegetation does not need to be run after. But there was one major problem. What about threatening carnivores? The answer lay in the development of armour or some sort of protective devices. Three different groups of quadrupedal bird-like dinosaurs appeared in the Mesozoic fossil record. Each adopted a somewhat different method of defence; each proved, for the time at least, successful.

First of such four-footed ornithischian groups to appear was that including *Stegosaurus* and his relatives of the late Jurassic and early Cretaceous. *Stegosaurus* was four-footed, but clearly shows his bipedal ancestry in his build (plate 14). His front legs had become greatly shortened during a preceding bipedal stage, and hence head and shoulders are low to the ground; to the rear, his back rises high over the long hind legs. A slow beast, and a harmless one. Defence? This was furnished by bony plates. Some earlier ornithischians (and even ancestral archosaurs) had had a double row of flat bony plates running along over the backbone. Stegosaurs had developed these into a double row of sharp-edged plates which projected upward from the back and would tend to fend off any aggressor attacking from above. The plates extended down over the tail; here, however, they took the form of spikes; and if the tail were flexible (as we hope, for *Stegosaurus*' sake, it was), a flailing-about of this weapon could have given an attacker a nasty surprise. The weak point of the armour was, of course, that it did not prevent an attack on the broad flanks, which were bare of armour (although perhaps covered with a tough hide). Despite this fault, *Stegosaurus* and his close relatives were for a time a flourishing group, and remains of this dinosaur type are known from America, Europe and Africa.

[1] The air tubes even extend into the backwardly projecting 'horn' sometimes developed, and many years ago I suggested in print, indiscreetly, that the animal used the 'horn' as a device for breathing under water. To my embarrassment, discovery of a perfectly preserved specimen showed that there was no opening at the end!

Seemingly a better type of armour was that developed by a later group, *Ankylosaurus* and his relatives of the late Cretaceous. Here the body was low, the legs short, and the armour developed into consolidated rows of bony plates stretching the width of the broad back (plate 14). The whole structure gives much the impression of a giant tortoise shell. The defensive adaptations were not, however, as good as those of the chelonians with which the ankylosaurs may be compared, for the typical modern turtle can draw head, tail, and legs into the shell. Nevertheless, these armoured dinosaurs tried bravely to defend these structures. The skull was reinforced above by an extra layer of armour plates of bone, and on either side of the carapace bony spikes extended outward over the legs to deter the enemy from taking a crippling snap. And the tail was transformed from a disability into an advantage, for it was heavily armoured in bone, sometimes furnished with spikes, and thus made a formidable club-like weapon.[1]

A third and final group of four-footed ornithischians was that of the horned dinosaurs, the ceratopsians, abundant in the late Cretaceous. Here the defences were of a very different order. The body was naked of bone, although presumably thick-skinned. Anteriorly, however, the neck region – a vulnerable spot, where one good bite could disable an animal – was protected by a great frill of bone extending back from the skull. Further, horns were developed in a fashion somewhat analogous to that of modern cattle. Horn development was variable. In some of the better-known forms such as *Triceratops* (plate 14) there were three horns present – a pair projecting up from the forehead above the eyes and a third rising over the nasal region. In some forms, however, the nasal horn was absent, while in others the nasal structure was the main or only weapon.

It is amusing to speculate on the behaviour of these horned dinosaurs if attacked. Because of vulnerability *a tergo*, obviously the ceratopsian would attempt to face up to the enemy. But if two or more carnivores had sense enough to co-operate in an attack, one would expect the ceratopsian to have been in an unfortunate position. Or would the ceratopsians have had enough brains to form herds, which when menaced could have formed a defensive circle? We shall never know.

The complete disappearance of these great reptiles at the end of

---

[1] There is an interesting parallel here to the extinct mammalian glyptodonts, heavily armoured giant relatives of the armadillos, in which the tail was armoured and sometimes spiked in closely comparable fashion.

the Cretaceous, leaving the surface of the world open for mammalian conquest, furnishes one of the major puzzles in the story of vertebrate evolution. What caused the extinction of dinosaurs – and of other major reptiles as well – in a geologically short space of time? To be sure, some types of dinosaurs were already on the wane before the end. But if, for example, we take certain areas in Wyoming, we find there beds which are definitely datable to the very end of the Creta ceous – the very end of the whole Mesozoic Age of Reptiles – in which duckbills, horned dinosaurs, and giant carnivores were present and flourishing. Above this level the shales and sands continued to be laid down with little if any indication of a break in time or break in deposition. But once above a certain level we are biologically at once in a different world, that of mammals. Not a trace of a dinosaur is to be found.

Why? Various explanations have been given, none too satisfactory. One often advanced is that the primitive mammals ate dinosaur eggs; no eggs, hence no more dinosaurs. But primitive mammals had already been in existence for many, many millions of years, and that they should have put on a campaign of extermination at this specific time is, to say the least, extremely improbable. Another suggestion is that they were exterminated by some epidemic of disease. But a type of disease which was specific for varied sorts of dinosaurs, and yet left such of their reptilian cousins as crocodiles, turtles, and lizards to continue serenely onward, is difficult to imagine. Today we are all – unfortunately – extremely conscious of radiation and its possible effects, and it has been suggested that the earth at that time chanced to pass through a belt of potent cosmic rays. But while novel ideas are welcome, this does not seem to fill the bill. The amount of harm done to an animal by radiation is in general proportionate to the amount absorbed in relation to its total bulk. The amount absorbed is proportionate to the amount of surface presented to the radiant source. But the amount of surface relative to bulk is small in large animals, great in small ones. Hence overdoses of cosmic radiation should have killed little animals, not big ones. Try again!

There is no complete solution to this puzzle, but we can at least nibble away at it. First, it is only the herbivorous dinosaurs whose extinction must be explained, for if the plant-eaters disappeared the carnivores which feasted on them would disappear too. What would cause the reduction and disappearance of the varied herbivores?

Two factors give a partial answer. The later part of the Cretaceous was a time of mountain building, when the Rocky Mountains and other chains were rising from formerly low-lying regions. The great sauropods were, we are sure, dwellers in lagoons and swamps, and if such environments were restricted in extent, we might expect at least reduction of such a group, if not complete extinction. Certainly the domain of the sauropods had become restricted before the end of the Mesozoic, for Cretaceous members of this group are relatively rare, and they are not met with at all in the famous late Cretaceous dinosaur beds of western Canada, Wyoming, and Montana. A second threat to dinosaur life lay in the changing flora of the world; types of plants characteristic of the Mesozoic were giving way to trees, shrubs and herbs of modern types. Certain of the dinosaurs may have been unable to shift in diet to new plant types, and the simple leaf-like teeth characteristic of such forms as the ceratopsians and ankylosaurs may have been ineffective in coping with different – and perhaps tougher – sorts of vegetation (the stegosaurs vanished early).

So far so good. Lack of swamps and lagoons and ineffectiveness of dentitions on new sorts of browse might have brought about the downfall of most herbivores – and the carnivores with them. But what about the duckbills? These were amphibious and needed ponds and swamps, it seems, and yet they were flourishing to the bitter end. And as for floral change and attendant difficulties, the duckbills, as we noted earlier, appear to have adapted their dentitions successfully to a new type of diet.

If we could account for the disappearance of the duckbills, we could regard the whole question of dinosaur extinction as well on the road to solution. But I admit that I am baffled. If, dear reader, you can give a reasonable explanation for duckbill demise, you would be doing science (and me, too) a great favour.

Chapter 13

Birds

EXCEPT for the lowly crocodilians, the Ruling Reptiles had become extinct by the end of the Age of Reptiles. But their contribution to the later history of vertebrate life was, even so, a major one. For the birds are their descendants.

To the lover of nature, no group of creatures is more fascinating or attractive than the birds. But Huxley's statement that a bird is, essentially, a 'glorified reptile' is a true one. We have seen that one group within the compass of the Archosauria developed flight – the pterosaurs. The birds are, from one point of view, merely a second group of Ruling Reptiles which took up flying habits in a different form – but have departed so far from the ancestral condition that we regard them as a distinct class of vertebrates.

Nearly all the structures and functions by which we define a bird are essentially flight adaptations. Feathers are, of course, one of the unique bird features. Pterosaurs and bats developed wing surfaces out of webs of skin; birds use feathers instead to give a wing-spread. Feathers are made of a material called keratin, as are horns, finger-nails – and reptile scales. Feathers, we have reason to believe, are derived from reptile scales, although their highly complex structure is a far remove from the simple ancestral scale pattern.

But furnishing wing surfaces (and steering tail) is not the whole reason for the existence of feathers. They form an excellent insulating device for the bird's body. Ancestral vertebrates had little control over their internal body temperatures, which tended to rise and fall pretty much in step with the temperature of the air (or water) surrounding them. But flying necessitates maintained activity, and it is necessary that body temperature be maintained. The clothing of the bird body gives an effective insulation.

But feathers are only one of many items in which the bird has been adapted for its life in the air. Its efficiency has been increased by a better system of blood circulation, as contrasted with reptiles, in a manner comparable to, but different from, that achieved in mammals; this brings a better supply of oxygen to its flight muscles. The bird brain is enlarged, although the increase in size seems to be related to the laying down of 'instinctive' behaviour patterns of complex types highly useful in its life in the air, rather than to increased intelligence. Smell is a sense of little importance to a bird, and it is underdeveloped; sight, on the other hand, is extremely important, and the eyes are usually well developed and large. Reproductive habits are improved. Reptiles generally abandon their eggs, once laid; birds' young are cared for as nestlings until they are ready for the complex business of flight.

The typical bird skeleton has been considerably modified from that of the archosaur ancestors. Like them, birds are bipeds, and their hind legs and feet are still very close in structure to those of Ruling Reptiles; so much so that when, a century and more ago, numerous footprints of dinosaurs were discovered in the Triassic rocks of the Connecticut Valley in New England, they were reasonably thought to have been made by gigantic birds. But in contrast with most archosaurs, the bird trunk is short and compact, and the tail reduced, the bird 'tail' being mainly a brush of feathers.

As with the pterosaurs, the potentiality of flight arose through the fact that with bipedal gait the front legs of the bird ancestors were freed, and hence available for a new function. But beyond this basic point the two groups diverged in flying adaptations. The bird wing skeleton is much closer to the original pattern, with rudiments of three toes (typically clawless), and lacking the extended 'finger' that supported the pterosaur wing membrane. Instead, the expanse of the wing is formed by a series of quills firmly bound to the back of the forearm and hand.

Quite surely the birds are descended from some member of the ancient thecodont stock of the Triassic period from which dinosaurs and pterosaurs also arose, although no one member of this group can be picked out as the actual bird ancestor. The oldest known true birds date from the end of the Jurassic period. In Bavaria, near the town of Solenhofen, there are deposits of readily splittable limestone, quarried, in part, for lithography. Here, over the course of a century, there have been found three skeletons plus one isolated feather of the ancestral bird *Archaeopteryx* (plate 15). The lithographic limestones are so fine-grained that they are capable of preserving delicate objects, and an array of feathers has been found associated with the skeletons.

This is fortunate, for in many regards the *Archaeopteryx* skeleton still preserves so many features of the ancestral archosaur pattern that, had feathers been absent, it might have been argued that we were dealing with some unusual type of very small dinosaur (*Archaeopteryx* was about the size of a crow). The skull, imperfectly known, appears to be avian in some regards, but teeth were still present, rather than a proper bird bill. There were, as in many dinosaurs, three clawed toes on a rather reptile-like front leg; but feather impressions show that quills along the back of the limb formed a modest wing. In strong contrast to modern birds, there was a long bony tail; but this carried a row of feathers along either side.

Along what adaptive path the bird ancestor travelled is none too certain. Majority opinion, however, holds that the reptilian ancestors of the birds were small tree-dwelling archosaurs, and that the flying habit evolved from the development of powers of gliding from branch to branch, or tree to ground.

Bird bones are fragile, and most birds small; hence avian fossils are relatively rarely found. Beyond the *Archaeopteryx* stage, there are practically no further traces of birds until nearly a full geologic period had elapsed and the late Cretaceous had been reached. The chalk rocks, which we have noted to have contained numerous remains of marine reptiles, have also yielded, particularly in Kansas, a restricted amount of fossil bird material. Our view of bird life at the time is, of course, limited to examples of oceanic birds, and we know nothing of what was happening in the evolution of birds on land. Nevertheless, two bird types present in these chalk rocks give us some idea of the advances and specializations that birds had accomplished since the days of *Archaeopteryx*.

Better known of the two is *Hesperornis* (plate 15). This was a rather large bird, and – remarkable at this early stage – a highly specialized one. The general structure of the skeleton suggests that the ancestor of *Hesperornis* had progressed a fair degree beyond *Archaeopteryx* toward a 'modernized' bird pattern – but then had shifted from flight to a life in the water. The front limbs are much reduced and flight out of the question; on the other hand, there are very stout hind legs for swimming. And a primitive feature is the retention of teeth.

A second sea-bird, *Ichthyornis*, was of a very different sort (plate 15). Nearly the whole postcranial skeleton is known; here the wings were very powerfully developed and in most regards this little bird –

about the size of a tern, and probably tern-like in habits – was essentially a modern bird type.

It was at one time firmly believed that *Ichthyornis* retained teeth, as was true of the contemporary *Hesperornis*. In consequence, it was assumed that all Cretaceous birds were still primitive in this regard, and that it was not until the Cenozoic era that the radiation of the modern orders began. Recently, however, it has come to be suspected that the tooth-bearing jaw bones thought to belong to *Ichthyornis* may pertain to a contemporary reptile, and (although we know almost nothing about the skull of this form) *Ichthyornis* may have been as 'modernized' a bird dentally as in other regards. The radiation of the modern bird groups may well have been under way in the Cretaceous.

As classified by most ornithologists, there are well over a score of orders of modern birds, most known from remains well back in the Cenozoic, and some of the fragmentary Cretaceous materials may well pertain to a number of these orders. Despite the variations in plumage, songs, and habits seen among modern birds, basic differences between most of the existing orders are relatively slight, and we shall not attempt here to trace out the various lineages. We will merely call attention to some of the more striking variants and problems connected with them.

Presumably the centre of bird evolution has always been on the continental areas. But, as was indicated by our account of Cretaceous finds, there early developed a trend toward life on or in the ocean, and this trend continued. The professional ornithologist customarily lists the major groups of birds in a specific order, and it is of interest that (apart from the ratites, which we will discuss later) this serial order, listing presumably primitive birds first, and ending up with the highly evolved song birds, begins with water-loving forms – loons, grebes, petrels, albatrosses, pelicans, gannets, cormorants. Many of these forms are, of course, primarily strong-winged flyers above the water, but some are excellent swimmers and divers. Most aberrant of all ocean-loving birds are the penguins of the Southern Hemisphere. Very probably they are descended from such oceanic flying forms as the albatrosses. But at least as far back as the very early Cenozoic they must have concentrated on swimming rather than flying, and all known penguins have powerful wings, but are incapable of flight. The wings, instead, are used as swimming organs. Penguins, living or fossil, are confined to the Southern Hemisphere, and they are mainly inhabitants of the South Temperate zone, although a few rear their young on the inhospitable icy shores of Antarctica, and, on the other hand, one species, which ventured up the west coast of South America in the chilly Humboldt Current, inhabits the Galapagos region, at the Equator.

Most interesting of bird variations from the main evolutionary track is the often repeated trend for birds of various sorts to abandon flying and take to living on the ground. The dodo of Mauritius, a large, rather grotesque, pigeon-like bird, now extinct, but abundant when that Indian Ocean island was discovered, is a familiar example.

Why should a bird fly, after all? For many birds today, seasonal migration from one favourable feeding area to another is important. But this 'reason' does not apply to the large proportion of the birds living in the tropics, and in earlier geologic times the present sharp temperature gradient between arctic and tropical regions appears not to have been marked, and major migrations may be a relatively new development. A second reason is that flight opens up food possibilities in the trees not available to a purely terrestrial creature. This, however, does not seem in general to be an overwhelming advantage; an animal that can hop about the limbs of a tree (as the bird ancestor probably could before he learned to fly) would be nearly as well off.

The major advantage of flight for most birds, it would seem, is that it protects them from ground-living enemies. And the corollary to this is that, given times and places where such enemies are absent, we might expect to find the evolutionary development of bird types which have abandoned flight, and become again ground-dwellers themselves.

The dodo (plate 16), safe on a remote island where, before the arrival of man and accompanying vermin, there were no enemies to force him to keep to the air, is a geologically recent case in point. But we find numerous examples of this sort scattered all through the geologic history of the Cenozoic and over almost every region of the world.

Most ancient of such examples are certain birds found in early Eocene deposits, far back in the Tertiary. At the end of the Cretaceous the dinosaurs became extinct and the surface of the earth was open for conquest by some other type of animal life. Two advanced groups were on the scene, the birds and the mammals. As we know, it was the mammals who won. But the birds made a try for it, it would seem. In early Eocene times the mammals had not advanced very far in their evolution; the typical horse of that day was, for example, no larger than a terrier, and although flesh-eating mammals were already present, many were small and most were apparently slow, ungainly, and, we suspect, stupid. The chances were fair, it would seem, for birds to become ground-dwellers and challenge the mammals for dominance. Some essayed this. Best known of these Eocene ground birds was *Diatryma* (plate 16), remains of which are known from Wyoming, standing seven feet in height, with reduced wings, sturdy legs, a massive skull, and a cruel beak. The attempt of these early birds to rival the mammals was, however, short-lived, and *Diatryma* and his kin soon disappear from the fossil record, overwhelmed by the advancing mammal hordes. It is amusing, if vain, to speculate what the world would be like today if the birds, rather than the mammals, had won. Would the earth be populated today by intelligent, 'civilized' birds? One major stumbling block which, as far as one can imagine, would have definitely ruled out any advanced material culture is the fact that the reduced wings of birds would have made it impossible for them to make or use even the simplest tools upon which, of necessity, any advance towards civilization must be based.

But although this early bird essay in ground life failed, there were later developments toward the evolution of large ground-dwelling birds whenever and wherever a good opportunity was present. A spectacular development of such forms occurred in mid-Cenozoic times in South America. That continent was isolated from the rest of the world at the time of dinosaur extinction, and remained isolated until just about the end of the Tertiary. Before the 'gate' from North America closed, a number of mammalian groups had already entered. These included a number of hoofed mammals of types now quite extinct and the ancestors of the sloths and armadillos. But no flesh-eaters of advanced types had gained entrance, and the only carnivores there were relatively inoffensive members of the marsupial group, of which the opossum is the prototype. Under these conditions, there was a fair opportunity for a second try at development of a ground-dwelling bird group. We find present in South American fossil deposits covering a good part of the Tertiary remains of large terrestrial birds of which *Phororhacos* is typical (plate 16). Here we have a type not dissimilar to *Diatryma*, although not a direct descendant.

This group of birds was destined to extinction by the close of the Tertiary, but there persist to this day members of a third group of great flightless birds – the ratites, of which the ostrich is the most familiar. For the most part, the features seen in the ostrich are characteristic of the ratites as a group: large size; powerful hind legs for rapid running; reduced, flightless wings; a fluffy type of plumage rather than the streamlined body cover of typical flying birds. In the ratites, in contrast to the older forms which attempted ground-dwelling, the head is small.

Ratites are widespread today and were even more widely distributed in the not distant past. Ostriches are at present found in the open deserts and semi-deserts of Africa, but not too long ago were present throughout much of Asia as well. In South America is the rhea, living in the open lands of Argentina. Australia is the home of both the cassowary and the emu (familiar, like the rhea, to crossword puzzle addicts). A final living form, the kiwi of New Zealand, departs, in its small size and long beak, from the typical ratite pattern. In addition to these living forms, two other sets of ratites are known which only recently became extinct. In Madagascar there are numerous remains of *Aepyornis*, the giant 'elephant bird'; its eggs, of enormous size, are found not infrequently in mascarene bogs and appear, *via* Arab traders, to have given rise to the legend of the roc. In New Zealand, in addition to the kiwi (plate 16) there flourished hordes of moas (*Dinornis*) of varied size, the largest with a spectacular height of twelve feet; there is evidence that some were still present when the Maoris arrived, only a few centuries ago.

The geographic distribution of the ratites bears out the general suggestion that the taking up of ground-dwelling by birds may occur in any area where terrestrial enemies are few or absent. Not a single mammalian flesh-eater was present in New Zealand in pre-human days. In South America, we have already noted, only marsupial carnivores were present until late in geological history, and in Australia only marsupials until man arrived and brought the dingo with him. In Madagascar there are small flesh-eaters of the civet group, but no representatives of the more dangerous cat and dog families. In Africa today we have a wide variety of carnivorous enemies for a ground-dwelling bird; but although the Tertiary history of Africa is poorly known, progressive carnivores may not have reached southern Africa until the ostriches were far enough evolved to become relatively large, fast, and safe.

Are these widespread ratites a natural group, or are they simply a miscellaneous set of birds which have independently, here and there, taken up ground-dwelling from a variety of flying ancestors as opportunity afforded. Most of the features seen in ratites – in wings, legs, fluffy plumage, and so on – are characters which might have evolved in any bird which had abandoned flying and grown to large size. There is, however, one technical feature which is shared by all the ratites. This is the possession of an old-fashioned (technically 'palaeognathous') type of palate, quite in contrast with that of more typical and advanced birds and rather reminiscent of that possessed by the birds' reptilian ancestors. In all the ratites except the ostrich the similarities are striking in this regard, and even here (despite some claims to the contrary) it is generally agreed that the basic pattern is comparable. This common structural bond suggests that we are really dealing with a natural group, descended from common ancestors.

Where are we to look for such ancestors? There is one good clue. The 'palaeognathous' palate is found in only one group of winged birds – the tinamous. These are relatively small South American birds which resemble the game birds of other regions in general habits, but are not related to them or to any other flying types. And, although winged, they are mainly ground-dwellers, who fly poorly, and only for short distances. We know almost nothing of the early fossil history of ratites, but the facts suggest that there may have been widespread in the Tertiary a group of birds, of which only the tinamous survive, which were feeble flyers and abandoned flight completely whenever conditions were suitable, thus giving rise to the later ratites scattered hither and thither over the globe.

Above we seem to have dilated on the less successful areas of bird evolution. But while, to be sure, their attempts at ground-dwelling have met with little success, we cannot gainsay them their overwhelming success in the air. The pterosaurs tried, and failed. Mammals have been highly successful in other regards, but their one attempt at flight, in the bats, has met with only modest success. The great Cenozoic era of the last 70 million years of earth history is generally termed the Age of Mammals. But there are considerable grounds for an alternative name, for it is, as well, the Age of Birds.

Chapter 14

Introducing the Mammals

THE remainder of this book will be devoted to the evolution of a final vertebrate class, the mammals, that group to which we ourselves belong, and which includes a large variety of animals, ranging from cats to bats, to rats, to whales, to cows, to horses – in fact, a great proportion of all animals familiar to us. Today, the fishes still dominate the life of the ocean, and such mammals as have invaded the waters – seals, porpoises, whales, sea-cows – make up but a small fraction of aquatic life. In the air, the birds are dominant, and the bats, interesting as they are, form but a minor element among winged vertebrates. On land, however, the story is a different one. Here the mammals have triumphed. The amphibians are a very minor element of the world's population, and even the reptiles are relatively unimportant.

How may one characterize a mammal? A few diagnostic characters are readily come by. As the name indicates, mammals nurse and care for their young, in contrast to the usual neglect of progeny in most vertebrate groups (birds excepted). Mammals have, generally, a covering of hair or fur, in contrast to the scales, scutes or feathers present in various other vertebrates. And so on. But a simple recital of technical points of this sort fails to bring out the features through which the mammals have attained the dominance they have today. The reasons for their success may, however, be summed up, essentially, in two words – *intelligent activity*.

Mammals are, by and large, active animals. To be sure, they have slothful periods and slothful representatives, and, on the other hand, a reptile may, at times, perform a rapid action – the strike of a rattlesnake, the sudden scuttling dash of an alarmed lizard. But it is only among the birds that we find a parallel to the restless energy that generally characterizes the mammals. The point of major importance here, of course, is the potentiality of activity at any time and under any circumstances – a potentiality which, as we have already discussed in the case of birds, is bound up with the maintenance of a constant

227

high body temperature, so that the energy necessary for action is always on tap.

In birds, as we have seen, insulation of the body from external cold by a feathery covering is a major factor. In mammals, other devices are developed. Internal sensory structures register temperature, and a brain centre (below the level of consciousness) receives this information and sets in motion, when necessary, regulating devices. Most mammals – but no other vertebrates – have abundant sweat glands, which may operate to give a cooling effect. The skin may be blanched or flushed by closing off or filling its numerous tiny blood vessels, and thus conserving heat or radiating out a surplus. And, for most mammals, the coat of hair – a structure peculiar to mammals – is a very efficient regulating device.

To maintain temperature and have on tap energy for potential activitity, a mammal must be able to supply its tissues constantly with oxygen to keep its internal metabolic fires burning – in plainer language, a mammal must be able to breathe constantly, without serious interruption. To be sure, in a few cases – whales, notably – there may be developed functional devices which enable the animal to submerge and cease breathing for a period. But for most mammals, as we are well aware, even a short interruption in breathing is rapidly fatal. Let us consider briefly one structure of the mammalian skull which, off-hand, one would think to be a minor feature but is actually of vital importance – the secondary palate in the roof of the mouth (figure 52).

In most lower land vertebrates the nostrils open internally into the mouth just behind the front teeth; the air drawn in here passes back through the mouth before entering the windpipe. Well and good, as long as the mouth is empty. But when the animal is eating, and the mouth filled with food, breathing is interrupted. For a 'cold-blooded' vertebrate – a frog, a turtle, a snake – no harm is done. But if the nasal apparatus of a mammal were built in this same fashion, the consequences would be serious if not fatal. If, in our own case, the air entered at the front and the mouth were filled with, say, a good portion of sausage-and-mashed, we would choke to death. This unfortunate result is, happily, avoided by the fact that in the mammals' ancestral line there evolved a shelf of bone and tissue in the roof of the mouth – a secondary palate (also developed, we have seen, in crocodilians for another purpose). Air coming in through the nostrils does not enter the front of the mouth; encountering this roofing structure, the air

228

turns backward in channels above this palatal bar to a point opposite the opening of the windpipe. We can, thus, eat and breathe at the same time, and only rarely is there such conflict between the two processes that we need to be patted on the back.

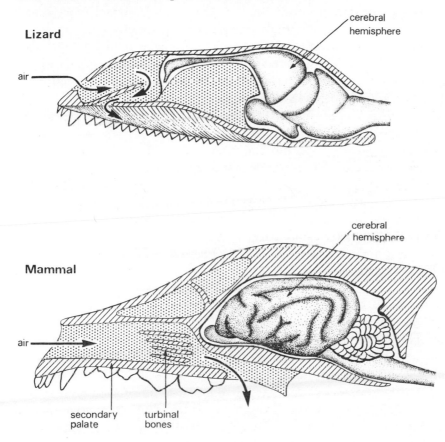

Figure 52. The greater size of the brain, and particularly of the cerebral hemispheres, shows clearly in these sections. In the mammal, the section shows also the turbinal bones whose mucous membrane covering warms and moistens the air as it enters, and the long secondary palate which separates the air passage from the food in the mouth.

More important, however, in mammalian success, than the potentiality of activity is the development of increased intellectual ability. We tend at times to look down on some of our mammalian cousins as stupid creatures. On the average, however, any mammal is an intellectual giant compared with most other vertebrates. We have earlier

229

noted that all vertebrates have a well-organized brain, into which information comes from the various senses, and from which, after this information is, so to speak, summed up, appropriate 'messages' are sent out to cause appropriate responses, usually in the way of muscular movements. But for the most part in 'lower' vertebrates these responses are essentially reflex patterns, generally rather simple in nature, inherent in the 'wiring' of the brain established when the animal is born. There appears to be in general little change in these patterns as a result of the experiences undergone by the animal – little learning ability. In most vertebrates the brain is an organ of modest proportions, occupying but a small area in the centre of the head region. There has tended to be a relative increase in its size in only two groups – birds and mammals.

The most anterior portions of the brain are the paired cerebral hemispheres (figure 52), small in most other vertebrates and mainly associated with reception of olfactory sensations. In birds there develop major masses of nervous tissue, associated in great measure with complex behaviour patterns, in the interior of the hemispheres. The even greater development of the hemispheres in mammals takes place in a different fashion. Great sheets of nervous tissue, the 'grey matter', develop over the outer surface of the expanded hemispheres as the cerebral cortex. Here, arranged in layers, are millions of nerve cells, connected with one another and with lower centres of the brain by countless nerve fibres. It is in this cortex that the highest mental faculties of a mammal are located. Into the cortex pour impulses from all the sense organs; here, on the basis of the sensory evidence, the appropriate 'decision' is made, and outgoing fibres pass appropriate 'orders' for action down through the brain stem and spinal cord to the muscles which may be concerned. As in lower vertebrates, some responses in mammals may be essentially reflex patterns. But the major feature of the mammalian grey matter is that much of the animal's behaviour is not innate in the nervous pattern, but is learned during the animal's life. The mammal's actions are in great measure determined by its experience; intelligence, in a broad sense of that term, is an attribute of every mammal.

Changes in reproductive processes are characteristic of mammalian evolution. As the name denotes, mammals nurse their young and care for them. A period of infancy is thus brought into the life story. The young are protected. But, more important, they can be trained; the potentialities of the highly developed brain can be put to use, and the young learn by experience and parental precept. Man prides himself on his educational institutions; the first educational institution came into being with the development of the nursing habit and the consequent association of young ancestral mammals and their parents. A further change in reproductive patterns in all but the most primitive of mammals took place when egg-laying was abandoned in favour of the live birth of the young – the viviparous habit, to use scientific terminology. In some reptiles (and some fishes as well) the eggs may be retained within the mother's body until hatching occurs. But in most of these cases in lower vertebrates there is no further contribution to the nourishing of the developing embryo than the yolk already present within the egg, and the young reptile born alive is no more advanced than if the egg were laid in normal fashion. Quite different is the mammalian situation. No shell is deposited around the egg; instead, the embryo, in a very early stage of development, embeds itself in the richly vascular wall of the maternal womb, and there develops the structure known as the placenta, whereby nutritive materials may be passed from the blood stream of the mother to that of the growing embryo. As a result, the young may continue growth within the mother's body to a size and to a stage of development far beyond that which would have been possible in the case of an egg laid out in the open. Viviparous development has an obvious advantage, in that the young have better protection than would have otherwise been the case. But it would seem that a major factor favouring this reproductive advance is to allow the greatest possible amount of time for the growth of the brain before birth, and the consequent beginning of utilization of this marvellous structure in the training and 'education' of the youngster. If one looks at figures of the embryo or foetus of man or any other mammal, a striking feature is the large size of the brain vault. Many organs of the body can, so to speak, take their time in development, and need not be perfected until well along in post-natal life. The brain, on the other hand, grows rapidly during embryonic life, and at birth is fully formed and ready to be put to use.

A fully evolved mammal is, I have tried to demonstrate, an organism with high potentialities for success. The evolutionary process leading to such forms was, however, a lengthy one.

Mammals are, of course, descended from reptiles. Because of their high degree of organization and the fact that their attainment of dominance came quite late in earth history, one would tend to think that the mammalian line sprang late from some advanced reptilian type.

231

Curiously, this is the reverse of the true situation. Apparently a group of reptiles which were to become ancestral to mammals diverged from the basic reptile stock at the very beginning of the history of that class, and had a long and flourishing history before such characteristic reptile groups as dinosaurs or lizards or turtles ever appeared on the evolutionary scene.

These mammal ancestors form a reptilian subclass, the Synapsida, within which we distinguish two successive orders, the Pelycosauria and the Therapsida.

I have worked, off and on, on pelycosaurs for much of my life, and am quite fond of these reptiles scientifically (although I imagine that if I ever could have encountered a live pelycosaur, my opinion would have changed radically for the worse). The oldest remains of pelycosaurs are found in the coal swamp deposits of the Upper Carboniferous. But although a few pelycosaurs were still persistently water-dwelling fish-eaters, most of them were essentially terrestrial forms, and in consequence the group is sparsely represented in Carboniferous rocks. In the early Permian, however, great series of reddish rocks were laid down in Europe and America under continental conditions. Particularly in the American South-west – and most especially in northern Texas – these 'redbeds' have yielded a considerable fauna of amphibians and early reptiles, in which the pelycosaurs are the dominant forms.

Some pelycosaurs, as was just said, were more or less persistently water-dwellers, with fish as the staple diet; a fraction turned to vegetable food. The main line, however, consisted of flesh-eaters – the dominant carnivores of early Permian days. In many ways, typical members of this pelycosaur group, such as *Sphenacodon* or *Dimetrodon* (figure 53), were still very primitive reptiles. The limbs were, for example, still in the primitive sprawled pose, with knee and elbow stretched far out on either side of the body; the trackway was broad, the speed slow. But, slow as these predators undoubtedly were, their limbs (as needs must be) were rather more slenderly and more efficiently built than those of their amphibian and more archaic reptile contemporaries. Only in two diagnostic features do these pelycosaurs foreshadow the mammals. In primitive vertebrates the sides of the skull behind the orbits were solidly covered by a bony shield, beneath which lay the jaw muscles. In reptiles, openings, bounded by bony arches, develop in varied patterns in the cheek region, giving freer play to the underlying muscles. In mammals there is a single larger

232

cheek opening on the side of the skull, bounded below by a narrow arch – the zygomatic arch. The pelycosaurs show the beginning of this cheek pattern, although the cheek opening is small and the arch below it broad.

Secondly, the dentition. In many lower vertebrates the teeth have much the same pattern in both front and back parts of the tooth row. In typical mammals (man is rather specialized), the dentition is highly differentiated into anterior nipping teeth, the incisors, at the front of the mouth, then a prominent stabbing canine, and beyond, a series of cheek teeth – premolars to molars. The pelycosaurs show the beginning of differentiation, for such a form as *Dimetrodon* has, behind anterior teeth of incisor type, a short series – typically only a pair on either side – of enlarged canine-like teeth (figure 53). This, however, is as far as the process of tooth differentiation has gone, for the cheek teeth are simple cones, with no grinding power.

A curious development in some pelycosaurs is the presence of a 'sail' along the back (figure 53). Independently in several different groups, we find that the spines always present at the top of each segment of the backbone have become long, slender structures, extending high above the back. There is considerable evidence indicating that in life a membrane of skin connected successive spines, to form a sail-like structure extending down the back from shoulder to hip region.

What was this seemingly absurd structure for? Cope, the American palaeontologist who first described the animals bearing it, jocularly suggested that it was to enable these pelycosaurs to go sailing on Permian lakes. Another idea was that a carnivore like *Dimetrodon* would lie in wait for his prey among the rushes, and that the spines would help in concealment by simulating rushes. However, the counter to this suggestion is obvious – the animal would be still better hidden in the rushes if it had no projecting spines. Still another suggestion was that the spines were protective; if the animal were attacked, the spines could be spread out sideways in hedgehog or porcupine fashion. But since the spines are an integral part of the joints of the backbone, spreading them out would involve dislocating every joint in the back – hardly a good idea.

Not many years ago, there finally dawned on me the seemingly correct solution. As discussed above, an important advance made by mammals was the ability to control internal temperature. May not the sail have been an early experiment in this direction? There is

233

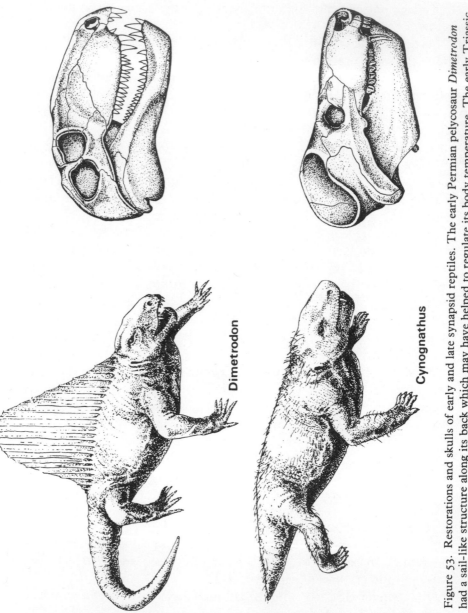

Dimetrodon

Cynognathus

Figure 53. Restorations and skulls of early and late synapsid reptiles. The early Permian pelycosaur *Dimetrodon* had a sail-like structure along its back which may have helped to regulate its body temperature. The early Triassic therapsid *Cynognathus* was far more mammal-like in appearance, and may have had a covering of hair.

evidence that it was richly supplied with blood vessels. If these could be regulated, to 'flush' or 'pale' the sail, here would be a vast skin area from which excess heat could be radiated off, or heat absorbed in sunlight. In more advanced therapsids, more properly mammalian methods may have developed; the sail may have been a first crude experiment in temperature control. It was unsuccessful in the long run; but 'sailed' pelycosaurs flourished for certainly some millions of years.

We cannot, of course, prove that the sail functioned in this fashion. But study of sail size in a variety of pelycosaur individuals furnishes suggestive evidence. In a big animal, the *volume* of the creature to be warmed or cooled increases by the cube of its linear measurements; but the *surface* of the sail, the supposed warming or cooling organ, increases only by the square of linear measurements. To be efficient for this function, the sail should become disproportionately tall in a big pelycosaur. And this it does! In a series of five specimens, small to large, it was found that the sail grew very high in the larger specimens, with the sail area efficiently keeping up with the animal's bulk.

The pelycosaurs had their day in the early Permian. Later in that period and on into the early and middle Triassic they were succeeded as dominant land vertebrates by the therapsids, their advanced and more mammal-like descendants.

The therapsids are known from thousands of fossil specimens representing hundreds of varied types, recovered from rocks ranging in age mainly from Middle Permian to Middle Triassic times – that is, roughly, over a period of about 40 million years. They are most common in South Africa, where a great part of Cape Colony and Orange Free State are covered by the Karroo system of rocks, the successive layers of which reach a thickness of 30,000 feet or so. But while this is the region most famous for fossils of mammal-like reptiles, these forms obviously existed the world over and, particularly in recent decades, numerous specimens of this group have been found and described from other areas – notably Russia west of the Urals, southern Brazil, and Argentina.

The central types among the therapsids were carnivores, continuing the flesh-eating tradition of the main pelycosaur stock, and such a well-known form as *Cynognathus* (figure 53) of the early Triassic of South Africa is typical of a moderately progressive therapsid. The scientific name, translatable as 'dog-jaw', refers to the rather dog-like appearance of the dentition; but actually the whole skull in

235

Cynognathus has come to have an appearance rather like that of a canid (figure 53). The small temporal opening seen in the pelycosaur cheek has enlarged, so as to leave below it a relatively narrow arch of bone comparable to that of mammals. Mammals have but a single bone in the lower jaw, compared to seven present in primitive reptiles; in *Cynognathus* and his kin all seven bones are present, but the one element destined to survive – the dentary – is by far the largest. We have seen that there was in many pelycosaurs a beginning of the differentiation of the dentition in a mammalian direction. This has proceeded farther in many therapsids; a single, sharply differentiated canine is seen in both upper and lower jaws in many therapsids, and in the cheek teeth some advanced forms tend to develop chewing or grinding surfaces rather in the fashion of mammalian molar teeth.

A very notable advance is found in the body skeleton of therapsids. Pelycosaurs, even the most ambitiously agile of them, we have seen, still progressed in an archaic fashion, with limbs sprawled widely sideways and much of the animal's energy necessarily devoted to keeping the body up off the ground instead of aiding in forward progress. All is changed in therapsids. Archosaurs, we noted, solved the locomotor problem by swinging the hind legs in toward the body and pretty much abandoning the front legs as hopeless. Not so in therapsids; here not only are knees turned in forward close to the body, but elbows are similarly pressed in backward, giving therapsids an efficient four-footed running pose which is essentially that found in many mammals today. With this radical shift in limb position and function went many changes in limb structure.

We will cite one such change as a sample. In primitive reptiles the number of free joints in the toes of hand or foot numbered successively 2, 3, 4, 5, 3, counting outward from 'thumb' or 'big toe'. The same count is present today in many lizards; in the sprawling pose there appears to be some advantage in greater toe length toward the outer side of the foot. Not so, however, in the new posture, where the feet are directed straight forward. There is a strong trend toward equalizing toe lengths, and in many therapsids there has been a reduction of joints to a count of 2, 3, 3, 3, 3, exactly that found to this day in many mammals – including ourselves.

The skeleton of the therapsids, thus, shows numerous features in which these very ancient reptiles had progressed far toward mammalian conditions. We are hence tempted to speculate as to whether they may not have also progressed in other features, of soft anatomy

236

and reproductive habits, concerning which we have, of course, little direct evidence. Did therapsids – or at least the more progressive ones – nurse and care for their young? Very likely, but we cannot be sure. Did they still lay eggs, or did they bear their young alive? Since some archaic mammals lay eggs even today, the chances are that most therapsids, at least, were egg-layers. Had the therapsids acquired the mammalian ability to maintain a high, constant body temperature? On this last point there is indirect but very suggestive evidence. I pointed out on an earlier page that for temperature maintenance the ability to breathe constantly is a necessity, and that in mammals the development of a secondary palate in the roof of the mouth aids greatly in keeping the flow of air to the lungs going during eating. No such structure was present in the pelycosaurs, nor even in the more primitive therapsids. But in the Triassic members of this latter group we see, in the fossil record, the gradual development of a secondary palate, independently in several lines within the order. Quite surely temperature regulation was evolving at this time, and one may well believe that, in addition to the evolution of the palate, other adaptations to the same end, such as the 'invention' of a hairy body covering, may have been progressing.

As mentioned above, the synapsids played a dominant role in the earlier phases of reptilian evolution from the beginnings of the history of the class up to about the middle of the Triassic period. If one collects from any characteristic continental fossil beds of Permian or early Triassic age, it will invariably prove that half or three-quarters – or even a larger fraction – of the entire collection will be remains of mammal-like forms. Most interesting from an evolutionary point of view are, of course, the flesh-eating forms from which the mammals were destined to arise. But available to the early reptiles was a great variety of vegetable life, and there evolved from the therapsid stock numerous forms which adapted themselves to a herbivorous mode of life. Commonest of the plant-eating side-branches of the therapsids were the dicynodonts, the 'two-tuskers' (figure 54). The general pattern of bodily build of these forms was similar to that of their predacious cousins, but since speedy locomotion was not as vital a necessity to them as to a carnivore, they are somewhat more clumsily built. Their heads were considerably modified. Teeth tended to be nearly completely lost, leaving in general only a pair of upper canine tusks. The jaw margins otherwise had an appearance somewhat like the beak of the turtles and, as in that group, were surely furnished

237

with a horny bill. Countless specimens of dicynodonts have been recovered, particularly in the late Permian rocks of the South African Karroo.

Figure 54. Such dicynodonts as six-foot-long *Deinodontosaurus* (above) from the Triassic of Brazil were the commonest land herbivores of the late Permian and early Triassic, ranging from rat-sized to rhino-sized.

But at long last the reign of therapsids came to an end. In the early Triassic appeared the first representatives of the archosaurs, the ruling reptiles discussed in an earlier chapter. The first of the archosaurs were modest in size and few in numbers. But as the Triassic progressed, archosaurs increased in numbers, in variety, and in size, and before the end of that period there had evolved the first of the dinosaur faunas, including speedy bipeds of large size, with highly predacious habits. The therapsids, it seems, were unable to stand up against this competition. By the late Triassic there were few forms remaining of this once dominant group; a single small survivor has been found in deposits of the succeeding Jurassic period.

The therapsids, however, were destined to live on in the form of their mammalian descendants. In rocks which in age lie close to the boundary between the Triassic and Jurassic periods have been found fragmentary specimens of a few small animals which seem to lie, as far as the evidence of the skeleton goes, close to the boundary between reptiles and mammals in structure. And in a few rare deposits of the Jurassic and Cretaceous periods, during the triumphant reign of the dinosaurs, there are present remains which are those of early mammals.

238

These mammals of the Mesozoic are very poorly known. From the entire stretch of time of these two periods – some 80 million years or so – we have not recovered even one complete mammal skeleton, and hardly a complete skull. For the most part, our deductions as to the nature of these ancestral forms must be based on scraps of material – individual teeth, occasional jaws, skull fragments, isolated limb bones. These remains have, of course, been studied attentively and are preserved with care in modern museums. But I expect that if (heaven forbid!) one were to scoop up these entire collections in one's hands the whole known assemblage would hardly fill a silk top hat.

Our Mesozoic mammal ancestors were obviously a very inconspicuous element in the faunas of dinosaurian times. Their rarity as fossil finds suggests rarity in numbers. And their size was small. Most had about the proportions of a mouse or rat, and the largest known Jurassic mammal is thought to have been no bigger than a half-grown kitten. Poor as their remains are, we can make some reasonable deductions as to their habits and mode of life. In most cases the teeth are sharp, and the canines well developed, as in their carnivorous therapsid ancestors. Quite surely they were eaters of animal food; but because of their small size they could seldom, one would expect, tackle anything above the level of insects as prey, although this diet may have been supplemented by worms, grubs, eggs, or baby lizards. Quite surely they were inconspicuous and shy in their habits, for over them lay the constant threat of death from their dinosaurian contemporaries. Very likely they kept to wooded or brushy areas; possibly (as in the case of many small mammals today) they may have been in great measure nocturnal.

A side-line leading to the living egg-laying mammals of Australia must have branched off from a very early stage in the development of archaic mammals. These forms, however, are so highly specialized that it is difficult to determine what their relationship to the older mammal stocks may be. The difficulty is heightened because most of the oldest fossil mammals are represented mainly by their dentitions, whereas in the Australian egg-layers the teeth have degenerated and been replaced by a horny bill.

These Australian egg-layers, known as the monotremes, include but two types – the platypus or duckbill (*Ornithorhynchus*) and the spiny anteater. Both have departed far from primitive conditions in structure and mode of life. The platypus, with a duck-like horny beak, is a stream-dweller, nesting in burrows in the bank (plate 17).

239

The anteater, with a long slender bill, has powerful digging feet to give it access to termite nests, and is protected by a stout spiny covering comparable to that of a hedgehog (plate 18).

The survival to the present day of these animals is an excellent example of isolation as a factor in the preservation of primitive forms of life. An animal may escape predation or competition with more progressive forms by geographic isolation, or may isolate itself by taking up an unusual, non-competitive mode of life. Both factors have operated in the case of the duckbill and spiny anteater. Their mode of life is one out of the ordinary, and they meet with little competition; and in Australia they dwell in a region in which most of their potential mammalian competitors are of a relatively unprogressive sort.

But to return from this side-branch of archaic forms to the main line of early mammalian history. As said above, this history, for some 80 million years, was one which seemingly played a very subordinate part in the life of the Jurassic and Cretaceous periods of reptile dominance. But for the mammals this long period was actually of crucial importance in preparing and perfecting them for the brilliant career which they were to have, once the great reptiles vanished. Certain advances toward the modern mammalian pattern had already been made by the therapsids. But in other regards the earliest mammals had not progressed far beyond a reptilian stage. Most notable is the situation with regard to the development of the brain, that outstanding feature leading to mammalian success. The skeletal remains of therapsids make it clear that even the most advanced members of that group were still in a reptilian condition as regards that organ. It is during the Mesozoic times of early mammalian subordination that the crucial advance in brain development took place. Living under the constant dinosaurian threat to their existence, the early mammals needed sharpened wits to survive. The Mesozoic was a time of trial for them, but it was a time of mental progress.

Progress, too, was made in reproductive habits, for it was during this period that the advance from egg-laying to the live birth of the young and the development of the placenta for foetal development took place. For the earliest fossil mammals, the evidence is too poor for us to gain any idea as to their reproductive habits. But in the late Cretaceous, shortly (geologically speaking) before the extinction of the dinosaurs, the fossil deposits show us that there already existed two more advanced types of mammals which bore their young alive.

Some 70 million or so years ago, the Mesozoic, the great Age of

Reptiles, came to an end. The dinosaurian hosts disappeared, and there began the Cenozoic era, the Age of Mammals. The surface of the earth, it would seem, lay open for conquest. By this time the mammals had completed their major evolutionary development, and were prepared to conquer.

Two advanced mammal groups were already present, the marsupials, the Metatheria, and the true placentals, the Eutheria. Most of the further story concerns the latter group; the history of the marsupials, or pouched mammals, may be considered at this point.

In the marsupials, of which the opossums and kangaroos are familiar representatives, a placenta is present, and the young are born alive. But the placenta in this group is generally an inefficient structure, and the offspring are born at a very tiny and immature stage. When born, the young of a large kangaroo are less than an inch in length; those of an opossum hardly as large as a bee. Obviously the young are not prepared at this stage to make a go of it on their own. The problem has been in considerable measure solved by the development in this group of mammals of a pouch – the marsupium – on the belly of the mother. Here the milk glands are situated and here, each clamped to a nipple, the youngsters stay and receive nourishment until they have attained more respectable proportions.

Most primitive of living marsupials are the opossums of the Americas (plate 19), and small opossum-like forms were already developed by the time of the extinction of the dinosaurs. For a time the marsupials appear to have had a modest degree of success, and in the early Cenozoic, opossums flourished in the Old World as well as in the New. But in general the marsupials were unable to compete successfully with the more advanced Eutheria – mammals more highly developed as regards placental developments – and flourished only when protected by regional isolation. South America and Australia are the only regions where they have had any degree of success. The former continent appears to have been cut off from connection with the north at the dawn of the Cenozoic. At that time a certain number of true placentals were present in South America, as well as opossum-like marsupials, but no true placental carnivores. In their absence there developed from the opossum stock a series of pouched mammals paralleling the placental flesh-eaters of other continents, with weasel-like, wolf-like, and cat-like forms – even a pouched parallel to the true sabre-tooth tigers! But at about the end of the Tertiary, connections with the north were re-established, and these interesting forms failed in competition with placental carnivores, leaving the opossums and one or two mouse-like forms as the only marsupial survivors.

In Australia the marsupials had better luck. That continent, too, was cut off from the rest of the world at about the end of the Cretaceous, and although some members of the rat family managed to migrate to Australia during the course of the Cenozoic, no other terrestrial placentals reached Australia until the arrival of man and animals introduced by him. Marsupials were already present, however, in Australia, and developed into a great variety of forms which are still present there, although becoming sadly depleted in numbers today. As in South America, carnivorous types evolved, but in addition there arose a varied series of other marsupials filling places in nature occupied by placental groups in the northern continents. Herbivores include, for example, such types as the rather squirrel-like phalangers, the wombat (plate 20), rather marmot-like, and the quaint arboreal koala, with much the appearance of a Teddy-bear. There is even a marsupial 'mole', a blind underground digger startlingly similar to some true placental moles. In one major respect only did the Australian marsupials fail to parallel the placentals. In other continents this more advanced group developed great series of ungulates – herbivores, frequently grazers in nature, with hoofed appendages that enable them to run speedily over the plains. Nothing of this sort developed among the marsupials. But although at first sight nothing would seem to be more absurd than to compare a kangaroo with an antelope or a horse, the kangaroo is essentially analogous to the placental ungulates, as a successful grazer and browser – and an animal which, like the ungulates, can travel speedily over the plains, albeit in a very different fashion.

But enough of the pouched mammals and their modest evolutionary achievements. The main success story of the Age of Mammals is the amazing evolutionary spread, following dinosaur extinction, of the Eutheria. These, the dominant animals of the post-dinosaur days, are generally termed the placental mammals. We shall use this term, although it is technically improper, since the marsupials, as well, have a placental connection between mother and embryo. But, as we have noted, the placenta of the marsupials is relatively inefficient, and the young are born at a very premature stage. In the placental mammals, in contrast, the young are plentifully supplied with nourishment through this medium, and attain a much higher degree of development before birth. This improved style of reproduction plus other advances (a rather better brain organization, for one thing) gave the placental mammals a considerable advantage over the pouched forms in the race for supremacy, and whenever the two have been in competition, the placentals have almost invariably triumphed over their rather more primitive cousins.

The first placentals, like the first marsupials, had evolved before the end of the Cretaceous period. Despite the advances they had achieved in brains and reproductive processes over their earlier mammalian forebears, they still lived much the same life as had the ancestral Mesozoic mammals. Like them, they were still quite small in size; like them (till the dinosaurs disappeared from the scene), they quite surely led lives of studied inconspicuousness; like them, they were would-be carnivores, but were still prevented by modest size from attacking much beyond insects as prey.

These oldest placentals were destined to give rise to a great series of varied descendants. A few placental types, however, still adhere fairly closely to the ancestral placental pattern (although with modifications of one sort or another) and are generally considered, together with their Cretaceous forebears, as constituting the order Insectivora. Least modified of these surviving forms are the shrews (plate 21), small creatures, mouselike in appearance, but very different in build and habits. They are widespread today, particularly in northern temperate regions, but are seldom seen, for they are – like their Mesozoic forebears – extremely shy and unobtrusive in habits. Like their ancestors, they are primarily insect-eaters, but, again like them, are would-be carnivores and will attack any form of animal life not too large to exceed their powers. Apart from the shrews, a few other surviving types are included in the insectivore order, such as the moles, which have gone underground in search of animal food in the shape of grubs and worms, and the hedgehogs, which have survived because of their prickly covering.

The remaining chapters of this book will view the amazing radiation of the placental mammals which began at the dawn of the Cenozoic and has continued to the present day. From the early, basic insectivore stock sprang a bewildering variety of mammals, which range in size from tiny shrews weighing only ounces to giant whales weighing scores of tons; from pure flesh-eaters to feeders on every type of vegetable material; from ground- and tree-dwellers to flying forms, to subterranean burrowers and to purely oceanic inhabitants. Our mammalian relatives are indeed a versatile assemblage.

Chapter 15

Carnivores

WE shall begin our description of the radiation of placental mammals with an account of the evolution of the Carnivora, since this is the group that, if we look at evolutionary history objectively, has written the final chapter to date of the main line of the upward progress of vertebrates. Nature preaches no moral; but if we attempt to abstract a moral from the broad story of animal evolution, this moral is a most unpleasant one to a person with any sense of ethics. For it is almost invariably carnivores that have been, in the long run, successful.

If we review the long history of vertebrate evolution from its beginnings, some hundreds of millions of years ago, upward to the evolution of placental mammals, the story is a bloodthirsty one. The most ancient jawless vertebrates, it is true, were lowly food-strainers, incapable of taking in any materials except detritus and tiny organisms. But when jaws were invented, the picture changed. The crossopterygians from which all land vertebrates evolved were, except for contemporary sharks, the most highly predacious forms of their day, feasting, we believe, on smaller ray-finned fishes. The early main line of amphibian evolution was, again, one of flesh-eaters (even today, except for frog tadpoles, amphibians keep to animal food). The ancestral reptiles, their dentitions indicate, were likewise carnivores. The pelycosaurs certainly included, as their main progressive line, the most bloodthirsty flesh-eaters of early Permian times, and among their therapsid descendants it is the carnivores that lead on upward to give rise to the ancestral mammals which, we are quite sure, were as predacious as their modest size would allow. Time after time, during the course of this history, there developed herbivorous side-branches of peaceful animal citizens of the world, which for a time might flourish greatly in numbers and variety. But never, in the whole story, has any herbivorous group been ancestral to any further major group on a higher level of evolutionary advancement. Always the end result has been extinction, and the replacement, eventually, of one

244

group of peaceful herbivores by another side-branch from a progressive carnivore stock.

This is a story highly unpalatable to Moral Man. In evolution, it has been the Huns and the Hitlers that have succeeded, not the Peaceful Citizens. We ourselves have wandered far off the main line of predators to become forms with an omnivorous diet, tending far toward vegetarianism. What is our future to be? Are the next dominant forms of life to be descendants of the weasel or wolf or cat? Or may we optimistically hope that our development of brains will change the general pattern of evolution?

Perhaps. But we, as individuals, will not be here to see.

Let us leave such unpleasant speculation, turn back to the past, and review the course of evolution (so far) of the mammalian flesh-eaters, consisting of the order Carnivora. They took origin, at the dawn of the Cenozoic, from the general placental stock of insectivores. The insectivores were carnivores by inclination, and with prominent piercing canine tusks and sharp pointed cheek teeth, already had a basic dental battery capable of active predation – once the dinosaurs were out of the way, and they were able to emerge into the open and grow to respectable size. Even in the earliest phases of the Cenozoic there tended to evolve, from the primitive placental stock, forms which, as will be presently discussed, shifted toward a plant-eating diet and became potential objects for predation. And, equally rapidly, other descendants of the early placental stock developed into predators, which fed upon them. The Palaeocene and Eocene epochs, the first two 'chapters' in the Cenozoic history, saw the rise of a variety of archaic flesh-eaters, often grouped (there were several families of them) as the creodonts.

To develop, a carnivore required little change in structure from the ancestral placental type. The ancestral mammalian dentition, with large stabbing canine tusks and sharp-cusped cheek teeth, was already fairly well fitted for attack. The only major change generally evolved was the development, in the cheek region on either side, of a pair of teeth termed 'carnassials', each with a long sharp fore-and-aft ridge, upper tooth shearing down over lower, which functioned in an important way in cutting and slicing hard pieces of food. (Notice, for example, how the house cat works a bone around to the side of the mouth to crack it.) Agility must be retained, and the skeleton of a typical carnivore differs little from that of generalized ancestral forms – this in contrast to many other animals, in which specializations for

245

climbing, digging, and so on may develop. Further, in order to seize the prey, claws must be retained and well developed, and there can be no development of the hoofed condition which we find in so many of the mammals discussed later.

Creodonts, the early carnivores, flourished for a time. In these older forms the limbs were short, and the speed, one may suspect, not very great; further, the fossil skulls show that the brain was relatively small and intelligence presumably nothing to boast of. But this, for the time being, made little difference, for the archaic ungulates upon which they fed were generally slow of gait, it would appear, and equally feeble in brain development. During the Eocene, however, there began to appear ungulates of more advanced nature, ancestral to, amongst others, the horse and cud-chewing forms (antelopes, deer, and so on) of later periods. Such animals were, in general, obviously speedier and apparently quicker in intellect than the older types. The archaic creodonts appear to have been unable to cope with these new types, became much reduced by Oligocene times, and eventually disappeared.

From among the older carnivores, only one family survived; this was the group ancestral to the 'modernized' carnivores, which are termed the fissipedes. These appear at about the beginning of the Oligocene epoch, and rapidly differentiate into a series of families of land carnivores which have progressed and survived to modern times.

To gain a general view of this evolutionary progress, we may note that these families may be arrayed in two series, of which the cat and dog are representative (although far from primitive) forms. Of the cat group, members of the civet family are the most primitive and closest to the basal fissipede stock. These are essentially tropical animals of the Old World (none reached the New), and include a long series of genera and species of which the civets, mongoose, and genets are the only forms with which an average reader may be familiar. Possibly the ancestral carnivores (and not impossibly the ancestral placentals) may have been arboreal in habits, and many civet types are arboreal to this day; as in ancestral forms, the limbs are usually short, and size generally small. One offshoot of the civet family, which did not appear until late Tertiary time, is that of the hyaenas, likewise confined to the Old World tropics, which have become relatively large and clumsy animals, with unpleasant habits as carrion feeders (with, today, a bit of grave-robbing on the side).

Most prominent derivatives of the civet stock, however, were the cats and their relatives of the family Felidae. Members of this group appeared at the beginning of the Oligocene, and numerous felids are present in the fossil record from that time on. Their general characteristics, well exemplified in the domestic cat, are familiar. In their body build, they are agile, well adapted for a stealthy approach and sudden pounce on the prey, but, in contrast to the dog-wolf group, most are not well adapted to a lengthy running-down of the prey. In nature the felids are essentially pure carnivores, and, as their short faces would indicate, have greatly reduced the cheek-tooth battery, so that while having an excellent pair of carnassials, they have little chewing ability. Notable in their history is the development of a long series of 'sabre-toothed' felines, now entirely extinct, in which the sharp-edged and sharp-pointed upper canines were greatly enlarged, capable of inflicting deep slashing wounds. It is probable that thick-skinned 'pachyderms', such as mammoths and mastodons, were a favourite prey. Countless skulls and bones of *Smilodon*, a Pleistocene American form, have been recovered from the La Brea tar pits in California, and skeletons are to be found in many museums. At La Brea there were, during the late Pleistocene, pools at which the animals of the region came to drink. Beneath the water, however, were deposits of soft tar, in which unwary animals were frequently entrapped. The presence of this potential prey attracted flesh-eaters, notably sabre-tooths, which were in turn trapped – and preserved for modern collectors.

The second major group of 'modernized' carnivores is that which we have characterized as the dog group. The canids, however, are not the primitive members of this assemblage; rather, it is the weasel family which appears to be primitive here. Like the civets among the feline series, the mustelids tend to be relatively small in size, short of leg, and primarily forest-dwellers in habits; they are, however, mainly temperate zone forms rather than tropical in distribution, and in contrast to the civet family have been present in North America as well as Eurasia since their first appearance in Oligocene days. Some are strictly carnivorous, as are the weasels and mink, for example; the wolverine of northern forests is a larger form with similar habits. Other mustelids, such as the badgers and odoriferous skunks, tend to more of a mixed diet. In the evolution of the family there have appeared two aquatic types – the graceful and attractive otters, mainly fresh-water fish-eaters, and the sea-otter, a nearly extinct mollusc-feeder of the northern Pacific.

From the early mustelid stock there rapidly developed the family Canidae, with the wolves, foxes, and various dogs and dog-like types as modern representatives. A few early canids closely resembled the mustelids, but there rapidly developed the typical dog characteristics which contrast strongly with those of their 'opposite numbers', the felids. The canids are less agile than the cats, but much better adapted for long-distance pursuit of prey. Although primarily carnivorous, they tend toward a mixed diet and (with a longer muzzle for its accommodation) have tended to keep more of a battery of cheek teeth for chewing use than have the cats. In great measure the members of the dog family are plains-dwellers, and since a great proportion of sediments of the various Tertiary epochs are deposits formed in plains areas rather than woodland regions, the fossil canid record is a relatively full one; some scores of genera and species of fossil dogs are known, including a variety of giant Tertiary types.

Related to the canids is the raccoon family (Procyonidae). The raccoons and their relatives are persistently arboreal forms; since, as implied above, sediments containing fossils are relatively rare in woodland areas, our record of the group is relatively poor, but several fossil genera are known from the Tertiary of North America, to which region the few typical living members of the group are confined. The raccoons have departed farther than the dogs from a purely carnivorous diet, and there is a rather good chewing surface present in the molar series of the procyonids. Usually associated with the raccoons are two eastern Asiatic animals, of which the fossil history is obscure. The true panda is an animal of modest size, which is nearly completely herbivorous in diet. Currently, however, this name has been popularly transferred to a much larger animal, properly called either the giant panda or parti-coloured bear – the latter name due to the fact that it is a primarily white animal but with patches and stripes of black. This has still better chewing ability and, despite its carnivorous pedigree, has abandoned flesh for a diet of bamboo shoots.

The giant panda, as its alternative name implies, has somewhat the appearance and habits of the bears, and in its basic structure as well shows suggestions of true relationship to the bear group, the family Ursidae. Quite clearly the bears are a late Tertiary offshoot of the canids, and a number of large canids, 'bear dogs', of the late Miocene and Pliocene, are transitional between the two families in structure. Although the bears are not purely herbivorous in nature (and the polar bear, in practical default of other nutriment, is a fish-eater), the bears have, even more than the raccoons, developed an expanded grinding surface in their molars capable of coping with plant materials. In the Pleistocene, bears were widespread in distribution; a common inhabitant of Ice Age caves in Europe was a gigantic relative of the Eurasian brown bear of today, and the Kodiak brown bear of Alaska is a living form of giant size.

A final group of carnivores is the suborder Pinnipedia, the seals and walruses. These appear in middle Tertiary times; while the early stages of their development are not too well represented in the fossil record, both certain technical features and (to the popular mind) the usually amiable disposition of these attractive creatures suggest a derivation from dog-like carnivores in the early Tertiary. The seals, fish-eating inhabitants of the cooler waters of both hemispheres, are well adapted to a marine existence; their limbs have been transformed into webbed flippers and, in default of a tail well developed enough to be re-adapted to locomotive functions, they have turned their hind legs backward to form effective swimming aids. The walruses are ponderous inhabitants of cold northern seas, mollusc-eaters, with large upper canine tusks which serve to root out the molluscs from their beds and stout peg cheek teeth for shell-crushing.

This, then, is the story of the evolution of the Carnivora, starting from small primitive would-be flesh-eaters at the dawn of the Tertiary, and expanding into a highly varied series of forms with a wide range of habits and a wide variety of tastes in diet.

Chapter 16

Hoofed Mammals

FROM the very beginning of the Cenozoic we find, among the host of mammal types radiating out from the ancestral insectivore stock, numerous forms which tended to grow to relatively large size and to take up vegetarian feeding habits. Early forms, it would seem, browsed on leaves and bushes; many later types adopted as food the grasses of the prairies which developed by middle Cenozoic days. The cheek teeth, originally rather small, sharp-cusped structures, tended to develop broad crowns and form a powerful battery of 'grinders' capable of dealing with tough vegetable material. Some early types were clumsily built, but many of these browsers and grazers developed fast-running and this aided these peaceful animals in escape from enemies and in rapidly traversing their grassland homes. Their legs were, in many cases, long and slender, and instead of walking more or less flat on palm and sole, many became capable of running on the tips of their fingers, supported by stout horny hoofs into which the ancestral claws had been modified. Hoof is translated *ungula* in Latin, and hence this great array of forms is generally termed the ungulates – the hoofed mammals.

A number of ungulates of rather archaic build were already evolved in the Palaeocene, at the very beginning of the Cenozoic, and archaic types remained common in the Eocene days which followed. A well-known and representative form is *Phenacodus* of the Lower Eocene of North America and Europe (plate 22). This herbivore had already gained a respectable size, with much the dimensions of a modern tapir. In its proportions, *Phenacodus* resembled to a degree the archaic creodont carnivores of those days, for body and tail were long, and the limbs still quite short and primitive in structure. However, there were already present some of the earmarks of a proper ungulate. In many later ungulates there is a reduction of the number of toes. *Phenacodus* had retained the full primitive complement, but each toe is capped by a small hoof; and the cheek teeth, although low-crowned, were already expanded for the chewing of vegetable food.

Phenacodus himself was a bit too large, and a bit too late in time to be considered actually ancestral to later groups of hoofed mammals, but he is representative of an order (the Condylarthra) which includes the probable base of many if not all of the later ungulate lines. Many of the groups which arose from such a base were aberrant in one way or another; various forms of this sort will be considered later in this chapter. We will at this point take up the history of the two great progressive orders which played a large role in ungulate history and are still present and varied in the modern fauna. These are the odd-toed and even-toed ungulates, constituting the orders Perissodactyla and Artiodactyla (figure 55).

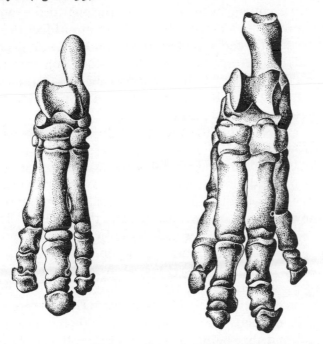

Figure 55. In the perissodactyl type of foot (left) the main axis runs through the middle toe, while in the artiodactyl type (right) it runs between the third and fourth toes.

Odd-toed Ungulates

The perissodactyls include among modern forms the horses, with their ass and zebra relatives, the rhinoceroses and the tapirs. Now represented by a relatively few genera and species, they were much more abundant in earlier stages of the Age of Mammals, and at that time included two further groups now extinct, the titanotheres and chalicotheres. Characteristic of this order is a type of foot in which the axis of symmetry runs through the middle toe. As, during their history, these forms tended to increase in speediness and rise off palm and sole to run on toe-tips, there was a trend for gradual reduction of toes on either side of the mid-line. Thumb and big toe, slanting off at an angle, were useless in this type of locomotion, and early disappeared. In the hind foot the 'little toe' likewise disappeared early, to give rise to a three-toed condition. This pattern persisted in many members of the group, but in later horses the two lateral digits dwindled and eventually were lost to give the one-toed – monodactyl – condition present in a modern horse. In the front foot the little toe was more persistent, and a modern tapir still has a four-toed 'hand'. In horses and rhinoceroses, however, a three-toed front foot developed early in the career of these families, and in the equids the front foot, like the hind, eventually became monodactyl.

Eohippus[1] is the earliest of horses and in many of its structures would appear to be close to the ancestry of the whole order (figure 56). This 'dawn horse' appears at the beginning of the Eocene, and its remains are abundant in deposits of that age, particularly in Wyoming. This was a small and slimly-built little fellow, some individuals being no larger than a fox-terrier. Toe reduction had begun, but there were still four functional toes in the front foot and three behind. The cheek teeth were well developed, but had low crowns, and were fit for use only with leaves and other soft vegetation. Early horses, such as *Eohippus*, were forest glade dwellers, with teeth suitable for forest food, and feet, with three or four spreading toes, well adapted for making as much speed as possible on a relatively soft forest floor.

Eohippus of the early Eocene inhabited both Eurasia and North America. Beyond that point in time, there developed in Eurasia a short side-branch of the early horse family, but the main evolutionary line of horses continued in North America through the Eocene, and all through every epoch of the Tertiary. In middle and late Eocene days *Eohippus* was succeeded by other genera, little changed (and, incidentally, much less common).

In the Oligocene, *Mesohippus* of North America represents a modest advance (figure 56). This was a somewhat bigger horse – averaging about collie size – and the 'little finger' had been lost; otherwise there

[1] More properly termed *Hyracotherium* by proper taxonomists.

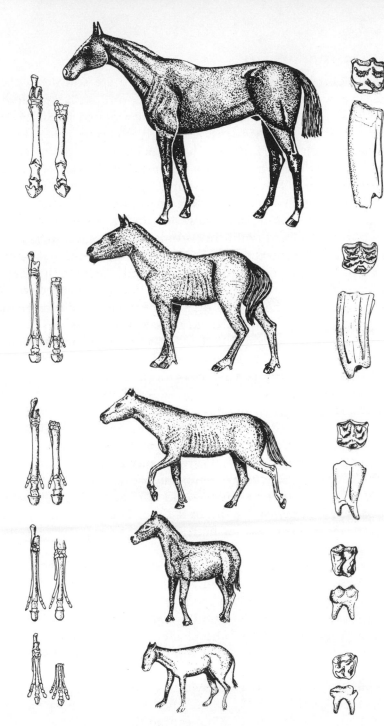

Figure 56. Little *Eohippus* (bottom) is the earliest known ancestor of the horse. Other types of horse shown in ascending order are *Mesohippus*, *Merychippus*, *Pliohippus* and the modern horse *Equus* (top). Beside each is shown its hind foot and fore foot (left) and side and top views of one of its molar teeth (right).

was little change from the Eocene type. We are still dealing with forest-dwelling browsers, and forms of this sort, with a gradual increase in size but conservatism in build, continued in diminishing numbers on into the Miocene and early Pliocene (one of them, *Anchitherium*, reaching Europe, where horses had been long absent).

But in the Miocene a new phase in horse evolution occurred. At this period of the Tertiary, grasslands appeared, and plains areas became increasingly abundant. Here there was open a new type of life, that of a grass-eating plains-dweller, and the main horse line became sharply modified to fill this promising ecological niche. Grass contains glass-like silica, and is hard on the teeth; Miocene horses, such as *Merychippus* (figure 56), adapted to this diet with the development of high-crowned teeth, capable of long and hard wear. The ground is firmer on the prairies than in the woods, and greater speed is possible; Miocene horses tended to reduce the side toes and concentrate on a single long slender toe. This process of adaptation continued, to produce, in *Pliohippus* of the Pliocene (figure 56), a horse of pony size which, except for the retention of tiny side toes, was by every standard as well developed as a modern horse. Another successful genus, *Hipparion*, invaded Eurasia and even reached Africa. These genera were succeeded by the end of the Pliocene by *Equus* (figure 56), the genus to which modern horses, asses, and zebras belong. Here the only change of note is the final disappearance of the small side toes to give the definitive monodactyl condition. *Equus* followed the pattern of *Hipparion* in colonizing Eurasia and Africa, and horse-like forms reached South America for the first time. During the Pleistocene, horses of one type or another flourished the world over, except for Australia.

But here, at the very end of the horse story, comes a curious quirk. North America had been, throughout, the stage on which the drama of horse evolution had been played. In the Pleistocene, horses persisted in America throughout the Ice Age. But then, just a few thousands of years ago, when all the changes and vicissitudes of glacial advances and retreats were over and modern conditions were approaching, horses vanished from the Western Hemisphere. When the Americas were discovered by Europeans, they had completely disappeared from the lands where they had lived and evolved for fifty million years and more. What caused this?

The disappearance of the horse from North America is but part of a much broader phenomenon of extinction. The horse is but one of a number of large mammals which inhabited North America during the Pleistocene but disappeared, apparently quite suddenly, at the end of the glacial epoch. Ground sloths, glyptodonts, giant armadillos, camels, mastodons and mammoths all roamed this continent not very many thousands of years ago. All now are gone. As far as we can discern from the fossil record, no small mammal became extinct; but of forms of any size there survive today only bear, deer of a few kinds, bison, mountain sheep and mountain goats (the last three recent immigrants). No adequate explanation has ever been given for this mass extinction of large North American mammals. The only new element in the environment at the end of the scene was man, a late comer to the Western Hemisphere. But he certainly played little direct part in killing off these great beasts, although it is possible that he may have had an indirect effect in upsetting some sort of delicate ecological balance within the fauna.

But let us return from this puzzling general problem to a recounting of the evolution of the perissodactyls. A second surviving family of the order is that of the tapirs, restricted today to South America and the Malay region. The modern tapirs are forest browsers, living very much the type of life led by *Eohippus*, resembling that primitive horse in retaining four toes in the front foot, and differing little structurally from earlier horses except in a rather stockier build, the development in the modern form of a protruding nose and (as a technical feature) the production in the upper molars of a pattern of two cross-ridges rather than the complex cusp pattern of the equids. In the Eocene a number of tapir-like forms, fairly similar to *Eohippus* in most regards, were common in both Eurasia and North America. From such types appeared the tapirs of the Oligocene and later epochs of the two northern continents. Tapirs, however, appear to be primarily warm-climate forms; and it would seem that they were driven by Pleistocene cold out of their former northern homes, never to return. Their presence in two widely separated tropical regions, with no representation in intervening land masses, is an excellent example of discontinuous distribution – a phenomenon which in earlier days frequently puzzled workers on geographical animal distribution. It now seems clear that the answer, in most cases, lies – as it does in the case of the tapirs – in restrictions in range caused by climatic changes.

The third, and last, of living perissodactyl types is that of the rhinoceroses. The living rhinoceroses include only a few species dwelling in southern Asia and in Africa – and these few, it would seem, are close to extinction. For most of their history they were a far more successful group.

The modern rhinoceroses are all of large size and ponderous build, with massive three-toed limbs. They are 'horned', but the 'horn' is formed of neither bone nor true horn, but of a matted-together mass of hair-like fibres (which does not preserve in fossil form). A key feature lies in the development in the upper molars of a Π-shaped pattern of ridges, the cross-bar at the outer rim of the tooth.

Far different from the modern types were the earliest rhinoceros-like forms of the Eocene, contemporaries of the early horse and tapir ancestors. These were slimly built as 'running rhinoceroses', four-toed still in front, hornless, and hardly identifiable as rhinoceroses except for the key afforded by the molar build. Slender running forms were still present in the Oligocene; but in that epoch began the evolution of more typical forms, with a trend toward larger size, heavier build, and loss (as in contemporary horses) of the 'extra' front toe; horns were relatively slow to make their appearance.

In the Oligocene and later epochs, rhinoceroses were amongst the most common of plains-dwellers in the northern continents, and variety of types developed. For example, *Baluchitherium* of the Oligocene of Asia, with somewhat the build of an enormous and ponderous giraffe, and a height estimated at seventeen feet, was the largest of known land mammals (plate 23). Among other Tertiary forms were short-legged amphibious types; in the Pleistocene there developed a woolly rhinoceros, adapted to cold glacial climates. Despite the earlier abundance of rhinoceroses, the close of the Tertiary saw a reduction in their numbers, their extinction in North America, and the beginning of the decline to their present lowly estate.

Two remarkable families now entirely extinct complete the roster of the perissodactyls. Of the titanotheres, the end forms such as *Brontotherium* found in the early Oligocene, and particularly common in the 'Big Badlands' of South Dakota, well merit the name of 'titanic beasts', for they were of ponderous build and some were of elephantine size (plate 23). Obviously slow of speed, these big herbivores seem to have been a source of prey for the larger carnivores of the day, and in relation to defence paired bony horns had developed above the nose region. The family is mainly a North American one, although represented in Asia as well. The earlier Eocene types were (as with tapirs and rhinoceroses) not too different from the early horses, but there was a rapid trend toward large size. Beyond the Lower Oligocene, these forms, not long since abundant, disappear completely. Reasons for their disappearance problably lie not in enemies but in the matter of food. Their cheek teeth were low-crowned and suitable only for the softest kinds of plant materials; even a slight change in the nature of the vegetation might have been enough to (literally) starve the titanotheres to death.

Finally, the chalicotheres such as *Moropus* (plate 23). Here, starting again with Eocene ancestors not dissimilar to early horses, still another evolutionary pattern was followed. The general body proportions were fairly similar to those of horses, but the teeth, on the contrary, were quite like those of titanotheres and in their feet the chalicotheres struck out on a line of their own, for the toes terminated not in hoofs but in huge claws – presumably used in digging a food supply of roots and tubers. Not uncommon in Tertiary deposits, they vanished before the Pleistocene was far advanced.

Even-toed Ungulates

The perissodactyls, as we have seen, were a flourishing and varied group in early and middle Tertiary times, but one which is close to the vanishing point today. Quite in contrast is the story of the order Artiodactyla, the even-toed ungulates. They were rare forms in early Eocene days, but as the Tertiary progressed they rapidly increased in numbers and variety, and they appear to be at the peak of their development at the present time, including such types as pigs and peccaries, the hippopotamus, camels, llamas, deer, giraffes, cattle, sheep, goats, and a host of antelopes.

Their popular name of 'even-toed' hoofed mammals is due to the type of toe reduction seen in this order. Perissodactyls, for the most part, reduced the toe count rapidly from five to three. Artiodactyls, on the contrary, generally lost the 'thumb' and 'big toe' at an early stage, but then tended to remain, at least for a time, in a four-toed condition, with toes three and four a prominent central pair, toes two and five bordering the principal ones on either side. Further progress might, and usually did, result in the reduction and often loss of the two side toes, producing the so-called 'cloven hoof' which is, of course, two closely appressed toes. A further distinctive character of the artiodactyls which has much to do with their development as speedy runners is concerned with one of the bones of the ankle region termed the astragalus. This forms the main articulation between leg

257

and foot, and in most mammals has a curved, and frequently pulley-shaped, upper surface to afford free movement but is flat below. In artiodactyls exclusively the lower as well as the upper end of the bone is pulley-shaped, thus giving unusual freedom of motion in running and bounding movements of the hind leg.

The earliest of Eocene artiodactyls show little evolutionary change, except for the characteristic astragalus, from the structural condition seen in lowly ungulates on the condylarth level. But before the end of that period differentiation had begun, and we see the initiation of types evolving in two contrasting directions.

In one major line of artiodactyl evolution the teeth tended to remain low-crowned with rounded cusps, suitable to a mixed type of diet (figure 57 A). Pigs are typical members of this group, and pig-like forms appear in Eurasian fossil beds in the late Eocene. Pigs are still four-toed, although the side toes are reduced; they are omnivorous in food habits, rather than proper herbivores; there are usually prominent canine tusks which generally curve outward and even upward on either side of the muzzle. Proper pigs are purely Old World forms and never reached the Americas, where we find in the Tertiary a related branch of the same stock – the peccaries (plate 24). These are pig-like, but more lightly built, and while the tusks are prominent they lack the peculiar curvature seen in the pigs. Peccaries passed most of their early history in North America, and even in the Pleistocene inhabited the ice-free portions of that continent; in the Pleistocene, however, they invaded South America, and today are present only in tropical and sub-tropical regions.

In the Tertiary there developed a number of variants of the pig-peccary type, of which the only survivor is the hippopotamus, a massively built amphibious form, now confined to Africa but present in the Eurasian Pleistocene in regions as far apart as England and China. Hippopotami as such can be traced no farther back than the late Pliocene; they appear, however, to have been derived from a group of swine relatives of large size – the anthracotheres – which can be traced back (mainly in the Old World) to the late Eocene.

Apart from the forms so far mentioned, nearly all artiodactyl groups from the late Eocene onward tended to evolve in quite a different direction. The general drift in such lines was toward a purely herbivorous diet; toward teeth, often high-crowned and with crescentic (selenodont) cusps (figure 57 B), capable of dealing efficiently with tough plant materials; toward a compartmentalized stomach and cud-

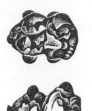

A   B

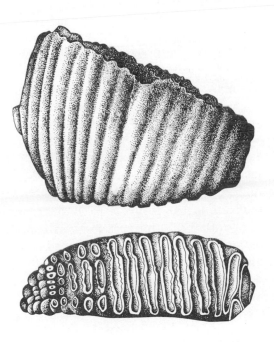

C

Figure 57. Side and crown views of the molar teeth of some herbivores. A, low-crowned tooth of a pig. B, high-crowned selenodont tooth of a camel. C, an elephant's tooth showing its great depth and the large number of cross ridges on its surface.

259

chewing 'rumination' for better digestion of such materials; and a final trend in most cases for greater speed, more slender limbs, and reduction of side toes in the feet.

Various types of artiodactyls progressed to various degrees along such lines of advance. We may note, as an example of a group which did not progress far in this direction, the oreodonts of North America, which nevertheless attained success for a considerable period of Tertiary time, and are the commonest of fossils in most Oligocene and Miocene formations. They are sometimes called, for want of a better name, 'ruminating swine', for the general proportions of the stocky body were pig-like, but the selenodont teeth are indicative of relationship to more advanced ruminants. A second characteristic American group is that of the camels. Today no members of the family are present in North America; the camels are restricted to the Old World, the llamas (plate 25) and their wild relatives to South America. In these forms the stomach is partly subdivided in the fashion of ruminants, the teeth are selenodont, and the side toes have been lost from the feet. Ancestral camels appeared in North America at about the beginning of the Oligocene, and camels of a variety of types were present in later Tertiary days in America – and America alone. In the Pleistocene, camels migrated to the Old World, ancestors of the llamas, alpacas and guanacos to South America. And in North America, at the end of the Pleistocene, the native camels disappeared as abruptly and mysteriously as did the native horses.

The main line of evolution toward higher modern types of ruminants seems to have had its centre in the Old World rather than the New. In most higher forms, to which the term 'Pecora' is often applied, the subdivision of the stomach is completed, cud-chewing is universal, horns or antlers of some sort are usually present, the side toes are reduced although remnants may remain as small 'dew claws', the two remaining long bones of the upper part of the feet fuse into a single 'cannon bone', and the upper front teeth – incisors – are lost.

Primitive forms leading toward the more progressive modern types appear in the Oligocene of Eurasia. Their more direct descendants survive today as the little chevrotains (plate 26), or 'mouse deer', of the Old World tropics. No bigger than hares, they look much like tiny deer, but lack horns or antlers, and are more primitive than proper pecorans in such features as the retention of complete if tiny side toes.

Proper pecorans developed into four families – two which retained ancestral habits as forest-dwelling browsers, two which became grass-eating inhabitants of open country. Of the two browsing types, the deer are the more widespread. A welter of primitive pecorans are known from the middle Tertiary; by the end of the Miocene there begin to appear true deer which became widespread over Eurasia and eventually reached the Americas. As persistent browsers, the teeth of deer remain low-crowned. A few small deer are 'hornless', but most develop structures which are often termed horns but are properly called antlers. These are branched bony outgrowths from the deer's forehead, covered during growth by the 'velvet' – a delicate furry skin; the antlers are shed and regrown annually.

The second family of browsing pecorans, likewise of Old World origin, and in this case purely Old World in distribution, is that of the giraffes. This group does not become clearly distinguishable from other browsing pecorans before the Pliocene. The familiar type is, of course, the giraffe, a tree-browser, well adapted for this life through its long front legs and long neck. Some of the extinct giraffe types have long been known to have had necks and legs of more normal proportions, but it was not until the present century that the okapi (plate 27), a living form of this sort, was discovered living in the forests of the Congo. Giraffes, as proper pecorans, have 'horns' of a sort. These are short, hair-covered nubbins of bone perched on top of the head; some fossil members of the family, however, possessed much larger, antler-like structures.

Of the two families of grazing pecorans, the less prominent one, which we shall mention first, is a North American product. The only living member is the prongbuck (plate 28), or so-called American antelope, of the western plains. A gracefully built animal, it has, like the members of the parallel Old World cattle group, high-crowned teeth for grass-eating. It has 'horns' of a peculiar type. Inside is a bony spike which like the horn core of cattle is permanent, not shed in antler fashion; it is sheathed by a partly-forked cover of true horn, which, in contrast to cattle horns, is shed annually. The prongbuck is, thus, a native American, *sui generis*, who refuses to conform to the customs of other members of the pecoran stock. The first members of the prongbuck group developed in the Miocene, when abundant grasslands first appeared, and a number of genera of prongbuck relatives flourished on the American prairies in the late Tertiary and even the Pleistocene; the reduction of the group to the sole surviving prongbuck series is very probably due to inability to compete with the bison, a Pleistocene invader from Asia which swarmed in immense numbers over the American prairies in late Pleistocene and Recent times.

Last, and most flourishing of all pecoran – and all ungulate – families is that of the cattle group, the bovids, which includes today not only cattle but bison, musk-ox, sheep, goats, and a swarm of other beasts which are highly varied but frequently lumped as 'antelopes'. These are the Old World parallels, as grazers, to the prongbucks of the New. They have, however, proved to be immensely more successful. The key character is their possession of true horns – structures often curved but never branched, and never shed, with a core of bone and a horny sheath. Like the prongbucks of North America, the bovids came into existence, as grazers, with the spread of grassy plains in the Miocene. By the Pliocene their numbers and variety had vastly increased, and some scores of antelope-like forms abounded on the plains of Europe and Asia. With the coming of the Pleistocene Ice Age their numbers in northern areas became greatly reduced, and it is to the African plains that we look today to see bovids at their best, in a series of antelopes still abundant despite human inroads. The sheep and goat types, including the ancestors of our domestic species, have been hill- and mountain-dwellers, rather than plains forms. The musk-oxen have adapted to cold climates. This animal apart, only a few bovids have ever reached the New World, and these are forms capable of living in relatively cold climates, such as the mountain sheep and goat of the American Rockies, and the bison which, reaching America during a Pleistocene interglacial stage, promptly populated the American grazing land.

Archaic Ungulates

The two orders to which most of the chapter thus far has been dedicated include in great measure progressive and successful ungulate types. We will now, to complete our task, discuss a variety of relatively unsuccessful forms, many of them departing far from typical ungulate patterns, and many of them extinct. Among the successful perissodactyls and artiodactyls, evolution and specialization progressed, for the most part, at a slow to moderate pace, and increase in size generally occurred but slowly. Quite in contrast is the history of some archaic types. We shall begin this section of the chapter with a brief mention of two groups, the pantodonts and uintatheres, which began their evolution in the Palaeocene, before either perissodactyls or artiodactyls had made their appearance, grew rapidly to large size – and shortly disappeared. Among the pantodonts there are known a number of Palaeocene age which were already of considerable size; best known of the group is *Coryphodon* (plate 30) of the Lower Eocene, represented in both Europe and America. A contemporary of little *Eohippus*, this animal stood some four or five feet high, with a ponderous body build and short and obviously slow-moving limbs. The uintatheres (plate 30), a North American group, were a bit later to appear than the pantodonts, none being known until the late Palaeocene. But like the pantodonts, they grew rapidly to large size; end forms in the late Eocene attained the size of a modern African rhinoceros, and were the giants of those days. These ponderous herbivores, pantodonts and uintatheres alike, were slow-moving and vulnerable to attack by carnivores; both *Coryphodon* and the uintatheres possessed sharp canine tusks which were presumably used in defence, and the uintatheres developed three pairs of knob-like horns on top of their long, low skulls. Whether the disappearance from the scene of these archaic ungulates was due to predation, or to a failure to compete for food with more progressive types, we do not know; but disappear they speedily did.

Hyraces

Under this head we shall begin a discussion of a group of animals which are highly diverse in nature, but which have common basic features and hence may form a natural group, possibly of African origin. These are the subungulates, amongst which may be ranged the conies or hyraces, the elephants and their fossil kin, and the seacows, as well as some fossil types.

Most modest in size and least unusual in nature of this assortment of subungulate types is that of the Hyracoidea, the conies or dassies (plate 29), living today in Africa and Syria. 'Coney' is an old English term, properly applied to rabbits, but used in the English Bible for the little animals now under discussion. The comparison is not too inappropriate, for the dassies have chisel-like front teeth and rather rabbit-like chewing habits; a better comparison, however, would be with a marmot or woodchuck, for the dassies lack the long rabbit ears and hind legs. But such comparisons are purely superficial; coney teeth are quite different from those of rodents, the feet end in little hoofs rather than claws, and the whole body structure is quite different from that of any other common mammalian group. The conies have had a long independent history, and are true African natives. The oldest known beds in Africa, in the Fayum district of Egypt, in which terrestrial animals are found, are, unfortunately, no older than late Eocene and early Oligocene. In these beds conies are already present and varied; one, in strong contrast with the small present-day forms, has the dimensions of a lion.

Proboscideans

There is considerable reason to believe that, in the earliest part of the Tertiary, Africa was an isolated continent, with no land connections with Asia or Europe; in the absence of such connections, there was an opportunity for the development in Africa of types of mammals quite distinct from those of other continental areas – notably the subungulate assemblage. The hyracoids, we have noted, appear in the oldest known Tertiary fossil beds of Africa, and other subungulates, some already far evolved, appear in these same beds. Among them we may briefly mention *Arsinoitherium* (plate 30), a gigantic herbivore, some eleven feet in length, bearing a huge pair of horns on its forehead. This great beast merits a position in a distinct order of its own, but some features of its structure are comparable with those of conies, elephants, and sea-cows, and suggest his inclusion in the subungulate assemblage.

Of broader interest in these same Egyptian beds are the oldest known representatives of the order Proboscidea, including the elephants and their kin, which thus prove to be of African origin and are a major subungulate stock. The evolutionary history of the proboscideans is fairly adequately known; it may be best understood if we consider the specialized structures seen in the modern elephants before describing their ancient African ancestors. The modern forms, and the related 'mammoths' of the Pleistocene, are large and massively built animals, with column-like legs, requisite for carrying the animal's great weight. The major specializations are seen in the head. There is, of course, a long and flexible trunk, and the only teeth in the front of the mouth are a pair of upper incisors which have developed into long tusks. The cheek teeth are few in number but of large size, very high-crowned, each consisting of a number of compressed parallel cross-ridges, fused tightly together, and capable of undergoing considerable wear (figure 57 C). The elephant's jaws are

264

short. There is room in each upper or lower jaw for but one molar tooth at a time; as this is worn down, it is replaced by a successor which forms meanwhile in a recess of the jaw behind it, and pushes forward to take its place.

Far different is the oldest and most primitive member of the order, *Moeritherium* (plate 31), found in the same late Eocene and early Oligocene beds of the Fayum district of Egypt in which the oldest hyrax remains are also present. This animal, probably somewhat amphibious in habits, shows little of the specializations of the modern elephants, and combines proboscidean features with structural resemblances to the conies, and, most especially, the sea-cows. *Moeritherium* was still a relatively small animal, of about pig size, and, except for a rather long body, of pig-like proportions. There was no trunk (although perhaps a somewhat pig-like snout). A number of teeth were present in the front of the mouth, but there was the beginning of tusk formation, one pair of both upper and lower incisor teeth being considerably enlarged. In the cheek there was a normal complement of teeth, all of them present at the same time, and each molar relatively small and low-crowned. However, the first faint beginning of the elephant tooth pattern is seen in the fact that two cross-crests are present.

The numerous forms intermediate between such a primitive type and that of an advanced elephant are generally called 'mastodons'. In these we see a series of progressive advances. In the front of the mouth the dentition is rapidly reduced to a single pair of incisor tusks above and below; these primitively extend straight forward, and the bony jaws, covered with flesh, are quite long. In progressive mastodons there is a concomitant lengthening of the tusks and a shortening of the jaws behind them. With this jaw shortening, the fleshy snout which originally extended farther is freed to become a flexible proboscis. In advanced mastodons the upper tusks continue to expand and frequently become curved; the lower ones persist in many mastodons, but in the line leading to the elephants are reduced and vanish, leaving only a projecting 'chin' to mark their former position. Meanwhile, in the cheek region, the individual grinders tend to increase in size and to increase the number of cross-ridges. In some advanced mastodons the molars come to be deeper and, with insufficient room in the jaws to accommodate the entire series at once, there begins the type of replacement characteristic of the elephants.

These advances did not take place rapidly, nor in a single phyletic line. The oldest mastodons, little more advanced than *Moeritherium*, are found in early Oligocene beds in the Fayum in which that genus still survived. By the early Miocene, mastodons had been able to reach Asia and Europe; by the end of the Miocene they were present in North America; in the Pleistocene they even gained a foothold in South America. In the Pliocene, particularly, a great variety of mastodons were to be found in both Eurasia and North America, but in the Pleistocene they became sharply reduced in numbers. The last survivor appears to have been the American mastodon (plate 31), a relatively primitive form, which appears to have lived until after the last retreat of the glaciers; numerous skeletons have been recovered from post-glacial bogs in the north-eastern United States.

In Asia, meanwhile, advanced mastodons had, before the end of the Pliocene, attained the character of primitive elephants, and in the Pleistocene a series of true elephants, usually called mammoths, were present in the northern continents and Africa. Notable was the development of a woolly mammoth, adapted to cold climates, common in the Pleistocene in both Eurasia and North America, and known not merely from skeletons but from the cave paintings of Old Stone Age artists and from frozen cadavers found in Siberian tundras. At the close of the Pleistocene the elephant tribe underwent strong reduction, to leave today only the Indian elephant and the rather more primitive African form.

Sirenians

A still further component of the subungulate series is that of the sirenians, the sea-cows. It seems absurd to list these aquatic vegetarians among the ungulates, but basic features in their structure suggest relationship to the proboscideans and conies. Members of the group are found in many Tertiary deposits. Today they are represented only by the manatee, present along both shores of the tropical Atlantic, and the dugong (plate 32) of the Red Sea region (a third sirenian, Steller's sea-cow, was formerly present in the North Pacific but was exterminated by man). The sirenians are purely aquatic, with the limbs much reduced, although the front pair serve as steering flippers, and with locomotion aided by a transverse tail flap. The dentition is much reduced, and is supplemented by horny plates and by a cropping mechanism of large fleshy lips; the cheek teeth, however, somewhat resemble those of primitive proboscideans.

The oldest sea-cows are found in the Eocene, and many of the known remains come from Egyptian sediments of an age similar to those containing remains of the earliest proboscideans. This fact, plus anatomical similarities, strongly indicates that we are here, again, dealing with members of an African radiation of subungulate forms. As suggested earlier, *Moeritherium* appears to have been close to the ancestry of both groups; although customarily brigaded with the mastodons and elephants, this animal was not improbably a marsh-loving animal, and may well have given rise to amphibious, and, eventually, truly aquatic descendants.

We may close our account of subungulates with the curious story of *Desmostylus* (plate 32). This name was given to specimens, mainly consisting of multi-cusped cheek teeth, which have long been known from Miocene shore deposits on either side of the North Pacific Ocean, notably California and Japan. The teeth are fairly comparable to those of sea-cows. Since the animal was obviously aquatic, it was assigned with little question to the sirenians, and it was assumed that its general structure would have been, were it known, similar to that of the mana-tee and dugong. Great was our astonishment when a skeleton was discovered in Japan a few years ago. The animal had well-developed limbs, quite capable of progression on land, in strong contrast to the reduced condition of the purely aquatic sea-cows. The general pro-portions were similar to the (quite unrelated) hippopotamus, and the mode of life of *Desmostylus* may have been similar, except that its amphibious existence was passed in and about salt-water coastal lagoons rather than the inland waters frequented by hippopotami.

South American Ungulates

In all the discussion of hoofed mammals earlier in this chapter, there has been no mention of South America, apart from notice of a few late intruders into that region. The reason for this omission is readily seen. As we have already noted, South America was separated from other continents for nearly the entire length of the Tertiary, and with few exceptions the mammalian faunas of that great region were de-veloped, in isolation, from the few forms which had reached there by very early Cenozoic times. Amongst the members of the sparse fauna known to have been present there in the Palaeocene were a few ungulates. From them developed a spectacular series of hoofed forms, of which remains of scores of genera have been discovered, principally in the rich fossil beds of Patagonia. We will limit our description of this varied array of ungulates to a very brief account, since the entire assemblage is now extinct and even the names of these forms are unfamiliar to all except the specialists in this particular area of palaeontology.

We believe that the primitive condylarths, mentioned at the beginning of this chapter, are close to the ancestry of many, if not all, of the more advanced ungulate groups. A few representatives of this order were among the early invaders of South America, and persisted for some time. In the Northern Hemisphere there sprang from the condylarths the important perissodactyl group; in South America the condylarths gave rise to the order Litopterna which there, in isolation, radiated out into a series of forms which paralleled their perissodactyl cousins in many regards. Notable was the series of forms analogous to the horses; there was a horse-like limb development, with the digits, as in horses, reduced to three, followed by decrease in size of the lateral toes. In one form, *Thoatherium* (plate 33) of the Miocene, we find a graceful little animal, about the size of *Mesohippus*, which had attained a one-toed condition at a time when true horses were still three-toed types.

Several other early types of South American hoofed forms paralleled archaic ungulates of northern continents in a precocious growth to large size. Most notable here is *Pyrotherium* (plate 33) of the Oligocene, a large and clumsy form which in its dentition closely paralleled the mastodons, then beginning their evolution on the opposite side of the Atlantic. But the greatest group of ungulates of South America was that of the order Notoungulata. Members of this order can be identified by technical features of the cheek teeth, and it is of interest that in the earliest Tertiary there are remains of small and primitive members of the group in other areas – the late Palaeocene of Mongolia, and the early Eocene of Wyoming. In the north, they failed, it seems, in competition with other groups of ungulates and rapidly disappeared; in South America, however, they flourished greatly in the Tertiary.

Although it is in general impossible to compare specific notoungulates with specific members of the more familiar northern orders, they appear to have produced types capable of fitting into nearly any niche which an ungulate could successfully occupy. We may mention as examples *Toxodon* (plate 33), which grew to large size and in appearance would have looked something like a cross between a rhinoceros and a hippopotamus, and the little typotheres such as *Typotherium* (plate 33). These latter were rather rodent-like in general build, and in some cases with long hind legs and a presumably rabbit-like hopping gait.

During the Tertiary, without enemies other than carnivorous marsupials, and without competition from other grazers and browsers, the native ungulates prospered. But in the Pleistocene, northern connections were established, and invaders poured in: carnivores (notably sabre-tooths) which preyed upon them; deer, camels, horses, and tapirs which competed with them for food. To these radically changed conditions the South American ungulates failed to adapt. By the end of the Pleistocene the entire host had vanished.

Chapter 17

A Mammalian 'Who's Who'

IN previous chapters we have outlined the evolution of flesh-eating mammals and the hoofed orders; in a final chapter we will conclude with an account of our own group, that of the primates. There still remains, however, a whole series of other orders of placental mammals, all products of that amazing radiation which took place at the dawn of the Tertiary. These we will review briefly in this chapter.

Bats

In terrestrial life, mammals have become supreme; in the air, however, they have failed to compete successfully with the birds. 'Planing' membranes have developed in a number of mammals, among marsupials as well as placentals, but only in the case of the bats – the order Chiroptera – has true flight evolved.

The bat wing is an efficient structure. A membrane, rather than feathers, forms the wing surface. Pterosaurs, we have seen, also evolved a membrane. That of the bat, however, is far superior. In the pterosaur the entire membrane was supported by a single long finger; there could be little manœvrability of the wing, and any tear would disable the whole structure. In the bat, in contrast, four fingers enter into the membrane support; flexibility is increased, danger of damage decreased. In addition to excellent wings, typical bats have a unique navigational aid through an echo-location system; high-pitched cries, inaudible to us, but not to the bat, echo back into his sensitive ears and aid in rapid avoidance of obstacles in the dusk or darkness in which bats usually fly.

But despite this, bats are but a minor element in the life of the air, and, except in insect-eating on the wing, have never been a serious threat to bird dominance of the atmosphere. What the full reasons are for mammals' failure in this sphere of activity it is difficult to determine. One factor in the situation, however, is clear. Birds can walk as well as fly. Bats cannot. They can fly; they can hang at rest upside down, suspended by their hind legs. But otherwise when not on the wing they are helpless. The differences here are clearly due to the differences in the nature of the terrestrial ancestors of the two groups. Birds, as we have seen, are descended from bipedal ruling reptiles; the front limbs could be transformed into wings without any impediment to the creature's walking ability. Bats, on the other hand, are descended from primitive insectivorous quadrupeds, which needed all four feet for ground locomotion. In consequence, when a bat through mischance finds himself grounded he is nearly helpless; the best he can do is a seemingly frantic series of flopping motions in the attempt to regain flight.

One family of large tropical bats have become fruit-eaters; we know almost nothing of the history of this type. For the most part, however, bats are insect-eating forms, and in this regard are clearly direct derivatives of the tiny primitive placental mammals which were similar in their diets. Of fossil bats, the record (apart from finds in Pleistocene cave deposits) is rather scanty, as would be expected in the case of such small and fragile animals. We are, however, fortunate in that deposits of Middle Eocene age both in Europe and in the Green River shales of Wyoming have yielded excellent specimens of bat skeletons, including the slender wing fingers. In these Eocene forms the wings, except in a few details, were completely evolved to the perfection seen in modern bats. We are here, in the geologic sequence, far back in the Age of Mammals, and these Eocene finds prove that the evolution of the bat group took place rapidly, surely starting well back in the Palaeocene. But we have no certain knowledge of connecting links between the full-fledged Eocene bats and the basal insectivore stock of placentals from which they sprang. Deposits of a sort which will preserve such a delicate structure as a bat wing are rare. In default of knowledge of wings – or lack of them – it is, at present, impossible to sort out possible bat ancestors amongst the varied but usually fragmentary remains of little insect-eaters of the earliest Tertiary.

Whales

Let us turn from the air to the other end of the range of possible environments – the sea. We have seen that the reptiles, whose ancestors had long since left the water, reinvaded that element, with – for the time – considerable success. The mammals, in their turn, have similarly invaded the sea. We have already mentioned the development of aquatic types amongst the carnivores and even amongst relatives of the hoofed mammals. But the mammals most highly adapted for an aquatic life and most successful in that environment are those constituting the order Cetacea, the whales and their smaller porpoise and dolphin relatives (figure 58).

Adaptations of this group for water-dwelling are so extreme that a whale or porpoise is helpless if stranded on a beach. Limbs have been sharply reduced; the hind legs lost (except for internal vestiges) and the front ones reduced to small steering devices. The whole body, in a modern whale or porpoise, has reverted to the torpedo-like streamlined shape of the fish ancestors, with shortening of the neck and with the redevelopment of a propulsive tail fin. In this last regard the newly developed tail is an effective swimming organ but is built on a different plan from that of fishes or even the ichthyosaurs. The mammalian tail was so reduced to begin with that resort had to be taken, as in the case of seals or sea-cows, to a new type of structure. Here, somewhat as in the sea-cows, there is present a pair of transverse flukes, which work in an up-and-down direction, at right angles to the direction in which primitive tail fins operate.

There are, of course, many aquatic adaptations apart from body shape. Breathing is a major problem for any terrestrial form which has returned to the water. Air intake in whales and porpoises is facilitated by the nostrils having moved up and back to form a blowhole on top of the head, and internal physiological adaptations are present which enable cetaceans to conserve oxygen and, in some cases, to remain submerged for considerable periods of time. Sea water is cold, and wet fur none too good an insulating device. Whales have lost all, or nearly all, of their original hairy covering and have, instead, an effective insulation in the form of a thick coat of blubber beneath the skin.

With, thus, numerous modifications of the structure of their terrestrial placental ancestors to facilitate life in their new environment, the cetaceans have become a successful marine order. The members living today can be divided into two groups – toothed forms and whalebone whales. The former group is by far the larger assemblage. It includes not only a number of large and proper whales, but all the smaller members of the order which we customarily call porpoises and dolphins, and which not only abound in the oceans the world over, but are even present in some of the larger rivers, such as the

Amazon, Ganges, and Yangtse. As the name implies, most of the members of this group are supplied with teeth, typically peg-shaped and often far in excess of that present in primitive placentals; this dentition enables them to cope successfully with the animal food – notably fish and squid – upon which they subsist.

Quite in contrast as regards feeding habits are the highly specialized whalebone whales. These are few in numbers today, and are all large forms, including the 'right whales' and the great blue whale, or sulphur-bottom; this noblest of all the cetaceans reaches as a maximum a length of nearly one hundred feet and an estimated weight close to 200 tons.

These largest of animals live on the smallest of food, particularly tiny shrimp-like crustaceans. Teeth have been lost from the margins of the huge mouth cavity. This is filled with a series of sheets of whalebone, fringed below with hairs and hanging down from the roof of the mouth in parallel rows, like the leaves of a book (figure 58, top). The whalebone (once popular for use as corset stays) is composed of hardened horny skin. In the roof of the mouth of many mammals (such as the dog) may be seen transverse skin ridges; the whalebone is formed by the elaboration of such ridges. Water taken into the whale's mouth is strained through the whalebone filter, and the edible materials deposited are licked off by the tongue.

Both modern whale types can be traced far back into Tertiary times. Even the specialized whalebone whales have representatives as far back as the Oligocene. The toothed whales have flourished greatly for a long period of time. All living types were already present in mid-Tertiary Miocene days; this epoch appears to have marked the peak of whale success, for Miocene strata have brought to light a variety of porpoises far more numerous than those surviving today. In the Oligocene, primitive members of the toothed whale group were present, but they were few in numbers.

To trace the more remote ancestry, we must turn to a third whale group, now entirely extinct but which flourished in the Eocene and survived in limited numbers into the following Oligocene epoch. These are the archaeocetes, the 'ancient whales', reasonably so called. There were already developed in these forms certain of the basic characters of the cetaceans, including the general body shape and limb modifications, but there were as well many primitive or transitional features. The nostrils had, in the oldest known forms, begun their migration back from the normal nose region, but were still far

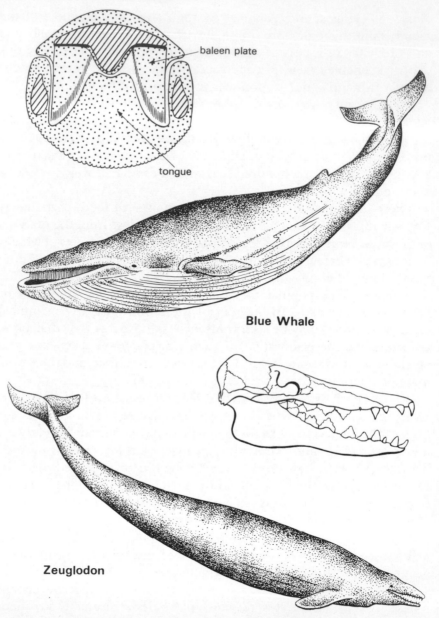

Blue Whale

Zeuglodon

Figure 58. The section through the head of the blue whale shows how the baleen plates, or 'whalebone', bear fringes which filter tiny crustaceans out of the water as the tongue forces it out between the plates. *Zeuglodon* is an Eocene whale which had not yet developed the large number of simple teeth found in later toothed whales.

274

from the ultimate position of the blowhole. There was a well-developed dentition (the whalebone specialization is not apparent in archaeocetes). But while the front teeth were peg-like, as in modern toothed whales, the cheek teeth in some archaeocetes are not unlike those of some primitive terrestrial carnivores. In one genus, at least, the tooth numbers – usually quite high in later toothed whales – were still at the low count found in the generality of primitive placentals.

Some of the archaeocetes were of relatively small size and unspecialized structure, and appear to represent a stock from which advanced whale types were descended. But apart from potential ancestors of later groups, the archaeocetes developed specializations of their own. The peak of their development was reached in the form generally known as *Zeuglodon* (figure 58), of which good remains are known from the south-eastern United States. This was a giant among early whales. Unlike modern forms, the body was slender, with the proportions which modern imagination ascribes to sea-serpents, and a length of seventy feet or so.

But although the archaeocetes are primitive, they are, nevertheless, whales. Their characters are such that we may believe them to have been an early offshoot from the primitive carnivores. We do not know their history before their first appearance in the Middle Eocene. A clue as to their place of origin is that the remains of these oldest members of the group are almost all from beds in Egypt which appear to have been laid down in African coastal waters. Quite probably the whales, like the subungulates, originated in Africa, and our lack of knowledge of transitional types is due to the absence in that continent of beds from the oldest Tertiary.

Edentates

The name 'edentate' is frequently applied to a considerable variety of mammals of odd types. Not all are truly related; most, however, do belong to a common group, as the order Edentata, of which South America is the seat, and of which the living component types are the armadillos, tree-sloths and anteaters of that continent. The name of 'toothless' animals is misleading, for, apart from the anteaters, they have a considerable supply of teeth. The teeth, however, are degenerate; no teeth are present in the front of the mouth, and those in the cheeks are simply blocks of dentine, without the normal covering of enamel. These odd South American forms have various further anatomical characters in common, including peculiar features in shoulder and hip girdles and in elements of the backbone. Most have large claws; many members of the group are terrestrial, but it is not improbable that the ancestors were tree-dwellers.

Of the three living types included in the order, only the South American anteaters (e.g. *Tamandua*, plate 34) are truly toothless; they feed on termites, gathered by a long sticky tongue into the small mouth at the end of a long snout. The tree-sloths (plate 35), which have a few peg teeth in either cheek, are grotesque arboreal leaf-eaters, nocturnal and slothful in habits, usually being found at ease hanging upside down from tree branches by their long claws (two or three in number). The armadillos, although toothless in front, have a large battery of cheek teeth. Apart from the toothed whales, they are the one group of living mammals which violate the 'rule' that only seven cheek teeth can be present in a single jaw ramus; there are as many as twenty-five teeth in one form. The most obvious characteristic of the armadillos is the development of rows of bony plates which cover the back and sides and even the top of the head of these inoffensive omnivores. Anteaters and tree-sloths are confined to South America, but one armadillo species extends northward through Mexico and currently appears to be expanding its range through the southern United States.

As mention of their present range suggests, most of the history of the group took place in South America. A few primitive relatives have been found in the Palaeocene and Eocene of North America, but left no descendants there. They early penetrated to South America, however, and are represented in the earliest mammalian fauna of that continent, that of the late Palaeocene. There they flourished during the Tertiary and Pleistocene and left an abundant fossil record. Tree-sloths are unknown as fossils, and little is known of anteaters, but there were many Tertiary types of armadillos, some of considerable size. In addition, there developed within the order two spectacular giant types, now extinct. The glyptodonts (plate 36) were armadillo relatives, some reaching ten feet or more in length, in which the armour formed a solid, domed carapace covering the entire trunk. Not only was the head, as well, protected by bony plates, but the tail was also ensheathed by armour and sometimes had projecting spikes at its tip, somewhat after the fashion of the Cretaceous armoured dinosaurs.

Paralleling the glyptodonts in their Tertiary development were the ground-sloths. These creatures are clearly related to the tree-sloths, and the peculiar construction of their oddly-clawed feet suggests that the ancestors were arboreal, descending to the ground when increase in bulk took place. These animals reached their peak in size and variety in the Pleistocene, where a dozen or more genera were present, several the size of an ox, one with the proportions of an elephant. The gait of these giants seems to have been of a clumsy shuffling type; they appear to have been able to rear up on their hind legs in bear fashion and crop leaves from the branches of the trees (plate 36).

When South America became reconnected with the north at the end of the Tertiary, the South American ungulates, as noted earlier, failed in competition with the newcomers and were rapidly exterminated. Not so the edentates, who appear to have been a sturdier stock. They not only held their own in South America during the Pleistocene, but even counter-invaded North America, where large glyptodonts have been found in Pleistocene Gulf Coast deposits, and where ground-sloths of several sorts ranged widely through temperate as well as southern regions. But by the end of the Pleistocene glyptodonts and ground-sloths became extinct in North and South America alike. This extinction, however, took place at a relatively recent date, for there is evidence both from the North American south-west and from Patagonia that they were still present when man, himself a late invader of the Western Hemisphere, reached these areas.

We may mention here two Old World types of termite eaters which are frequently called edentates, but which are quite unrelated to the South American group. The aardvark of Africa (plate 37) is a grotesque and clumsy beast with long ears, long snout, long tongue, and powerful claws. Some mid-Tertiary remains of the creature are known from Africa and southern Europe, but give little clue to his pedigree, although certain features suggest a remote relationship to the early ungulates of the condylarth group. The pangolins of southern Asia and Africa (plate 38) have somewhat similar termite-eating adaptations in the long snout and tongue and good claws; their most notable characteristic, however, is their protective covering of large overlapping horny scales, which gives them somewhat the appearance of living pine cones. Of their fossil history and possible relationships we know nothing whatever.

Rodents

If variety of forms and numbers of individuals be an acceptable criterion, the gnawing animals of the order Rodentia are the most successful of mammals. Squirrel, rat and guinea pig are among the numerous familiar forms. In general the body structure is relatively uniform, anatomically suitable for four-footed scampering over the ground or on tree limbs, and with the feet generally furnished with good claws that make for facile digging. The major specializations are in the dentition. In the front of the mouth there are only two incisor teeth above and below; but these are powerful chisel-like gnawing weapons, growing from persistent roots so that their length is maintained despite heavy wear. After a gap comes a battery of cheek teeth, few in number (usually three or four only in each jaw ramus). These cheek teeth are complexly and variably built, and in most cases are high-crowned, so that they can stand hard wear before dental senility is reached; frequently they grow, like the incisors, from persistent roots. The jaw muscles are powerful and complex, making the jaws not only capable of good chiselling and biting but also efficient in chewing tougher foods. The rodents are a hardy folk, mostly of modest size, able to exist on almost any variety of food that presents itself, and to live under almost any type of terrestrial condition, from arctic to tropics, from forest and swamp to desert. The first rodents appear in the record at the end of the Palaeocene; primitive rodents became numerous in the Eocene, and the order has thrived increasingly ever since. Whence the first rodents came is, however, still unknown. Ultimately, of course, they were derived from the primitive placental insectivore stock; but the rodent structural pattern, notably that of the dentition, was fully developed in the very first forms known, and there are no direct links to any members of the Palaeocene insectivore stocks.

How to classify the hordes of rodents, living and fossil, and what the form of their evolutionary family tree has been are problems that even the most competent of specialists confess themselves incapable of fully understanding. It seems, however, fairly clear that a large proportion of rodents can be arrayed in three general categories, of which the squirrels, guinea pigs and mice are fairly representative. The squirrels and a small American animal, the 'mountain beaver' or sewellel of the Rocky Mountains, are the only living representatives of the more primitive of the three groups, to which most of the Eocene rodents pertain; the squirrels are somewhat modified in certain technical features, but persistently primitive in many others.

Much more successful in the long run have been the two other major types. To the mouse-rat group pertain not only the numerous forms recognizable under these names, but also such forms as the jerboas, kangaroo rats (plate 39) and other jumping forms, the dormice and the curious burrowing 'pocket gophers' of America. Members of this group had evolved by the early Oligocene, and became widespread before the Tertiary period was much farther advanced. Some of the forms mentioned have met with but modest success, but the more typical rats and mice have become, in later Cenozoic and Recent times, the most abundant of all mammalian forms in both numbers of genera and species and, one may be sure, in numbers of individuals concerned. Much of the evolution of this rodent group appears to have taken place in Eurasia, but rats and mice are present the world over. They are abundant in Africa and North America; they invaded South America in the Pleistocene; and, before the end of the Tertiary, rats of special sorts had reached Australia, presumably by gradual migration down the East Indian chain. They are the only terrestrial placentals which had reached that continent before the arrival of man.

The third and in some ways the most interesting group of rodents is that of which the guinea pig is typical. This group is for the most part confined to South America where, apart from some invading mouse types, its members make up the entire rodent fauna of the continent. There are some scores of genera, few of which, apart from the domesticated guinea pig, will be known to any reader not an inhabitant of that region. Possibly familiar names are the chinchilla and 'nutria' (coypu), prized for their fur; the giant of all rodents is the carpincho or capybara (*Hydrochoerus*) (plate 40), the amphibious 'water hog' of Brazil, which reaches a weight of nearly one hundred pounds. One type, exceptional in the fact that its range is extended to North America, is that of the New World porcupines, which are related to the typical South American rodents and, despite their quills, are not (except, of course, that both are rodents) related to the equally spiny Old World porcupines.

As their present distribution leads one to suspect, the evolution of this group took place in South America. Quite surely the guinea-pig group is an offshoot of the early squirrel-like forms. They were not, however, present in South America at the beginning of the Tertiary, but appear suddenly in the Oligocene. Presumably they (like the South American monkeys discussed in the next chapter) had reached South America from the north by gradual migration down the island chain which presumably filled part of the water gap between the two western continents in Tertiary days. With the resumption of land connections at the end of the Tertiary, the native rodents were subject to some competition from invading 'foreign' rodents. On the whole, however, they have stood their ground well, and the porcupines native to the southern continent successfully invaded North America.

Hares and Rabbits

We will conclude this 'who's who' of mammalian orders by a brief mention of the Lagomorpha. This is a small group, including only a relatively few genera of hares and rabbits and, as a somewhat more primitive relative, the 'mountain hare' or pika of the American Rockies and Asia. In early days this group was often included in the rodents; but apart from the fact that there are chisel-like incisor teeth in both groups, they have nothing in common, and have quite distinct pedigrees. Even in the gnawing apparatus the two differ, for while the true rodents have but a single pair of upper chisels, the lagomorphs have a smaller accessory pair of upper incisors behind the principal pair.

As in the case of the rodents, the first lagomorphs appeared in the late Palaeocene; as with the rodents, there is no sure clue as to their derivation from primitive placental ancestors. Throughout the Tertiary the lagomorphs are present as fossils in modest numbers in the northern continents and in Africa. In the Pleistocene they reached South America, but have not greatly flourished there. Australia they did not reach until introduced by man; there, until struck by a virus disease, they multiplied in disastrous fashion. On the whole, their history has been an uneventful one. Only one 'improvement' has occurred. The little 'mountain hare' has hind legs of normal length, and presumably this was the case with the ancestral lagomorph. The development of longer hind legs in hares and rabbits has presumably been responsible for such modest success as the group has attained.

Chapter 18

Primates

WE will conclude this volume with an account of the evolution of the order Primates, a mammalian group of particular, personal interest, since it includes not only lemurs, monkeys, and great apes, but also man himself; in studying primate evolution we are climbing our own family tree. A matter of this sort deserves, from selfish interests, particularly detailed consideration, and another volume in this series will discuss the ascent of man at greater length; here we shall cover the ground more briefly, considering the primates and man a bit more casually and objectively as merely one of the numerous sets of creatures developed out of the primitive placental stock during the course of the Cenozoic.

Although, as members of the group, we have a great interest in the palaeontological story of primate evolution, the fossil record of the order is a disappointing one. Primates, with a few exceptions (such as men and baboons), are tree-dwellers, and fossil deposits with remains of forest-dwellers are relatively rare. Further, most primates are, and seemingly always have been, inhabitants of warm climates; most of our better-known fossiliferous beds are found in what are now temperate zones, giving another reason for the paucity of primate remains – except for the earliest stages of the Cenozoic, when climates of more equable nature appear to have been present farther north than is now the case.

How to give a common characterization of all primates, from tree shrews to apes and men, is a difficult matter. In part, the definition must be a negative one. In many regards a primate can be defined by the absence of specializations found in many other orders of placentals. Many mammals have modified their limbs into efficient hoofed running organs, frequently with loss of toes, or into wings or swimming paddles; primates have done none of these things, and, except for somewhat better grasping ability in hand (and often foot), the limbs – and indeed nearly the whole skeleton – have tended to remain in a rather generalized and fairly primitive condition. Primates are rather omnivorous in their feeding habits, although with a trend toward vegetarianism, and the dentition, apart from some shortening of the tooth row, is little specialized; there is lacking the strong development of grinding molars seen in many specialized herbivores or, on the other hand, the stabbing, biting and shearing specializations found in carnivores.

Primates, however, do have strong positive features, most of them little developed in primitive types but emphasized in advanced forms. Almost every one of these features is associated directly with the arboreal life which is characteristic of nearly all members of the order.

As mentioned, hand and foot show modifications related to life in the trees. Some small tree-dwellers (squirrels, for example) can scurry about over the trunk and branches by digging their claws into the bark. For a larger form, gaining a grasp around a bough or twig is a more satisfactory procedure. Primitive mammals which are adequately known show a structure of hand and foot in which the thumb and big toe are somewhat opposable to the other fingers and toes. Some grasping power was thus present at an early stage, and it may well be that ancestral mammals were arboreal to some degree. It is, however, only among the primates that an arboreal trend with a good grasping power became highly developed, as it is even in the lowly lemurs of today and in early Eocene relatives of these forms. Nearly all primates have been, of course, four-footed climbers, and in most primates below the human level the big toe is better developed and has a better grasping power than the thumb. Claws are of lessened importance in this mode of locomotion, and in most primates have been modified into flattened nails of the sort which we ourselves possess.

Arboreal life has had a profound effect upon the sense organs. In primitive mammals smell is of the highest importance, sight in great measure secondary. The reverse is true with the tree-dwelling primates – the higher members of the group, at least. A man recognizes his dog, as he nears home, by sight; the dog recognizes his master by smell long before sight will assure him of identity. Higher primates have an exceedingly poor sense of smell, whereas in most mammals olfaction is extremely highly developed, obviously with many nuances which we cannot even imagine. In most mammals sight is developed only to a moderate degree with, as far as our studies can determine, little possibility of perception of detail. Further, in primitive mammals the eyes are essentially directed laterally, with little overlap of the fields of vision and no development of a sense of depth. To a typical mammal, the world of vision consists of two sets of pictures, each flat and somewhat fuzzy. In higher primates the story is a very different one. The eyes are turned forward, so that the two fields of vision tend to be identical; further, the brain circuits are so built that in the mind the two nearly identical pictures are superimposed to give stereoscopic vision, a three-dimensional picture in which depth is present and judgment of distances is possible. Still further, in higher primates a special central area is developed in each eye retina in which details are readily visible, contrasting with the less distinct picture seen peripherally.

These changes in sense organs in the evolution of primates are clearly useful adaptations for efficient arboreal life. On the ground, the nose is very useful in giving information as to the presence nearby of friend, foe or prey. In a tree, the mere presence of other animals nearby has in itself little meaning; the important thing is whether the friend or foe is in the primate's own tree and hence readily accessible, or in another tree. This the nose cannot tell; but the eye, if well developed, can give this vital information. Still more important is the need for good vision in tree locomotion. A modest development of vision is enough for normal terrestrial travel. In the tree, jumping from branch to branch, a mere knowledge that the next limb is somewhere about is not sufficient; its exact distance must be gauged for the jump, and it may be a matter of life or death to be able to see this limb well enough to determine whether it is sound and will bear your weight – or let you crash to the ground.

All mammals have relatively good brains, but it is among primates – even if we exclude man – that we find brains which are, proportionate to body size, far larger than in any other mammal group. This trend, particularly notable in monkeys, apes, and men, seems, again, definitely related to tree-dwelling. Tree locomotion requires great agility and muscular co-ordination, requiring well-developed motor centres in the brain; and it may be significant that most of the highest mental faculties in man are apparently developed in areas of the 'grey matter' alongside the brain motor centres. Again, the development of good eyesight makes available to primates a far broader knowledge of the environment than is possible for a mammal mainly dependent on smell. Even more important, perhaps, in the development of mental faculties in primates has been the development of the hand as a sensory aid in the grasping of objects – and as an aid in their manipulation.

Not merely man, but other higher primates as well, can see a broad range of objects to incite their mental curiosity and, through their hands, often have the ability to satisfy that curiosity. 'Monkey curiosity' is proverbial. And intellectual curiosity, together with the scientific or scholarly investigation which follows up this curiosity, has been a major factor in advancing man to his present estate.

Brain growth, olfactory reduction, emphasis on vision and some reduction in tooth row length have all tended to modify considerably skull proportions and head contours in higher primates. The face is shortened, the snout reduced, the eye sockets are turned forward to nearly meet above the reduced nose, and the skull vault swollen to enclose the expanded brain.

Living today in the East Indies are the tree shrews (plate 41). As the name implies, they are often classed with the shrews as members of the primitive order Insectivora and indeed, in most regards, they are exceedingly primitive placental mammals. They do, however, show a few technical features suggesting that they represent a primitive arboreal group from which the primates sprang. Almost nothing, however, is known of the tree shrews as fossils, and it is to the lemurs, fossil and living, that we must turn for knowledge of primitive forms which are definitely members of the primate order.

The lemurs (plate 42) today are Old World tropical forms, mainly found in Madagascar; the survival there of these primitive forms is primarily due to isolation, the absence from that island of many of the carnivores which could prey upon them were they dwellers on the major continental areas. They are arboreal, and nocturnal in habit; this latter, together with the ghostly sound of their cries, is responsible for there having been bestowed on them a name which the Romans applied to the night-haunting souls of the dead. In a number of regards, such as, for example, their highly developed grasping power, they are reasonably classed with the primates; but they are far more primitive in many ways than monkeys or other higher members of the order. They have thick fur, contrasting with the sparser hairy covering of more advanced types, and a long bushy tail; the claws are sometimes retained on part of the toes; in many, the face is still a long fox-like muzzle, the nose still well developed, the eyes primitive in basic structure and more to the side than forward.

Primitive primates, abundant in variety and numbers (although mainly represented by fragmentary remains) are found in the Palaeocene and Eocene of Europe and North America. Some are so primitive in nature that we feel uncertain as to whether to consider them as advanced insectivores or very primitive primates. Others show various specializations indicating that they were straying away from the line leading to more advanced members of the order. Still others, however, including some of which complete skeletons have been recovered, exhibit a structure of generalized, if primitive, nature, and one very close to that preserved by certain of the living Madagascar forms.

Beyond the Eocene, however, the lemurs disappear from our fossil deposits in northerly regions. The general history of world climates indicates that in the early stages of the Cenozoic the climate was an equable one, with fairly warm temperatures extending far toward the poles, but that, as the Tertiary progressed, climatic gradients became more sharply marked, the tropics warmer, the temperate and arctic zones increasingly colder. It would appear that by the Oligocene the northern temperate zones were becoming too chilly for lemur occupancy, and that from this time on they were confined to the tropics. But due to the paucity of tropical fossil deposits we have little knowledge of the later history of the lemurs, except for fossil remains in the Madagascar Pleistocene.

A clear cut above the lemurs in the living primate assemblage is *Tarsius* (plate 43), a curious little animal from the East Indies and the Philippines. *Tarsius* has some aberrant features, such as a hopping gait associated with elongation of the ankle (technically termed the tarsal region – hence the scientific name of the creature). But in a number of regards, *Tarsius* clearly represents a stage in primate evolution above that of lemurs, although below that of monkeys. The braincase is large; the large and well-developed eyes are turned forward, with a considerable development of clear and stereoscopic vision; the nose is reduced to a mere nubbin below the eyes. We have here not a typical animal snout but a face (although rather a caricature of a face). If we turn to the fossil record we find, again, in the early Cenozoic deposits of North America and Europe a series of forms which appear to represent this tarsioid stage in primate evolution. As in the case of the lemurs, many of the specimens are too fragmentary to be accurately identified as *Tarsius* relatives, and dental characters alone are hardly diagnostic enough to sort out tarsioids from other primitive primates. In a few cases, however, there are good skulls which definitely show the swollen braincase, forwardly turned eyes, and reduced snout which characterize this stage of primate evolution. As was true of the lemurs, tarsioids disappear from the fossil record of northern regions at an early stage of the Tertiary, leaving a long gap in time between the days of the primitive *Tarsius*-like forms and the survivor in the modern tropics.

With the advances seen in the tarsioids, we have progressed far toward, but not reached, the upper of the two sub-groups into which the primates are often subdivided. Lemurs and tarsioids are frequently 'lumped' as a suborder Prosimii; monkeys, apes, and man grouped together as the suborder Anthropoidea (the latter name due to the fact that the monkeys and apes are very man-like – i.e., anthropoid – in many structural features).

Monkeys, of course, occupy the lowest bracket in this anthropoid assemblage. As we find them today in the tropics of both Old and New Worlds, we find expressed in their structures the fulfilment of many of the advanced tendencies present in *Tarsius*. As was already true in *Tarsius*, the eyes are very large and turned forward; but in addition to the stereoscopic vision permitted by this shift, there is present in even the lowest of monkeys a central area for clear perception of detail; the monkey's eye is on a par with our own. With this advance in vision, the sense of smell is, as was already true in *Tarsius*, much reduced, and the snout in general short. Monkeys are normally four-footed walkers, but there is a strong tendency toward an upright sitting posture and a consequent freeing of the hands for manipulation of food – and the satisfying of curiosity. The brain is large and well developed, and, for what it is worth, the relative size of brain to body is higher in some small South American monkeys than in ourselves. Two groups of monkeys evolved from forms on the tarsioid level, one in South America, the other in the tropics of Africa and southern Asia. Both have achieved a modest success. The South American forms have persistently kept to the trees, and many of them have increased their arboreal agility by the development of a 'fifth hand' in a prehensile tail (never found in Old World forms). In the Old World we find, as well as arboreal types, a series of large monkeys which have tended toward life on the ground – the baboons, drills, and the (to us) repulsively coloured mandrills of Africa. As purely tropical forms, our knowledge of fossil monkeys is scanty.

In recent years considerable scientific interest has been given to a primate known as *Oreopithecus* from the Pliocene of Italy which, of monkey size and formerly regarded as a member of the Old World monkey family, shows some anatomical features suggestive of human relationships. The majority opinion, however, is that these resemblances are purely a parallelism, and that the human pedigree passes upward from the monkey level in common with the line leading to the great apes of the Old World, which are thus our closest relatives. The living types of such apes are four in number – gibbon, orang-utan, chimpanzee, and gorilla. The skeleton is rather close to the human type, and that of a chimpanzee or gorilla can be matched bone for bone with that of man, although the elements vary in their proportions. The hands are fairly similar to those of man, but the thumb is generally relatively short, the other four fingers elongate. The arms are long; the legs, on the contrary, short. The foot is, as in lower primates, still an excellent grasping organ, with the toes long and the big toe, in hand-like fashion, opposable to the other four.

These features, particularly those of the arm, appear to be correlated with the great ape type of locomotion. Most monkeys still climb about the tree limbs on all fours. But many tree limbs will not support such a heavy weight as that of the great apes; it is safer if the ape rests his hind feet on one branch and grasps the next above with his hands, with the body now in a partially erect posture. From this it is but a step to a type of locomotion termed brachiation, in which the gibbon and orang are particularly adept, the apes swinging by their hands from bough to bough.

The brain is large in the great apes, but even in the largest gorillas is far below human proportions, so that the forehead is low, and there may be heavily developed bony brow ridges. The great apes are primarily vegetarians in food habits; in relation to this, the grinding teeth in the cheeks tend to be large, and the tooth-row long, giving a more projecting face than in man. The canine teeth are generally prominent, and, as in mammals generally (and even primitive human types), there is no development of a chin.

Smallest and in many ways most primitive of the living great apes are the gibbons of the Malay region, with a stature not exceeding three feet. They are marvellous arboreal acrobats, with very long arms and with the brachiating type of locomotion highly developed. The orang-utan, the 'wild man' of Borneo and Sumatra, is considerably larger, the males reaching nearly five feet in height. The orang brain may reach a maximum of about 500 cubic centimetres in volume, whereas that of modern man, with about the same body size, may reach 1,500 cubic centimetres or more in cubic capacity. Brain size is not, of course, an accurate index of intelligence, but it seems clear that the great apes are far below human standards.

Rather higher in organization and, it is believed, somewhat closer to the human line are the two great apes of Africa, the chimpanzee and gorilla. In these forms, in contrast to the gibbon and orang, there is a trend away from purely arboreal life. The chimpanzees do spend much of their existence in the trees, but are much less adept in locomotion there than are the gibbons or orangs; the gorillas – particularly those of the African highlands – are mainly ground-dwellers, who take to the trees but little, except for a nightly nest. Both are animals of considerable size, and although the weight and height of the chimpanzee is considerably below that of most human races, old male gorillas are said to weigh as much as 600 pounds. Chimpanzees, in particular, appear to have a degree of intelligence which is high for a non-human form, but the brain is, even in these higher apes, far below the size characteristic of any modern human race; 630 cc in an exceptional gorilla seems to be the record brain size in any great ape.

The great apes are, quite surely, man's closest relatives. But we are not, of course, descended from any of these living types; we and they are varied descendants from a common ancestral stock. It is highly improbable that our ancestors ever developed to any degree the agile brachiating type of locomotion so highly developed in gibbons, particularly. The great apes are not our ancestors, but our cousins, who have followed different evolutionary lines – with relatively little success.

In attempting to follow out the pedigree of the higher primates, we encounter the same stumbling block that we have met in the case of lower primates. Except for developed man, we are dealing with warmth-loving animals, and fossil deposits in tropical and subtropical regions are little known. Decade by decade, however, one find after another of fossil ape material has been made, and we are beginning to acquire at least the rough outline of the story.

The oldest traces of man-like apes are found in early Oligocene beds of the Fayum region of western Egypt. There have long been known from there fragmentary remains – mainly teeth and a jaw – of a primate, *Propliopithecus*, no bigger than a typical monkey, but showing technical features of the dentition that indicate that we are dealing with a man-like ape, although a small and primitive one, and recently further remains of related forms have been discovered. In rocks of the succeeding Miocene period, particularly from the Siwalik

Hills of India, there have long been known a series of very incomplete remains – mainly individual teeth and jaw fragments – to many of which have been applied the pleasant name *Dryopithecus*, the 'oak ape' (because the first specimen discovered was from a deposit filled with leaf impressions from an ancient oak forest). As far as one can tell from these materials, *Dryopithecus* might well have been ancestral to one or both of the higher great apes – or to man. But these remains are too fragmentary to give us positive answers. Somewhat better is the evidence from a considerable suite of fossil ape materials more recently discovered in East Africa. To them has been given a separate name, *Proconsul*, but the animals represented are certainly close to, if not identical with, *Dryopithecus*. There appear to be several related species of variable size represented by these remains – and these remains are far better than the *Dryopithecus* fragments, for the nearly complete skull is known, as well as a fair amount of postcranial material. As we surmised in the case of *Dryopithecus*, so we find in *Proconsul* that we are here dealing with an advanced but rather generalized ape, with little to debar it from ancestry to chimpanzee or gorilla or man (plate 44). Further, there is some suggestion from the nature of the skeleton that it may have progressed to some degree on the ground.

We think of ourselves as far removed in nature from even advanced apes, but in fact the structural features which distinguish the body of an ape from that of a man are comparatively few. Bone for bone, muscle for muscle, organ for organ, every ape feature is repeated in the human body. The differences are mainly in proportions and relationships of the structures concerned; differences related mainly to methods of locomotion and brain growth and, as lesser features, the shortening of the face, reduction of canine teeth and, in modern man, development of a chin.

With man's adoption of an upright pose (foreshadowed to some degree in higher apes), and the reduction of whatever trend toward brachiation may have been present in his ancestors, we find that the arms show none of the relative elongation seen in a gibbon or orang, and the legs, vitally important for bipedal locomotion, are long and straight. The hands of man are closely comparable to those of other primates; but with the shift to erect posture, the feet have become radically changed. The divergent big toe of a monkey or ape was an excellent adaptation for climbing about the branches, but a sprawled-out foot of this sort gives poor support to an erect body; in man the big toe has been swung forward parallel with the others to give a broad sole to the foot, and the heel bone has developed strongly at the back as a supporting prop.

The sole anatomical feature in which man can properly take pride is his more highly organized brain, and this has involved a very considerable increase in the bulk of this organ, as well as an increase in the complexity of the folding of the surface grey matter of the cerebral cortex, in which man's higher faculties reside. Apart from occasional variants, the brain size in living human races ranges, roughly, from about 1,200 to 1,500 cc in volume – on the average, that is, two or three times the brain volume found in any of the great apes. Brain expansion has, of course, been responsible for marked changes in the general contours of the head, such as the development of a high, rounded cranium, and high forehead, with, in advanced human types, reduction of the heavy brow ridges common in apes.

How and why did man descend from the trees to become a ground-dweller? To leave the protection of the trees and venture into a terrestrial existence, one would think that an animal would need to be a fast runner to escape the predacious forms present on the ground, or be a powerful creature, competent to protect himself against attack. Primitive man was neither. Particularly in his early career, his locomotion would have been far from speedy, and, compared with most mammals of any size, man is not a particularly strong creature. It may be, however, that growing brain development gave the human ancestor a degree of cunning which would partially, at least, compensate for his physical deficiencies in his attempt to grasp the advantages which might be obtained by leading a venturesome terrestrial life. Or it may be that his transformation into a terrestrial animal was not entirely of his own choosing. Rather than man having left the trees, the trees may have left him. In modern East Africa we find today savanna conditions – a type of country in which groves of trees are common, but are separated by grasslands. There is evidence suggesting that similar conditions were already present in that region in the days when *Proconsul* and other apes were present there; in many other areas in those late Tertiary times there was similarly under way a process of reduction of forest areas and replacement by grassy savannas. Even if a pre-hominid wished to remain a tree-dweller, his living area would be much restricted unless he were able to venture out into the open in travelling from one tree cluster to another, and in this fashion gradually accustom himself to terrestrial life.

Above I have minimized the anatomical differences between men and apes. But relatively slight as these differences may be, we long lacked, in our fossil evidence, any true transition between ape and human patterns; even the most primitive of fossil human types seemed clearly on the human side of the dividing line. In the last few decades, however, the seeming clear distinction between ape and human evolutionary grades has been broken down by discoveries, mainly in limestone caves of the Transvaal, of 'ape men', most of them included in the genus *Australopithecus*. These forms may have been in existence for a considerable period of time, but seem to have flourished mainly at about the beginning of the Pleistocene epoch – upward of a million or so years ago. The first specimen discovered, in the '20's, was the skull of an ape-man child, but in the years that have followed, a number of adult skulls and jaws have been discovered in South African cave deposits. Recently a good specimen of this general type was found in East Africa, and there is evidence suggesting that *Australopithecus* may have once been widespread over the warmer areas of the Old World continents.

In their cranial features the members of the *Australopithecus* group neatly split the differences between ape and man, but the consensus of opinion is that, on the whole, they must be considered as men, although at an exceedingly low level among human types. The australopithecines were small in stature; skeletal remains do not allow too positive a statement, but their height may have been about four feet or so. The dentition is closer to that of men than of apes in the pattern of the molar teeth (which are remarkably large), and in the fact that the canines, although stout, do not project as tusks in the common ape fashion (plate 45). There is a projecting muzzle, but one less prominent than in the apes, and although the brain is not very much larger than in apes (about 700 cc appears to be maximum) and the forehead is low, the brow ridges are less developed than in most apes, and the skull roof is more domed than it is in our simian relatives. Little is known of body structures, but there is definite evidence, both from the way in which the skull is posed on the backbone and from the typically human form of the hip bones, that these pre-humans could walk erect in manlike fashion.

The final section of our story is that of ascending stages of the evolution of man himself. The details of this history, as far as known, are, naturally, of great interest to us as members of this specific lineage, and entire books can be – and have been – devoted to this one subject.

291

In a modest work of the present sort, in which we are attempting to cover the entire panorama of animal life, it would be highly improper to cover this story in detail; I shall merely present its main outlines.

The evolution of man took place during the Pleistocene epoch, the last chapter of the geologic story before Recent times. As compared with the five epochs preceding it, the Pleistocene was short in duration, including, at the most, but a million and a half years or so. Nevertheless, it allowed sufficient time for modern man to have evolved from the australopithecine stage which had already been reached in the early part of the epoch. The Pleistocene is of interest as the time of the most recent Ice Age in the earth's history. In the early Cenozoic the world's climate appears to have been lacking marked climatic zonation; plant evidence, particularly, suggests that relatively mild climates extended north into the Arctic, and it is probable that temperatures were only mildly high in the present tropical regions. As the Cenozoic progressed, however, climatic gradients tended to become steeper, the tropics hotter, the polar regions increasingly colder, until, a million or so years ago, glaciation developed. Major ice centres developed in the Arctic regions of North America and the Scandinavian mountains and minor centres were present farther south – in the Alps and Rockies, for example. Four times during this Ice Age the glaciers advanced from the northern centres to cover large fractions of North America and Europe, four times the glaciers retreated, to give, in the inter-glacial periods, climates in the modern temperate regions which were considerably warmer than we have at present, so that (for example) hippopotami and other tropical forms flourished in southern England.

For the history of pre-human forms, our evidence is almost entirely that furnished by skeletal remains. But man was surely, from an early stage, a user and then a maker of tools. Many of the objects used and made by early human types were presumably of perishable materials – sticks and plant fibres, skins and hides – which rarely persist in fossil form. But early man learned the value of bone and, especially, of stone – particularly flint – for tools, and countless examples of flint hand tools – knives, scrapers, and so on – have been discovered and studied. Presumably early men, and pre-men, first picked up such sticks, bones, and stones as came to hand, with little or no preparation or shaping. It is hard to identify objects of this sort, although there are indications that even australopithecines were to some extent tool users. For later, definitely man-made tools, students of early human evolution have defined sequences of flint tool cultures associated with early human types. We shall not discuss them here; but anyone who undertakes a more thorough study of early human history will soon become familiar with such terms as Chellean (Abbevillian), Acheulean, and Mousterian to characterize primitive human cultures, and Aurignacian, Solutrian, Magdalenian, and so on, to describe the series of stone implements made by 'modernized' races of man in late Pleistocene and 'sub-Recent' geologic times.

The story of human evolution is an Old World story. Indian and pre-Indian types appear to have invaded the Americas via Siberia and Alaska toward the end of the Ice Age, somewhere between ten and twenty thousand years ago; but these invaders were men advanced physically to general present-day standards, and all early phases of the history of man, as of apes, are to be found in Eurasia and Africa. In the latter part of the story human remains are not uncommon in caves and other deposits close to the glaciated regions; as a result, the term 'cave man' is in popular use as a general term for primitive human types. But man's ancestors, with presumably little hairy covering to protect their bodies, were warm-climate forms, and it was probably not until man had advanced far enough in culture to clothe himself in skins and furs that he was able to penetrate far north except in the warmer, inter-glacial stages.

Despite the variations man exhibits today in skin colour, stature, and so on, it is generally agreed that all living races, from Australian Aborigines, Bushmen, Pygmies, and Negroes to Nordics, Mongolians, and American Indians, are not merely members of a single genus, *Homo*, but, further, despite their variations, of a single species named (with a touch of conceit) *Homo sapiens*. What of more primitive types of men now long extinct? Over-enthusiastic scientists describing such remains have tended to describe many of them as belonging not merely to species different from the modern one, but often to distinct genera. Actually, however, once above the *Australopithecus* level, the differences between these various fossil types of men are relatively minor ones, in such features as brain size, development of brow ridges, and so on. Most modern workers have tended to adopt a saner theory, and include all the forms mentioned below in the genus *Homo*, and many consider all but the most archaic of extinct races as merely primitive members of our own species.

The australopithecines appear to have been the characteristic hominids of the earliest part of the Pleistocene, before the initiation of the glacial stages. Some recent evidence from Africa suggests that there may have been some overlap between late survivors of the *Australopithecus* group and the earliest representatives of the genus *Homo*. For the most part, however, such evidence as we have indicates that the establishment of the earliest phase of true men took place during Middle Pleistocene days – the earlier part of the Ice Age, covering the times between half a million and a million years before our present era.

The earliest well-recognized form of this early stage in the rise of true men was the so-called ape-man of Java, of which the first described remains, found in the 1890's, consisted of a skull cap, a femur, and one or two teeth; further and better skull remains have since been unearthed in Java. The original describer of this material assigned it to a separate genus from modern man, as *Pithecanthropus erectus*, the 'erect ape-man'. But while the Java type certainly shows enough differences from modern man to consider it as a separate species, it is best considered as lying within the lower limits of our own genus – *Homo erectus* is a preferable name. Remains of skeletons very similar in nature to those from Java have been discovered in a number of other regions. In the '20's and '30's excavation of a large cave near Peking, China, yielded a considerable series of skulls and jaws of a man which was at first thought to be distinct from the Java man, but later was recognized as clearly identical in species. It was long thought that *Homo erectus* was confined to the Orient, and that other types of men may have been present in the West, but within the last decade specimens of this human type have been discovered in Africa. It seems probable that in the Middle Pleistocene times mankind included but a single species, widespread over the Old World. We know little of the postcranial skeleton of '*Pithecanthropus*' except for the femur, distinctly human in type, which proves that the creature walked erect. In the skull, the cranial vault was low, despite the fact that the roofing bones are thick, and the average brain capacity of skulls of this type, although well above the *Australopithecus* level, was far below modern standards, estimates based on a number of individuals ranging from a low of 835 cc to a high of 1,200 cc. In correlation with a low forehead (plate 46), massive brow ridges were developed above the eye sockets, and there was some forward protrusion of the muzzle with (the facial pattern suggests) a large but flattened nose. There is evidence, in the case of the Chinese form, at least, that *Homo erectus* had the beginnings of cultural development in the shaping of very crude tools, and had gained a knowledge of the use of fire. One may suspect that were we able to meet this ancestor of ours in the flesh, we would not find him a very attractive specimen, to say the least. And the fact that every known skull of this race appears to have been broken open before its burial brings the repulsive suggestion that he was cannibalistic, with brain apparently considered a delicacy.

There remains a gap, although not a major one, between the australopithecines and the *Homo erectus* type of primitive true man. Even that, however, may be bridged presently, for very recent finds in East Africa suggest the presence there of a human type still more primitive than '*Pithecanthropus*' as a contemporary of the last australopithecines and a descendant of that group.

For later phases of the Pleistocene, before the appearance of truly modern types at its very close, our evidence is scattered and does not give us, as yet, a very coherent story. As far as can be seen, however, it appears that there was, on the whole, a slow but steady upward progress, with mankind remaining a single, widespread species, although developing racial differences in various Old World regions. In deposits as far apart from one another as the Solo River in Java, a cave worked for minerals in Zambia, and a considerable series of Ice Age caves in western and central Europe, there have been found remains of relatively late Pleistocene human types which in great measure split the difference between *Homo erectus* and modern humankind. In all the skull vault is low, there are great brow ridges, a somewhat projecting muzzle and a chin of the old-fashioned 're-treating' type. Brain size is somewhat variable, it would seem, but the Solo and Zambian types have endocranial capacities on the order of 1,300 cc, thus well above the average of the '*erectus*' forms. In the best-known members of this series, the Neanderthal man (plate 47), who appears to have persistently occupied European caves until a relatively late stage of the last Pleistocene glaciation, the skull, though low-vaulted, is long and expanded posteriorly, allowing brain proportions as great as those in highly developed modern races.

I will interrupt the story of the evolution of modern man to give a brief account of the one major hoax that has been perpetrated on honest and unsuspecting scientists in the domain of human palaeontology – the story of 'Piltdown man'.

A bit over a half century ago, an amateur archaeologist named Dawson presented to a distinguished English palaeontologist specimens representing the greater part of the braincase of a human skull said to have been excavated from a gravel deposit of early Pleistocene date near Piltdown Manor in Sussex, England. Further excavation in these gravels in later years brought to light other remains – a lower jaw, a canine tooth, nasal bones. These materials aroused a high degree of interest and discussion amongst palaeontologists and anatomists, for the braincase was high and vaulted, and essentially modern in type; the jaw, on the other hand, was exceedingly primitive in structure, obviously not up to even the level of the most primitive known human fossil types, and, in fact, resembled that of an orangutan. This puzzling combination of a very advanced skull and a very primitive jaw presented a picture conflicting strongly with any reasonable theory of human evolution (such as that we have presented here). Were there two separate evolutionary lines, one represented by the forms we have considered and a second by a line which Piltdown represented, in which the brain grew rapidly to the modern condition but the jaw remained persistently primitive?

For many years students of human evolution were disturbed by this seemingly insoluble puzzle. A decade ago, however, came the solution. An anatomist, restudying the Piltdown materials with care, found signs of 'wear' on the lower teeth which looked suspiciously as if made by a file rather than by the animal's chewing action. Further investigation made it clear that 'Piltdown man' was a gigantic hoax. The jaw is actually that of a modern orang, broken and artificially stained to give an appearance of great age. The skull fragments may be of some modest antiquity, but of doubtful provenance; the gravel pit it would seem, was 'salted' by someone (?Dawson) with specimens to be later excavated as seeming authentic fossils.

That such a hoax could be readily perpetrated is easily understandable. Scientists may disagree widely over the interpretations of their findings, but are scrupulously honest in the presentation of the facts, and it does not in general occur to them that standards of honesty may be lower – or absent – in men of other callings.

But let us return from quackery to science, and conclude our story of the evolution of modern man. Before our diversion into the Piltdown story, we noted the presence in various parts of the Old World in late Pleistocene stages of forms transitional in structure between the archaic '*Pithecanthropus*' type and modern man, with Neanderthal the best-known, although somewhat aberrant, representative of this intermediate stage. In Europe there finally appear, at a time towards the close of the Pleistocene which is difficult to determine precisely, but was at the most only a few tens of thousands of years ago, men of true modern type; to them, despite variations, the term Cro-Magnon man is frequently applied (plate 48). There have also been found remains of 'modernized' forms of the same general sort in scattered deposits of, roughly, the same general late Pleistocene age, in regions ranging from Africa to China. In these ancestors of living men, the brain is almost uniformly up to modern standards; the skull vault and forehead are high, the brow ridges reduced, the face short, and a projecting chin developed. As to where and when these advanced forms first arose we are still uncertain. Definitely they did not come from the Neanderthal race which preceded them in Europe, for the transition from the Neanderthals to their successors in the strata in the caves is a sharp one, and no transitional individuals are known in Europe. Presumably the modern racial types originated in some area of Asia or Africa from ancestral forms on the general Neanderthal level of evolution, but from forms less specialized than the Neanderthal group of Europe. A few fragmentary remains of Neanderthal types well back in the Upper Pleistocene appear to be rather more generalized members of this stage, and are thought to be possibly ancestral; and in caves in Mount Carmel in Palestine have been found skeletons which show a mixture of Neanderthal and modern features. But it is possible that the Mount Carmel individuals are racial hybrids rather than ancestral in nature, and the solution of the exact time and place of origin of modern man is as yet uncertain.

Cro-Magnon man and his late Pleistocene contemporaries were still in a stone age culturally. But in their body build and, we believe, in mental ability, these men were already on our own level. The remainder of the story of man is one for the archaeologist and, later, the historian, rather than the palaeontologist. The time since the appearance of the modern type has been too short for any notable evolutionary change to have taken place; the advances have been on the cultural, not the physical level.

The future? It is unsafe to extrapolate from the past on into the unknown. Looking back at past major events, we can see that frequently the dominant form of one era becomes extinct, to be replaced by some very different type of life. It is somewhat discouraging to reflect that man is one of the very few animals known which wantonly destroys members of his own species, and he now has the ability to eradicate himself (and much of the rest of the living world with him). Perhaps he is doomed to become extinct and replaced by members of some other group. But perhaps – one may hope – intelligence may triumph, and something better and finer evolve from man himself.

References

BARNES, R.D.(1963) *Invertebrate zoology.* Saunders: Philadelphia and London
BUCHSBAUM, R.(1938) *Animals without backbones.* University of Chicago Press and Pelican Books: London
HYMAN, L.H.(1940–67) *The invertebrates.* McGraw-Hill: New York
MOORE, R.C.(Ed.)·(1953–) *Treatise on invertebrate Paleontology.* Geological Society of America: New York
PIVETEAU, J.(Ed.)(1952–) *Traité de paléontologie,* vols. 1–7. Masson: Paris
ROMER, A.S.(1956) *Osteology of the reptiles.* University of Chicago Press
—— (1962) *The vertebrate body,* 3rd ed. Saunders: Philadelphia and London
—— (1966) *Vertebrate paleontology,* 3rd ed. University of Chicago Press
SWINNERTON, H.H.(1961) *Outlines of palaeontology.* Arnold: London
YOUNG, J.Z.(1962) *The life of vertebrates,* 2nd ed. Oxford University Press

Chapter 1

CAIN, A.J.(1954) *Animal species and their evolution.* Hutchinson: London
DARWIN, C.(1872) *The origin of species.* 1956 reprint of 6th ed. Oxford University Press
DE BEER, G.R.(1951) *Embryos and ancestors.* Oxford University Press
DOBZHANSKY, I.(1951) *Genetics and the origin of species,* 3rd ed. Columbia University Press: New York
—— (1955) *Evolution, genetics and man.* Wiley: New York
DUNBAR, C.O.(1967) *The earth.* Weidenfeld and Nicolson: London
FORD, E.B.(1938) *Mendelism and evolution.* Methuen: London
HOLMES, A.(1966) *Principles of physical geology.* Nelson: London
HUXLEY, J.(1963) *Evolution in action.* Pelican Books: London
KUMMEL, B.(1961) *History of the earth.* Freeman: San Francisco and London
LAMARCK, J.B.(1802) *Recherches sur l'organisation des corps vivants.* Maillard: Paris
—— (1809) *Philosophie zoologique.* Savy: Paris
MAYR, E.(1963) *Animal species and evolution.* Belknap Press: London
NOÜY, LECOMTE DU (1948) *L'homme et sa destinée.* La Colombe: Paris
ROMER, A.S.(1949) Time series and trends in animal evolution. In *Genetics, paleontology and evolution* (Ed. Jepsen, Simpson and Mayr), 103–120. Princeton University Press
SIMPSON, G.G.(1949) *The meaning of evolution.* Yale University Press
SMITH, J.M.(1958) *The theory of evolution.* Pelican Books: London
WELLS, A.K.(1938) *Outline of geological history.* Allen and Unwin: London
ZEUNER, F.E.(1958) *Dating the past,* 4th ed. Methuen: London

299

Chapter 2

BURTON, M. (1963) *A revision of the classification of sponges.* British Museum (Natural History): London

CLARK, R. B. (1964) *Dynamics in metazoan evolution.* Clarendon Press: Oxford

CORLISS, J. (1960) Comments on the systematics and phylogeny of the Protozoa. *Systematic Zoology 8*: 169–190

DARWIN, C. (1896) *The structure and distribution of coral reefs.* Murray: London

DOUGHERTY, E. C. (Ed.) (1963) *The lower Metazoa : comparative biology and phylogeny.* University of California Press

GRIMSTONE, A. V. (1961) Fine structure and morphogenesis in Protozoa. *Biological Reviews 36*: 97–150

HADZI, J. (1963) *The evolution of the Metazoa.* Pergamon Press: Oxford

HAYASHI, T. (1961) How cells move. *Scientific American 205* (3): 268–289

HICKSON, S. J. (1924) *An introduction to the study of Recent corals.* University of Manchester Press

JÄGERSTEN, G. (1955) On the early phylogeny of the Metazoa. *Zoologiska Bidrag från Uppsala 30*: 321–354

—— (1959) Further remarks on the early phylogeny of the Metazoa. *Zoologiska Bidrag från Uppsala 33*: 79–108

JAHN, T. L., & JAHN, F. F. (1949) *How to know the Protozoa.* Brown: Dubuque

JONES, D. J. (1956) *Introduction to microfossils.* Harper: New York

LENHOFF, H. M., & LOOMIS, W. F. (Eds.) (1961) *The biology of Hydra and of some other coelenterates.* University of Miami Press

PITELKA, D. (1962) *The electron microscopic structure of Protozoa.* Pergamon Press: Oxford

STEPHENSON, T. A. (1935) *The British sea anemones.* Ray Society: London

VICKERMAN, K., & COX, F. E. G. (1967) *The Protozoa.* Murray: London

WOLPERT, L. (1965) Cytoplasmic streaming and amoeboid movement. *Society for General Microbiology Symposium 15*: 270–293

Chapter 3

AX, P. (1963) Relationships and phylogeny of the Turbellaria. In *The lower Metazoa* (Ed. E. C. Dougherty), 191–224. University of California Press

BAYLIS, H. A. (1938) Helminthes and evolution. In *Evolution*, essays presented to E. S. Goodrich (Ed. G. R. de Beer), 249–270. Oxford University Press

BEKLEMISHEV, E. M. (1963) On the relationship of the Turbellaria to other groups of the animal kingdom. In *The lower Metazoa* (Ed. E. C. Dougherty), 234–244. University of California Press

DALES, R. P. (1963) *Annelids.* Hutchinson: London

LAPAGE, G. (1957) *Animals parasitic in man.* Penguin Books: London

STEPHENSON, J. (1930) *The Oligochaeta.* Oxford University Press

WALCOTT, C. D. (1911) Middle Cambrian annelids. *Smithsonian Miscellaneous Collection 57*: 109–144

WELLS, G. P. (1957) The life of the lugworm. *New Biology 22*: 39–55. Penguin Books: London

Chapter 4

BRISTOWE, W. S. (1958) *The world of spiders*. Collins: London

CALMAN, W. T. (1939) The structure of the trilobites. *Nature 141*: 1077

CARPENTER, F. M. (1953) The evolution of insects. *American Scientist 41*: 256–270

GARSTANG, W., & GURNEY, R. (1938) The descent of the Crustacea from the trilobites and their larval relations. In *Evolution*, essays presented to E. S. Goodrich (Ed. G. R. de Beer), 271–286. Oxford University Press

GLAESSNER, M. F. (1957) Evolutionary trends in the Crustacea. *Evolution 11*: 178–184

HUTCHINSON, G. E. (1930) Restudy of some Burgess Shale fossils. *Proceedings of the U.S. National Museum 78*: 14–22

IMMS, A. D. (1959) *Outlines of entomology* (revised O. W. Richards and R. G. Davies) Methuen: London

LANKESTER, E. R. (1881) *Limulus* an arachnid. *Quarterly Journal of Microscopical Science 21*: 504–548

RAW, F. (1953) The external morphology of the trilobite and its significance. *Journal of Paleontology 27*: 82–129

—— (1957) Origin of the chelicerates. *Journal of Paleontology 31*: 139–192

TIEGS, O. W., & MANTON, S. M. (1958) The evolution of the Arthropoda. *Biological Reviews 33*: 255–337

Chapter 5

EALES, N. B. (1950) Torsion in gastropods. *Proceedings of the Malacological Society 28*: 185–196

GHISELIN, M. T. (1966) The adaptive significance of gastropod torsion. *Evolution 20*: 337–348

HAAS, O. (1942) Recurrence of morphological types and evolutionary cycles in Mesozoic ammonites. *Journal of Paleontology 16*: 643–650

LEMCHE, H., & WINGSTRAND, K. G. (1959) The anatomy of *Neopilina galatheae*. *Galathea Reports 3*: 9–71

MORTON, J. E. (1958) *Molluscs*. Hutchinson: London

SCHENK, H. C. (1945) Geological application of biometrical analysis of molluscan assemblages. *Journal of Paleontology 19*: 504–521

SCHINDEWOLF, O. (1934) Concerning the evolution of the Cephalopoda. *Biological Reviews 9*: 458–459

SPATH, L. F. (1933) The evolution of the Cephalopoda. *Biological Reviews 8*: 418–462

TRUEMAN, A. E. (1941) The ammonite body chamber, with special reference to the buoyancy and mode of life of the living ammonite. *Quarterly Journal of the Geological Society of London 96*: 339–383

YONGE, C. M. (1950) *Oysters*. Collins: London

Chapter 6

ATKINS, D. (1932) The ciliary feeding mechanism of the endoproct polyzoans and a comparison with that of the ectoproct polyzoans. *Quarterly Journal of Microscopical Science 75*: 393–423

—— (1960) The ciliary feeding mechanism of the Megathyridae (Brachiopoda) and the growth stages of the lophophores. *Journal of the Marine Biological Association of the United Kingdom 39*: 459–479

BASSLER, R. S. (1953) Bryozoa. In *Treatise on invertebrate paleontology* (Ed. R. C. Moore), Part G

BATHER, F. A. (1900) The Echinoderma. In *Treatise on zoology* (Ed. E. R. Lankester), Part 3. Black: London

BUDINGTON, R. A. (1942) The ciliary transport system of *Asterias forbesi*. *Biological Bulletin 83*: 438–450

DURHAM, J. W. (1966) Evolution among the Echinoidea. *Biological Reviews 41*: 368–392

ELLIOTT, C. F. (1953) Brachial development and evolution in terebratelloid brachiopods. *Biological Reviews 28*: 261–279

FELL, H. B. (1963) The phylogeny of sea-stars. *Philosophical Transactions of the Royal Society, London (B) 246*: 381–435

NICHOLS, D. (1962) *Echinoderms*. Hutchinson: London

—— (1964) Echinoderms: experimental and ecological. *Annual Review of Oceanography and Marine Biology 2*: 393–423

SPENCER, W. K. (1938) Some aspects of evolution in echinoderms. In *Evolution, essays presented to E. S. Goodrich* (Ed. G. R. de Beer), 287–303, Oxford University Press

Chapter 7

BARRINGTON, E. J. W. (1965) *The biology of Hemichordata and Protochordata*. Oliver and Boyd: London

BERRILL, N. J. (1955) *Origin of vertebrates*. Oxford University Press

BONE, Q. (1960) The origin of the chordates. *Journal of the Linnean Society, London 44*: 252–269

DELSMAN, H. C. (1912) *The ancestry of vertebrates*. Valkhoff: Amersfoort

FELL, H. B. (1948) Echinoderm embryology and the origin of chordates. *Biological Reviews 23*: 81–107

GARSTANG, W. (1928) The morphology of the Tunicata, and its bearings on the phylogeny of the Chordata. *Quarterly Journal of Microscopical Science 72*: 51–187

GASKELL, W. M. (1908) *The origin of vertebrates*. Longmans: London

PATTEN, W. (1912) *The evolution of vertebrates and their kin*. Churchill: London

WHITEAR, M. (1957) Some remarks on the ascidian affinities of vertebrates. *Annals and Magazine of Natural History 12* (x): 338–348

WILLEY, A. (1894) *Amphioxus and the ancestry of vertebrates* Macmillan: New York and London

Chapter 8

ARAMBOURG, C., & GUIBÉ, J. (1958) Sous-classe des dipneustes. In *Traité de zoologie* (Ed. J. Piveteau) *13* (3): 2522–2540. Masson: Paris

BRODAL, A., & FANGE, R. (1963) *The biology of Myxine*. Oslo University Press

BROUGH, J. (1936) On the evolution of bony fishes during the Triassic period. *Biological Reviews 11*: 385–405

DENISON, R.H.(1941) The soft anatomy of *Bothriolepis*. *Journal of Paleontology* *15*: 553–561

—— (1956) A review of the habitat of the earliest vertebrates. *Fieldiana: Geology* *11*: 359–457

GREGORY, W.K., & RAVEN, H.C.(1941) A new restoration of the skeleton of *Eusthenopteron*, with remarks on the origin of the tetrapod stem. *Annals of the New York Academy of Sciences 42*: 293–412

HEINTZ, A.(1932) *The structure of Dinichthys: a contribution to our knowledge of the Arthrodira.* Bashford Dean Memorial Volume. American Museum Press: New York

MARSHALL, N.B.(1965) *The life of fishes.* Weidenfeld and Nicolson: London

MILES, R.S.(1965) Some features in the cranial morphology of acanthodians and the relationships of the Acanthodii. *Acta zoologica 46*: 233–255

MILLOT, J., & ANTHONY, J.(1958 and 1965) *Anatomie de Latimeria chalumnae* (2 vols.). Centre National de la Recherche Scientifique: Paris

MOY-THOMAS, J.A.(1939) The early evolution and relationships of the elasmobranchs. *Biological Reviews 14*: 1–26

NORMAN, J.R.(1963) *A history of fish.* 2nd ed., revised by P.H.Greenwood. Benn: London

PATTERSON, C.(1964) A review of Mesozoic acanthopterygian fishes. *Philosophical Transactions of the Royal Society, London (B) 247*: 213–482

—— (1965) The phylogeny of the chimaeroids. *Philosophical Transactions of the Royal Society, London (B) 249*: 101–219

RAYNER, D.H.(1941) The structure and evolution of the holostean fishes. *Biological Reviews 16*: 218–237

ROMER, A.S.(1955) Fish origins – fresh or salt water? *Deep-Sea Research*, supplement to vol. *3*: 261–280

—— (1956) The early evolution of land vertebrates. *Proceedings of the American Philosophical Society 100*: 157–167

—— (1942) Cartilage an embryonic adaptation. *American Naturalist 76*: 394–404

STENSIÖ, E.A.(1927) Downtonian and Devonian vertebrates of Spitzbergen. *Skrifter om Svalbard og Nordishavet 12* (2 vols.)

Chapter 9

COWLES, R.B.(1958) Additional notes on the origin of the tetrapods. *Evolution 12*: 419–421

COX, C.B.(1966) The Amphibia – an evolutionary backwater. In *Looking at animals again* (Ed. D.R.Arthur), 97–118. Freeman: London

—— (1967) Cutaneous respiration and the origin of the modern Amphibia. *Proceedings of the Linnean Society, London 178*: 37–47

GOIN, C.J.(1960) Amphibians, pioneers of terrestrial breeding habits. *Smithsonian Report 1959*: 427–445

—— & GOIN, O.B.(1962) *Introduction to herpetology.* Freeman: San Francisco and London

JARVIK, E.(1955) Ichthyostegalia. In *Traité de paléontologie* (Ed. J.Piveteau) *5*: 53–66. Masson: Paris

NOBLE, G.K.(1931) *The biology of the Amphibia*. McGraw-Hill: New York. Reprinted 1954, Dover Publications: New York

PARSONS, T., & WILLIAMS, E.E.(1963) The relationships of the modern Amphibia: a re-examination. *Quarterly Review of Biology 38*: 26–53

PIVETEAU, J.(1937) Un amphibien du Trias inférieur. *Annales de paléontologie 26*: 135–176

ROMER, A.S.(1937) The braincase of the Carboniferous crossopterygian *Megalichthys nitidus*. *Bulletin of the Museum of Comparative Zoology, Harvard 82*: 3–73

——— (1947) Review of the Labyrinthodontia. *Bulletin of the Museum of Comparative Zoology, Harvard 99*: 1–368

——— (1958) Tetrapod limbs and early tetrapod life. *Evolution 12*: 365–369

——— (1964) Problems in early amphibian history. *Journal of Animal Morphology and Physiology 11*: 1–20

SAWIN, H.J.(1945) Amphibians from the Dockum Triassic of Howard County, Texas. *University of Texas Publication 4401*: 361–399

SZARSKI, H.(1962) The origin of the Amphibia. *Quarterly Review of Biology 37*: 189–241

WESTOLL, T.S.(1943) The origin of the primitive tetrapod limb. *Proceedings of the Royal Society, London (B) 131*: 373–393

——— (1943) The origin of the tetrapods. *Biological Reviews 18*: 78–98

WHITE, T.E.(1939) Osteology of *Seymouria baylorensis* Broili. *Bulletin of the Museum of Comparative Zoology, Harvard 85*: 325–409

Chapter 10

BELLAIRS, A.D'A., & UNDERWOOD, G.(1951) The origin of snakes. *Biological Reviews 26*: 193–237

BOLTT, R.E., & EWER, R.F.(1964) The functional anatomy of the head of the puff adder, *Bitis arietans* (Merr.). *Journal of Morphology 114*: 83–106

CAMP, C.L.(1945) *Prolacerta* and the protorosaurian reptiles. *American Journal of Science 243*: 17–32 and 84–101

CARROLL, R.L.(1964) The earliest reptiles. *Journal of the Linnean Society, London (Zoology) 45*: 61–83

FOX, R.C., & BOWMAN, M.C.(1966) Osteology and relationships of *Captorhinus aguti*. *Paleontological Contributions of the University of Kansas 11*: 1–79

GANS, C.(1961) The feeding mechanism of snakes and its possible evolution. *American Zoologist 1*: 217–247

HAUGHTON, S.H., & BOONSTRA, L.D.(1929–1934) Pareiasaurian studies 1–11. *Annals of the South African Museum 28* and *31*

HOFSTETTER, R.(1962) Revue des récentes acquisitions concernant l'histoire et la systématiques des squamates. In *Problèmes Actuels de Paléontologie (Evolution des Vertébrés) 104*: 243–279. Centre National de la Recherche Scientifique: Paris

JAEKEL, O.(1916) Die Wirbeltierfunde aus dem Keuper von Halberstadt. II. Testudinata. *Paläontologisches Zeitschrift 1*: 155–214

MERTENS, R.(1960) *The world of amphibians and reptiles*. Harrap: London

PEYER, B.(1931) Die Triasfauna der Tessiner Kalkalpen. II. *Tanystropheus longobardicus* Bass sp. *Schweizerische Paläontologische Abhandlungen 50*: 7–110

ROMER, A. S. (1957) Origin of the amniote egg. *Scientific Monthly 85*: 57–63

TIHEN, J. A. (1960) Comments on the origin of the amniote egg. *Evolution 14*: 528–531

Chapter 11

BLACKETT, P. M. S., BULLARD, E., & RUNCORN, S. K. (Eds.) (1965) Symposium on continental drift. *Philosophical Transactions of the Royal Society, London (A)*: 258

CAMP, C. L. (1942) California mosasaurs. *Memoirs of the University of California 13*: 1–68

DREVERMANN, F. (1933) Das Skelett von *Placodus gigas* Agassiz in Senckenberg Museum. *Senckenbergische Naturforschende Gesellschaft Abhandlungen 38*: 319–364

FRAAS, E. (1910) Plesiosaurier aus dem oberen Lias von Holzmaden. *Palaeontographica 57*: 105–140

HAY, O. P. (1908) The fossil turtles of North America. *Publications of the Carnegie Institute, Washington 75*: 1–568

HUENE, F. von (1922) Die Ichthyosaurier des Lias und ihre Zusammenhänge. *Monographien zur Geologie und Paläontologie 1* (1): 1–112

—— (1941) Osteologie und systematische Stellung von *Mesosaurus*. *Palaeontographica 92A*: 45–58

OSBORN, H. F. (1899) A complete mosasaur skeleton, osseous and cartilaginous. *Memoirs of the American Museum of Natural History 1*: 167–188

ROMER, A. S., & LEWIS, A. D. (1959) A mounted skeleton of the giant plesiosaur *Kronosaurus*. *Bulletin of the Museum of Comparative Zoology, Harvard 112*: 1–15

TOIT, A. L. DU (1937) *Our wandering continents*. Oliver and Boyd: Edinburgh

WEGENER, A. (1924) *The origin of continents and oceans*. Methuen: London

WELLES, S. P. (1952) A review of the North American Cretaceous elasmosaurs. *University of California Publications in Geological Science 29*: 47–144

Chapter 12

BROWN, B., & SCHLAIKJER, E. M. (1940) The structure and relationships of *Protoceratops*. *Annals of the New York Academy of Sciences 40*: 133–266

CAMP, C. L. (1930) A study of the phytosaurs with description of new material from western North America. *Memoirs of the University of California 10*: 1–161

CASIER, E. (1960) *Les iguanodons de Bernissart*. Institut Royal des Sciences Naturelles de Belgique: Brussels

COLBERT, E. H. (1947) Studies of the phytosaurs *Machaeroprosopus* and *Rutiodon*. *Bulletin of the American Museum of Natural History 88*: 53–96

—— (1961) *Dinosaurs – their discovery and their world*. Hutchinson: London

—— & MOOK, C. C. (1951) The ancestral crocodilian *Protosuchus*. *Bulletin of the American Museum of Natural History 97*: 143–182

EATON, G. F. (1910) Osteology of *Pteranodon*. *Memoirs of the Connecticut Academy of Science 2*: 1–38

EWER, R. F. (1962) The anatomy of the thecodont reptile *Euparkeria*. *Philosophical Transactions of the Royal Society, London (B) 248*: 379–435

GILMORE, C. W. (1914) Osteology of the armoured Dinosauria in the United States National Museum, with special reference to the genus *Stegosaurus*. *Bulletin of the United States National Museum 89*: 1–143

—— (1925) A nearly complete articulated skeleton of *Camarasaurus*, a saurischian dinosaur from the Dinosaur National Monument, Utah. *Memoirs of the Carnegie Museum 10*: 347–384

JANENSCH, W. (1950) Die Wirbelsäule von *Brachiosaurus brancai*. Die Skelettrekonstruktion von *Brachiosaurus brancai*. *Palaeontographica*, Supplement 7: 27–103

LAMBE, L. M. (1917) The Cretaceous theropodous dinosaur *Gorgosaurus*. *Memoirs of the Geological Survey of Canada 100*: 1–84

LULL, R. S. (1933) A revision of the Ceratopsia or horned dinosaurs. *Memoirs of the Peabody Museum of Natural History 3* (3): 1–135

MOOK, C. C. (1934) The evolution and classification of the Crocodilia. *Journal of Geology 42*: 295–304

OSBORN, H. F. (1917) Skeletal adaptations of *Ornitholestes*, *Struthiomimus*, *Tyrannosaurus*. *Bulletin of the American Museum of Natural History 35*: 733–771

OSTROM, J. H. (1961) Cranial morphology of the hadrosaurian dinosaurs of North America. *Bulletin of the American Museum of Natural History 122*: 33–186

—— (1962) The cranial crest of hadrosaurian dinosaurs. *Postilla, Yale Peabody Museum 62*: 1–29

—— (1964) A reconsideration of the paleoecology of hadrosaurian dinosaurs. *American Journal of Science 262*: 975–997

RUSSELL, L. S. (1940) *Edmontia rugosidens* (Gilmore), an armoured dinosaur from the Belly River series of Alberta. *University of Toronto Studies, Geological Series 43*: 3–28

—— (1965) Body temperature of dinosaurs and its relationships to their extinction. *Journal of Paleontology 39*: 497–501

YOUNG, C. C. (1964) On a new pterosaurian from Sinkiang, China. *Vertebrata Palasiatica 8*: 239–255

Chapter 13

DE BEER, G. R. (1954) *Archaeopteryx lithographica*. British Museum (Natural History): London

—— (1956) Evolution of Ratites. *Bulletin of the British Museum (Natural History)*, *Zoology 4*: 59–70

HEILMANN, G. (1926) *The origin of birds*. Witherby: London

HOWARD, M. (1955) Fossil birds. *Los Angeles County Museum, Science Series 10*: 1–40

MARSH, O. C. (1880) Odontornithes: a monograph on the extinct toothed birds of North America. *Report of the Geological Exploration of the 40th Parallel 7*: 1–201

MATTHEW, W. D., & GRANGER, W. (1917) The skeleton of *Diatryma*, a gigantic bird from the Lower Eocene of Wyoming. *Bulletin of the American Museum of Natural History 37*: 307–326

OWEN, R. (1879) *Memoirs on the extinct wingless birds of New Zealand*. Van Voorst: London

PYCRAFT, W. P. (1910) *A history of birds*. Methuen: London

THOMSON, A. L. (Ed.) (1964) *A new dictionary of birds*. Nelson: London

TUCKER, B. W. (1938) Functional evolutionary morphology: the origin of birds. In *Evolution*, essays presented to E. S. Goodrich (Ed. G. R. de Beer), 321–336. Oxford University Press

WOLFSON, A. (Ed.) (1955) *Recent studies in avian biology*. University of Illinois Press: Urbana

Chapter 14

BRINK, A. S. (1957) Speculations on some advanced mammalian characteristics in the higher mammal-like reptiles. *Palaeontologia africana* 4: 77–96

BROILI, F., & SCHRÖDER, J. (1934–37) Beobachtungen an Wirbeltieren der Karroo-formation. 1–28. *Sitzungsberichte der Bayerischen Akademie der Wissenschaften, München, 1934–37*

BROOM, R. (1932) *The mammal-like reptiles of South Africa and the origin of mammals*. Witherby: London

BURRELL, H. (1927) *The platypus*. Angus and Robertson: Sydney

COX, C. B. (1965) New Triassic dicynodonts from South America, their origins and relationships. *Philosophical Transactions of the Royal Society, London (B) 248*: 457–516

CROMPTON, A. W. (1955) A possible explanation for the origin of the mammalian brain and skull. *South African Journal of Science 52*: 130–133

KÜHNE, W. G. (1956) *The Liassic therapsid Oligokyphus*. British Museum (Natural History): London

OLSON, E. C. (1944) Origin of mammals based upon cranial morphology of the therapsid suborders. *Special Paper, Geological Society of America 55*: 1–136

—— (1961) The food chain and the origin of mammals. *International colloquium on the evolution of mammals*. Koninklijke Vlaamse Academie voor Wetenschappen: Brussels

—— (1962) Late Permian terrestrial vertebrates, U.S.A. and U.S.S.R. *Transactions of the American Philosophical Society 52* (2): 1–224

OWEN, R. (1878) *Researches on the fossil remains of the extinct mammals of Australia*. Royal Society: London

PARRINGTON, F. R., & WESTOLL, T. S. (1940) On the evolution of the mammalian palate. *Philosophical Transactions of the Royal Society, London (B) 230*: 305–355

RIDE, W. D. L. (1959) On the evolution of Australian marsupials. In *The evolution of living organisms*. Melbourne

ROMER, A. S. (1948) Relative growth in pelycosaurian reptiles. *Royal Society of South Africa, Special Publication, Robert Broom Commemorative Volume*. 45–55

—— & PRICE, L. I. (1940) Review of the Pelycosauria. *Special Paper, Geological Society of America 28*: 1–538

SIMPSON, G. G. (1940) The development of marsupials in South America. *Physis 14*: 373–398

—— (1945) The principles of classification and a classification of mammals. *Bulletin of the American Museum of Natural History 85*: 1–450

—— (1962) Evolution of Mesozoic mammals. *International colloquium on the evolution of mammals*. Koninklijke Vlaamse Academie voor Wetenschappen: Brussels

YOUNG, J. Z. (1957) *The life of mammals*. Oxford University Press

Chapter 15

BUTLER, P.M.(1948) The evolution of carnassial dentitions in the Mammalia. *Proceedings of the Zoological Society, London 116* (2): 198–220

DAVIS, D.(1964) The giant panda. A study of evolutionary mechanisms. *Fieldiana, Zoology Memoir 3:* 1–339

ERDBRINK, D.P.(1953) *A review of fossil and Recent bears of the Old World.* de Lange: Deventer

GAZIN, C.L.(1957) A skull of the Bridger Middle Eocene creodont, *Patriofelis ulta* Leidy. *Smithsonian Miscellaneous Collection 134* (8): 1–20

GREGORY, W.K., & HELLMAN, M.(1939) On the evolution and major classification of the civets (Viverridae) and allied fossil and recent Carnivora: a phylogenetic study of the skull and dentition. *Proceedings of the American Philosophical Society 81:* 309–392

KELLOGG, R.(1922) Pinnipeds from the Miocene and Pleistocene deposits of California . . . and a résumé of current theories regarding the origin of the Pinnipedia. *University of California Publication: Bulletin of the Department of Geological Science 13:* 23–132

MATTHEW, W.D.(1910) The phylogeny of the Felidae. *Bulletin of the American Museum of Natural History 28:* 289–316

—— (1930) The phylogeny of dogs. *Journal of Mammalogy 11:* 117–138

MERRIAM, J.C., & STOCK, C.(1932) The Felidae of Rancho La Brea. *Publication of the Carnegie Institute, Washington 422:* 1–231

McGREW, P.O.(1938) Dental morphology of the Procyonidae with a description of *Cynarctoides*, gen.nov. *Publication of the Field Museum of Natural History; Geology Series 6:* 323–339

VAN VALEN, L.(1966) Deltatheridia: a new order of mammals. *Bulletin of the American Museum of Natural History 132:* 1–126

WORTMAN, J.L.(1901–2) Studies of Eocene Mammalia in the Marsh Collection, Peabody Museum. I. Carnivora. *American Journal of Science*, Series 4, vols. *11, 12*

Chapter 16

ANDREWS, C.W.(1906) *A descriptive catalogue of the Tertiary Vertebrata of the Fayûm, Egypt.* British Museum (Natural History): London

BOHLKEN, H.(1960) Remarks on the stomach and the systematic position of Tylopoda. *Proceedings of the Zoological Society, London 134:* 207–215

COPE, E.D.(1883) The genus *Phenacodus*. *American Naturalist 1883:* 535

GRANGER, W., & GREGORY, W.K.(1943) A revision of the Mongolian titanotheres. *Bulletin of the American Museum of Natural History 80:* 349–389

MACDONALD, J.R.(1956) The North American anthracotheres. *Journal of Paleontology 30:* 615–645

MARSH, O.C.(1884) Dinocerata, a monograph of an extinct order of gigantic mammals. *Monograph of the United States Geological Survey 10:* 1–255

OSBORN, H.F.(1923) The extinct giant rhinoceros *Baluchitherium* of western and central Asia. *Natural History 23:* 209–228

—— (1929) The titanotheres of ancient Wyoming, Dakota and Nebraska. *Monograph of the United States Geological Survey 55:* 1–953

—— (1936–42) *Proboscidea : a monograph of the discovery, evolution, migration and extinction of the mastodonts and elephants of the world.* (2 vols.) American Museum Press: New York

PILGRIM, G. E. (1947) The evolution of the buffaloes, oxen, sheep and goats. *Journal of the Linnean Society, London 279*: 272–286

RADINSKY, L. B. (1964) *Paleomoropus*, a new early Eocene chalicothere (Mammalia, Perissodactyla), and a revision of Eocene chalicotheres. *American Museum Novitates 2179*: 1–28

—— (1965) Evolution of the tapiroid skeleton from *Heptodon* to *Tapirus*. *Bulletin of the Museum of Comparative Zoology, Harvard 134*: 69–103

REINHART, R. H. (1959) A review of the Sirenia and Desmostylia. *University of California Publication, Geological Science 36*: 1–146

SCOTT, W. B. (1910) Litopterna of the Santa Cruz Beds. *Report of the Princeton University Expedition to Patagonia 6*: 287–300

SIMPSON, G. G. (1932) Fossil Sirenia of Florida and the evolution of the Sirenia. *Bulletin of the American Museum of Natural History 59*: 419–503

—— (1951) *Horses.* Oxford University Press

SINCLAIR, W. J. (1909–1928) Mammalia of the Santa Cruz Beds. *Report of the Princeton University Expedition to Patagonia 6*: 1–110 and 239–342

SINGER, R., & BONÉ, E. L. (1960) Modern giraffes and the fossil giraffids of Africa. *Annals of the South African Museum 45*: 375–548

SIMONS, E. L. (1960) The Paleocene Pantodonta. *Transactions of the American Philosophical Society 50* (6): 3–81

WATSON, D. M. S. (1946) The evolution of the Proboscidea. *Biological Reviews 21*: 15–29

WOOD, H. E. (1941) Trends in rhinoceros evolution. *Transactions of the New York Academy of Sciences*, series 2, *3*: 83–96

ZEUNER, F. E. (1945) New reconstructions of the woolly rhinoceros and Merck's rhinoceros. *Proceedings of the Linnean Society, London 156*: 183–195

Chapter 17

JEPSEN, G. L. (1966) Early Eocene bat from Wyoming. *Science 154*: 1333–1339

KELLOGG, R. (1928) The history of whales: their adaptation to life in the water. *Quarterly Review of Biology 3*: 29–76 and 174–208

—— (1936) A review of the Archaeoceti. *Publication of the Carnegie Institute, Washington 482*: 1–366

SCOTT, W. B. (1903–4) Mammalia of the Santa Cruz Beds: Edentata. *Report of the Princeton University Expedition to Patagonia 5*: 1–364

SIMPSON, G. G. (1931) *Metacheiromys* and the Edentata. *Bulletin of the American Museum of Natural History 59*: 295–381

SLIJPER, E. J. (1962) *Whales.* Hutchinson: London

STOCK, C. (1925) Cenozoic gravigrade edentates of western North America. *Publication of the Carnegie Institute, Washington 331*: 1–206

WOOD, A. E. (1957) What, if anything, is a rabbit? *Evolution 11*: 417–425

—— (1959) Eocene radiation and phylogeny of the rodents. *Evolution 13*: 354–361

—— (1965) Grades and clades among rodents. *Evolution 19*: 115–130

Chapter 18

BROOM, R., & SCHEPERS, G.W.H.(1946) The South African fossil ape-men, the Australopithecinae. *Memoirs of the Transvaal Museum 2*: 1–272

CLARK, W.E.LE GROS (1960) *The antecedents of man: an introduction to the evolution of the primates.* Nelson: London

—— (1962) *History of the primates* (8th ed.). British Museum (Natural History): London

—— (1964) *The fossil evidence for human evolution* (2nd ed.). University of Chicago Press

—— & LEAKEY, L.S.B.(1951) The Miocene Hominoidea of East Africa. *British Museum (Natural History), Fossil Mammals of Africa 1*: 1–117

FEREMBACH, D.(1959) Les limnopithèques du Kenya. *Annales de paléontologie 44*: 149–249

GAVAN, J.A.(Ed.) (1955) *The non-human primates and primate evolution.* Detroit

HOWELLS, W.(1962) *Ideas on human evolution.* Harvard University Press

LEAKEY, L.S.B.(1961) *The progress and evolution of man in Africa.* Oxford University Press

PIVETEAU, J.(1948) Recherches anatomiques sur les lémuriens disparus: le genre *Archaeolemur. Annales de Paléontologie 34*: 125–172

ROBINSON, J.T.(1962) Australopithecines and the origin of man. *Annual Report of the United States National Museum, for 1961.* 479–500

SIMONS, E.L.(1962) A new Eocene primate genus, *Cantius*, and a revision of some allied European lemuroids. *Bulletin of the British Museum (Natural History), Geology 7* (1): 1–36

—— (1963) A critical reappraisal of Tertiary primates. In *Evolutionary and genetic biology of primates* (Ed. J. Buettner-Janusch). Academic Press: New York

—— (1964) The early relatives of man. *Scientific American 211* (1): 50–62

—— & PILBEAM, D.R.(1965) Preliminary revision of the Dryopithecinae. *Folia Primatologica 3*: 81–152

SIMPSON, G.G.(1940) Studies on the earliest primates. *Bulletin of the American Museum of Natural History 77*: 185–212

—— (1962) Primate taxonomy and recent studies of nonhuman primates. *Annals of the New York Academy of Sciences 102*: 497–514

Index

numbers in italics refer to pages on which figures appear